FIFTY FAMOUS
SEA STORIES

In the same Series:

Fifty Famous Stories for Girls
Fifty Famous Stories for Boys
Fifty Famous Animal Stories

FIFTY FAMOUS

SEA STORIES

Selected & edited

by

"MAINSAIL"

BURKE ★ LONDON

First published September 1961
Second impression September 1967

222 69125 5

BURKE PUBLISHING COMPANY, LTD.
14 JOHN STREET, LONDON, W.C.1.

MADE AND PRINTED BY OFFSET IN GREAT BRITAIN BY
WILLIAM CLOWES AND SONS, LIMITED, LONDON AND BECCLES

CONTENTS

CONTENTS

7

CONTENTS

INTRODUCTION

The British are an island people, a race which owes its birth and its existence to the sea and to the ships and sailormen who bring food and all that is needed for human survival. Stories of the men who sail salt water, naturally, appeal to everyone. What is more, some of the best tales, fact as well as fiction, are bound up with the men who go down to the sea in ships; so many of them that it is very difficult to select fifty for this book.

An attempt has been made, therefore, to choose those which appeal most to everyone who has salt running in his veins, and that means most of us. Some are true, some are stories well-known and loved, as well as many which the old-time shellbacks spun on the forehatch of tall ships, in warm latitudes, during the Dog-watch before the night's work began. In those two halcyon hours of the Second Dog the seamen entertained themselves and their shipmates in the short spare time they had before rounding either the Horn or the Cape of Good Hope.

I trust that these fifty stories will bring you the tang, the feel and the scent of salt water, and show you a little of the spirit of the men who still plough the ocean-lanes.

"MAINSAIL"

VENGEANCE IS MINE

By CHARLES KINGSLEY

Driven by his rage-filled lust for vengeance on Don Guzman de Soto, Sir Amyas Leigh pursues the Spanish galleon after the dispersal of the Armada. As last, close to Lundy Island, he sights the enemy.

At the fifty-seventh degree of latitude, the English fleet, finding themselves growing short of provision, and having been long since out of powder and ball, turn southward toward home, "thinking it best to leave the Spaniard to those uncouth and boisterous northern seas." A few pinnaces are still sent onward to watch their course: and the English fleet, caught in the same storms which scattered the Spaniards, "with great danger and industry reached Harwich port, and there provided themselves of victuals and ammunition," in case the Spaniards should return; but there is no need for that caution. Parma, indeed, who cannot believe that the idol at Halle, after all his compliments to it, will play him so scurvy a trick, will watch for weeks on Dunkirk dunes, hoping against hope for the Armada's return, casting anchors, and spinning rigging to repair their losses.

> "But lang lang may his ladies sit,
>   With their fans intill their hand,
>   Before they see Sir Patrick Spens
>   Come sailing to the land."

The Armada is away on the other side of Scotland, and Amyas is following in its wake.

For when the Lord High Admiral determined to return, Amyas asked leave to follow the Spaniard; and asked, too, of Sir John Hawkins, who happened to be at hand, such ammunition and provision as could be afforded him, promising to repay the same like an honest man, out of his plunder if he lived, out of his estate if he died; lodging for that purpose bills in the hands of Sir John, who, as a man of business, took them, and put them in his pocket among the thimbles, string, and tobacco; after which Amyas, calling his men together, reminded them once more of the story of the Rose of Torridge and Don Guzman de Soto, and then asked—

"Men of Bideford, will you follow me? There will be plunder for those who love plunder, revenge for those who love revenge; and for all of us (for we all love honour) the honour of having never left the chase as long as there was a Spanish flag in English seas."

And every soul on board replied, that they would follow Sir Amyas Leigh around the world.

There is no need for me to detail every incident of that long and weary chase; how they found the *Sta. Catharina,* attacked her, and had to sheer off, she being rescued by the rest; how when Medina's squadron left the crippled ships behind, they were all but taken or sunk, by thrusting into the midst of the Spanish fleet to prevent her escaping with Medina; how they crippled her, so that she could not beat to windward out into the ocean, but was fain to run south, past the Orkneys, and down through the Minch, between Cape Wrath and Lewis; how the younger hands were ready to mutiny, because Amyas, in his stubborn haste, ran past two or three noble prizes which were all but disabled, among others one of the great galliasses, and the two great Venetians, *La Ratta* and *La Belanzara* — which were afterwards, with more than thirty other vessels, wrecked on the west coast of Ireland; how he got fresh water, in spite of certain "Hebridean Scots" of Skye, who, after reviling him in an unknown tongue, fought with him awhile, and then embraced him and his men with howls of affection, and were not much more decently clad, nor more civilised, than his old friends of California; how he pacified his men by letting them pick the bones of a great Venetian which was going on shore upon Islay (by which they got booty enough to repay them for the whole voyage), and offended them again by refusing to land and plunder two great Spanish wrecks on the Mull of Cantire (whose crews, by-the-by, James tried to smuggle off secretly into Spain in ships of his own, wishing to play, as usual, both sides of the game at once; but the Spaniards were stopped at Yarmouth till the council's pleasure was known — which was, of course, to let the poor wretches go on their way, and be hanged elsewhere); how they passed a strange island, half black, half white, which the wild people called Raghary, but Cary christened it "the drowned magpie"; how the *Sta. Catharina* was near lost on the Isle of Man, and then put into Castleton (where the Manx-men slew a whole boat's-crew with their arrows), and then put out again, when Amyas fought with her a whole day, and shot away her mainyard; how the Spaniard blundered down the coast of Wales, not knowing whither he went; how they were both nearly lost on Holyhead and again on Bardsey Island; how they got on a lee shore in Cardigan Bay, before a heavy westerly gale, and the *Sta. Catharina* ran aground on Sarn David, one of those strange subaqueous pebble-dykes which are said to be the remnants of the lost land of Gwalior, destroyed by the carelessness of Prince Seithenin the drunkard, at whose name each loyal Welshman spits; how she got off again at the rising of the tide, and fought with Amyas a fourth time; how the wind changed, and she got round St. David's Head;—these, and many more moving incidents of this eventful voyage, I must pass over without details, and go on to the end; for it is time that the end should come.

It was now the sixteenth day of the chase. They had seen, the evening before, St. David's Head, and then the Welsh coast round Milford Haven, looming out black and sharp before the blaze of the inland thunder-storm; and it had lightened all round them during the fore part of the night, upon a light south-western breeze.

In vain they had strained their eyes through the darkness, to catch, by the fitful glare of the flashes, the tall masts of the Spaniard. Of one thing at least they were certain, that with the wind as it was, she could not have gone far to the westward; and to attempt to pass them again, and go northward, was more than she dare do. She was probably lying-to ahead of them, perhaps between them and the land; and when, a little after midnight, the wind chopped up to the west, and blew stiffly till day-break, they felt sure that, unless she had attempted the desperate expedient of running past them, they had her safe in the mouth of the Bristol Channel. Slowly and wearily broke the dawn, on such a day as often follows heavy thunder; a sunless, drizzly day, roofed with low dingy cloud, barred and netted, and festooned with black, a sign that the storm is only taking breath awhile before it bursts again; while all the narrow horizon is dim and spongy with vapour drifting before a chilly breeze. As the day went on the breeze died down, and the sea fell to a long glassy foam-flecked roll, while overhead brooded the inky sky, and round them the leaden mist shut out alike the shore and the chase.

Amyas paced the sloppy deck fretfully and fiercely. He knew that the Spaniard could not escape; but he cursed every moment which lingered between him and that one great revenge which blackened all his soul. The men sat sulkily about the deck, and whistled for a wind; the sails flapped idly against the masts; and the ship rolled in the long troughs of the sea, till her yard-arms almost dipped right and left.

"Take care of those guns. You will have something loose next," growled Amyas.

"We will take care of the guns, if the Lord will take care of the wind," said Yeo.

"We shall have plenty before night," said Cary, "and thunder too."

"So much the better," said Amyas. "It may roar till it splits the heavens, if it does but let me get my work done."

"He's not far off, I warrant," said Cary. "One lift of the cloud and we should see him."

"To windward of us, as likely as not," said Amyas. "The devil fights for him, I believe. To have been on his heels sixteen days, and not sent this through him yet!" And he shook his sword impatiently.

So the morning wore away, without a sign of living thing, not even a passing gull; and the black melancholy of the heaven reflected it-self in the black melancholy of Amyas. Was he to lose his prey after all? The thought made him shudder with rage and disappointment. It was intolerable. Anything but that.

16

"No, God!" he cried, "let me but once feel this in his accursed heart, and then — strike me dead, if Thou wilt!"

"The Lord have mercy on us," cried John Drimblecombe. "What have you said?"

"What is that to you, sir? There, they are piping to dinner. Go down. I shall not come."

And Jack went down, and talked in a half-terrified whisper of Amyas's ominous words.

All thought that they portended some bad luck, except old Yeo.

"Well, Sir John," said he, "and why not? What better can the Lord do for a man, than take him home when he has done his work? Our captain is wilful and spiteful, and must needs kill his man himself; while for me, I don't care how the Don goes, provided he does go. I owe him no grudge, nor any man. May the Lord give him repentance, and forgive him all his sins: but if I could but see him safe ashore, as he may be ere nightfall, on the Mortestone or the back of Lundy, I would say, 'Lord, now lettest Thou Thy servant depart in peace,' even if it were the lightning which was sent to fetch me."

"But, master Yeo, a sudden death?"

"And why not a sudden death, Sir John? Even fools long for a short life and a merry one, and shall not the Lord's people pray for a short death and a merry one? Let it come as it will to old Yeo. Hark! There's the captain's voice!"

"Here she is!" thundered Amyas from the deck; and in an instant all were scrambling up the hatchway as fast as the frantic rolling of the ship would let them.

Yes. There she was. The cloud had lifted suddenly, and to the south a ragged bore of blue sky let a long stream of sunshine down on her tall masts and stately hull, as she lay rolling some four or five miles to the eastward: but as for land, none was to be seen.

"There she is; and here we are," said Cary; "but where is here? And where is there? How is the tide, master?"

"Running up Channel by this time, sir."

"What matters the tide?" said Amyas, devouring the ship with terrible and cold blue eyes. "Can't we get at her?"

"Not unless some one jumps out and shoves behind," said Cary. "I shall down again and finish that mackerel, if this roll has not chucked it to the cockroaches under the table."

"Don't jest, Will! I can't stand it," said Amyas in a voice which quivered so much that Cary looked at him. His whole frame was trembling like an aspen. Cary took his arm, and drew him aside.

"Dear old lad," said he, as they leaned over the bulwarks, "what is this? You are not yourself, and have not been these four days."

"No. I am not Amyas Leigh. I am my brother's avenger. Do not reason with me, Will: when it is over I shall be merry old Amyas again," and he passed his hand over his brow.

"Do you believe," said he, after a moment, "that men can be possessed by devils?"

"The Bible says so."

"If my cause were not a just one, I should fancy I had a devil in me. My throat and heart are as hot as the pit. Would to God it were done, for done it must be! Now go."

Cary went away with a shudder. As he passed down the hatchway he looked back. Amyas had got the hone out of his pocket, and was whetting away again at his sword-edge, as if there was some dreadful doom on him, to whet, and whet forever.

The weary day wore on. The strip of blue sky was curtained over again, and all was dismal as before, though it grew sultrier every moment; and now and then a distant mutter shook the air to westward. Nothing could be done to lessen the distance between the ships, for the *Vengeance* had had all her boats carried away but one, and that was much too small to tow her and, while the men went down again to finish dinner, Amyas worked on at his sword, looking up every now and then suddenly at the Spaniard, as if to satisfy himself that it was not a vision which had vanished. About two Yeo came up to him.

"He is ours safely now, sir. The tide has been running to the eastward for this two hours."

"Safe as a fox in a trap. Satan himself cannot take him from us!"

"But God may," said Brimblecombe simply.

"Who spoke to you, sir? If I thought that He — There comes the thunder at last!"

And as he spoke an angry growl from the westward heavens seemed to answer his wild words, and rolled and loudened nearer and nearer, till right over their heads it crashed against some cloud-cliff far above, and all was still.

Each man looked in the other's face: but Amyas was unmoved.

"The storm is coming," said he, "and the wind in it. It will be East-ward-ho now, for once, my merry men all!"

"Eastward-ho never brought us luck," said Jack in an undertone to Cary. But by this time all eyes were turned to the north-west, where a black line along the horizon began to define the boundary of sea and air, till now all dim in mist.

"There comes the breeze."

"And there the storm, too."

And with that strangely accelerating pace which some storms seem to possess, the thunder, which had been growling slow and seldom far away, now rang peal on peal along the cloudy floor above their heads.

"Here comes the breeze. Round with the yards, or we shall be taken aback."

The yards creaked round; the sea grew crisp around them; the hot air swept their cheeks, tightened every rope, filled every sail, bent her over. A cheer burst from the men as the helm went up, and they staggered away before the wind, right down upon the Spaniard, who lay still becalmed.

"There is more behind, Amyas," said Cary. "Shall we not shorten sail a little?"

"No. Hold on every stitch," said Amyas. "Give me the helm, man. Boatswain, pipe away to clear for fight."

It was done, and in ten minutes the men were all at quarters, while the thunder rolled louder and louder overhead, and the breeze freshened fast.

"The dog has it now. There he goes!" said Cary.

"Right before the wind. He has no liking to face us."

"He is running into the jaws of destruction," said Yeo. "An hour more will send him either right up the Channel, or smack on shore somewhere."

"There! he has put his helm down. I wonder if he sees land?"

"He is like a March hare beat out of his country," said Cary, "and don't know whither to run next."

Cary was right. In ten minutes more the Spaniard fell off again, and went away dead down wind, while the *Vengeance* gained on him fast. After two hours more, the four miles had diminished to one, while the lightning flashed nearer and nearer as the storm came up; and from the vast mouth of a black cloud-arch poured so fierce a breeze that Amyas yielded unwillingly to hints which were growing into open murmurs, and bade shorten sail.

On they rushed with scarcely lessened speed, the black arch following fast, curtained by one flat grey sheet of pouring rain, before which the water was boiling in a long white line; while every moment behind the watery veil, a keen blue spark leapt down into the sea, or darted zigzag through the rain.

"We shall have it now, and with a vengeance; this will try your tackle, master," said Cary.

The functionary answered with a shrug, and turned up the collar of his rough frock, as the first drops flew stinging round his ears. Another minute and the squall burst full upon them, in rain, which cut like hail — hail which lashed the sea into froth, and wind which whirled off the heads of the surges, and swept the waters into one white seething waste. And above them, and behind them, and before them, the lightning leapt and ran, dazzling and blinding, while the deep roar of the thunder was changed to sharp ear-piercing cracks.

"Get the arms and ammunition under cover, and then below with you all," shouted Amyas from the helm.

"And heat the pokers in the galley fire," said Yeo, "to be ready if the rain puts our linstocks out. I hope you'll let me stay on deck, sir."

"I must have someone, and who better than you? Can you see the chase?"

No; she was wrapped in the grey whirlwind. She might be within half a mile of them, for aught they could have seen of her.

And now Amyas and his old liegeman were alone. Neither spoke; each knew the other's thoughts, and knew that they were his own. The squall blew fiercer and fiercer, the rain poured heavier and heavier. Where was the Spaniard?

"If he has laid-to, we may overshoot him, sir!"

"If he has tried to lay-to, he will not have a sail left in the bolt-ropes, or perhaps a mast on deck. I know the stiff-neckedness of those Spanish tubs. Hurrah! There he is, right on our larboard bow!"

There she was indeed, two musket-shots off, staggering away with canvas split and flying.

"He has been trying to hull, sir, and caught a buffet," said Yeo, rubbing his hands. "What shall we do now?"

"Range alongside, if it blow live imps and witches, and try our luck once more. Pah! How this lightning dazzles!"

On they swept, gaining fast on the Spaniard.

"Call the men up, and to quarters; the rain will be over in ten minutes."

Yeo ran forward to the gangway; and sprang back again, with a face white and wild—

"Land right ahead! Port your helm, sir! For the love of God, port your helm!"

Amyas, with the strength of a bull, jammed the helm down, while Yeo shouted to the men below.

She swung round. The masts bent like whips; crack went the foresail like a cannon. What matter? Within two hundred yards of them was the Spaniard; in front of her, and above her, a huge dark bank rose through the dense hail, and mingled with the clouds; and at its foot, plainer every moment, pillars and spouts of leaping foam.

"What is it, Morte? Hartland?"

It might be anything for thirty miles.

22

"Lundy!" said Yeo. "The south end! I see the head of the Shutter in the breakers! Hard a-port yet, and get her close-hauled as you can, and the Lord may have mercy on us still! Look at the Spaniard!"

Yes, look at the Spaniard!

On their left hand, as they broached-to, the wall of granite sloped down from the clouds toward an isolated peak of rock, some two hundred feet in height. Then a hundred yards of roaring breaker upon a sunken shelf, across which the race of the tide poured like a cataract; then, amid a column of salt smoke, the Shutter, like a huge black fang, rose waiting for its prey; and between the Shutter and the land, the great galleon loomed dimly through the storm.

He, too, had seen his danger, and tried to broach-to. But his clumsy mass refused to obey the helm; he struggled a moment, half hid in foam; fell away again, and rushed upon his doom.

"Lost! Lost! Lost!" cried Amyas madly, and throwing up his hands, let go the tiller. Yeo caught it just in time.

"Sir! sir! What are you at? We shall clear the rock yet."

"Yes!" shouted Amyas in his frenzy; "but he will not!"

Another minute. The galleon gave a sudden jar, and stopped. Then one long heave and bound, as if to free herself. And then her bows lighted clean upon the Shutter.

An awful silence fell on every English soul. They heard not the roaring of wind and surge; they saw not the blinding flashes of the lightning; but they heard one long ear-piercing wail to every saint in heaven rise from five hundred human throats; they saw the mighty ship heel over from the wind, and sweep headlong down the cataract of the race, plunging her yards into the foam, and showing her whole black side even to her keel, till she rolled clean over, and vanished for ever and ever.

"Shame!" cried Amyas, hurling his sword far into the sea, "to lose my right, my right! When it was in my very grasp! Unmerciful!"

A crack which rent the sky, and made the granite ring and quiver; a bright world of flame, and then a blank of utter darkness, against which stood out, glowing red-hot, every mast, and sail, and rock, and

Salvation Yeo as he stood just in front of Amyas, the tiller in his hand. All red-hot, transfigured into fire; and behind, the black, black night.

A whisper, a rustling close beside him, and Brimblecombe's voice said softly,—

"Give him more wine, Will; his eyes are opening."

"Hey day?" said Amyas faintly, "not past the Shutter yet! How long she hangs in the wind!"

"We are long past the Shutter, Sir Amyas," said Brimblecombe.

"Are you mad? Cannot I trust my own eyes?"

There was no answer for awhile.

"We are past the Shutter, indeed," said Cary very gently, "and lying in the cove at Lundy."

"Will you tell me that that is not the Shutter, and that the Devil's-limekiln, and that the cliff—that villian Spaniard only gone—and that Yeo is not standing here by me, and Cary there forward, and—why, by-the-by, where are you, Jack Brimblecombe, who were talking to me this minute?"

"Oh, Sir Amyas Leigh, dear Sir Amyas Leigh," blubbered poor Jack, "put out your hand, and feel where you are, and pray the Lord to forgive you for your wilfulness!"

A great trembling fell upon Amyas Leigh; half fearfully he put out his hand; he felt that he was in his hammock, with the deck beams close above his head. The vision which had been left upon his eyeballs vanished like a dream.

"What is this? I must be asleep? What has happened? Where am I?"

"In your cabin, Amyas," said Cary.

"What? And where is Yeo?"

"Yeo is gone where he longed to go, and as he longed to go. The same flash which struck you down, struck him dead."

"Dead? Lightning? Any more hurt? I must go and see. Why, what is this?" and Amyas passed his hand across his eyes. "It is all dark—dark, as I live!" And he passed his hand over his eyes again.

There was another dead silence. Amyas broke it.

"Oh, God!" shrieked the great proud sea-captain, "Oh, God, I am blind! Blind! Blind!" And writhing in his great horror, he called to Cary to kill him and put him out of his misery, and then wailed for his mother to come and help him, as if he had been a boy once more; while Brimblecombe and Cary, and the sailors who crowded round the cabin-door, wept as if they too had been boys once more.

Soon his fit of frenzy passed off, and he sank back exhausted.

They lifted him into their remaining boat, rowed him ashore, carried him painfully up the hill to the old castle, and made a bed for him on the floor, in the very room in which Don Guzman and Rose Salterne had plighted their troth to each other, five wild years before.

Three miserable days were passed within that lonely tower. Amyas, utterly unnerved by the horror of his misfortune, and by the over-excitement of the last few weeks, was incessantly delirious; while Cary, and Brimblecombe, and the men, nursed him by turns, as sailors and wives only can nurse; and listened with awe to his piteous self-reproaches and entreaties to Heaven to remove that woe, which, as he shrieked again and again, was a just judgment on him for his wilfulness and ferocity. The surgeon talked, of course, learnedly about melancholic humours, and his liver's being "adust by the over-pungency of the animal spirits," and then fell back on the universal panacea of blood-letting, which he effected with fear and trembling during a short interval of prostration; encouraged by which he attempted to administer a large bolus of aloes, was knocked down for his pains, and then thought it better to leave Nature to her own work. In the meanwhile, Cary had sent off one of the island skiffs to Clovelly, with letters to his father, and to Mrs. Leigh, entreating the latter to come off to the island: but the heavy westerly winds made that as impossible as it was to move Amyas on board, and the men had to do their best, and did it well enough.

On the fourth day his raving ceased: but he was still too weak to be moved. Toward noon, however, he called for food, ate a little, and seemed revived.

25

"Will," he said, after a while, "this room is as stifling as it is dark. I feel as if I should be a sound man once more if I could but get one snuff of the sea-breeze."

The surgeon shook his head at the notion of moving him: but Amyas was peremptory.

"I am captain still, Tom Surgeon, and will sail for the Indies, if I choose. Will Cary, Jack Brimblecombe, will you obey a blind general?"

"What you will in reason," said they both at once.

"Then lead me out, my masters, and over the down to the south end. To the point at the south end I must go; there is no other place will suit."

And he rose firmly to his feet, and held out his hands for theirs.

"Let him have his humour," whispered Cary. "It may be the working off of his madness."

"This sudden strength is a note of fresh fever, Mr. Lieutenant," said the surgeon, "and the rules of the art prescribe rather a fresh blood-letting."

Amyas overheard the last word, and broke out,—

"You pig-sticking Philistine, wilt thou make sport with blind Samson? Come near me to let blood from my arm, and see if I do not let blood from thy cox omb. Catch him, Will, and bring him me here!"

The surgeon vanished as the blind giant made a step forward; and they set forth, Amyas walking slowly, but firmly, between his two friends.

"Whither?" asked Cary.

"To the south end. The crag above the Devil's-limekiln. No other place will suit."

Jack gave a murmur, and half-stopped, as a frightful suspicion crossed him.

"That is a dangerous place!"

"What of that?" said Amyas, who caught his meaning in his tone. "Dost think I am going to leap over cliff? I have not heart enough for that. On, lads, and set me safe among the rocks."

So slowly, and painfully, they went on, while Amyas murmured to himself, "no, no other place will suit; I can see all thence."

So on they went to the point, where the cyclopean wall of granite cliff which forms the western side of Lundy, ends sheer in a precipice of some three hundred feet, topped by a pile of snow-white rock, bespangled with golden lichens. As they approached, a raven, who sat upon the topmost stone, black against the bright blue sky, flapped lazily away, and sank down the abysses of the cliff, as if he scented the corpses underneath the surge. Below them from the Gull-rock rose a thousand birds, and filled the air with sound; the choughs cackled, the hacklets wailed, the great blackbacks laughed querulous defiance at the intruders, and a single falcon, with an angry bark, dashed out from beneath their feet, and hung poised high aloft, watching the sea-fowl which swung slowly round and round below.

It was a glorious sight upon a glorious day. To the northward the glens rushed down toward the cliff, crowned with grey crags, and carpeted with purple heather and green fern; and from their feet stretched away to the westward the sapphire rollers of the vast Atlantic, crowned with a thousand crests of flying foam. On their left hand, some ten miles to the south, stood out against the sky the purple wall of Hartland cliffs, sinking lower and lower as they trended away to the southward along the lonely ironbound shores of Cornwall, until they faded, dim and blue, into the blue horizon forty miles away.

The sky was flecked with clouds, which rushed toward them fast upon the roaring south-west wind; and the warm ocean-breeze swept up the cliffs, and whistled through the heather-bells, and howled in cranny and in crag.

> "Till the pillars and clefts of the granite
> Rang like a God-swept lyre;"

while Amyas, a proud smile upon his lips, stood breasting that genial stream of airy wine with swelling nostrils and fast-heaving chest, and seemed to drink in life from every gust. All three were silent for a while; and Jack and Cary, gazing downward with delight upon the glory and the grandeur of the sight, forgot for a while that their companion saw it not. Yet when they started sadly, and looked into his face, did he not see it? So wide and eager were his eyes, so bright and calm his face, that they fancied for an instant that he was once more even as they.

A deep sigh undeceived them. "I know it is all here—the dear old sea, where I would live and die. And my eyes feel for it; feel for it—and cannot find it; never, never will find it again for ever! God's will be done!"

"Do you say that?" asked Brimblecombe eagerly.

"Why should I not? Why have I been raving in hell-fire for I know not how many days, but to find out that, John Brimblecombe, thou better man than I?"

"Not that last: but Amen! Amen! And the Lord has indeed had mercy upon thee!" said Jack, through his honest tears.

"Amen!" said Amyas. "Now set me where I can rest among the rocks without fear of falling—for life is sweet still, even without eyes, friends—and leave me to myself awhile."

It was no easy matter to find a safe place; for from the foot of the crag the heathery turf slopes down all but upright, on one side to a cliff which overhangs a shoreless cove of deep dark sea, and on the other to an abyss even more hideous, where the solid rock has sunk away, and opened inland in the hillside a smooth-walled pit, some sixty feet square and some hundred and fifty in depth, aptly known then as now, as the Devil's-limekiln; the mouth of which, as old wives say, was once closed by the Shutter-rock itself, till the fiend in malice hurled it into the sea, to be a pest to mariners. A narrow and untrodden cavern at the bottom connects it with the outer sea; they could even then hear the mysterious thunder and gurgle of the surge in the subterranean adit, as it rolled huge boulders to and fro in darkness, and forced before it gusts of pent-up air. It was a spot to curdle weak blood, and to make weak heads reel: but all the fitter on that account for Amyas and his fancy.

"You can sit here as in an arm-chair," said Cary, helping him to one of those square natural seats so common in the granite tors.

"Good; now turn my face to the Shutter. Be sure and exact. So. Do I face it full?"

"Full," said Cary.

"Then I need no eyes wherewith to see what is before me," said he, with a sad smile. "I know every stone and every headland, and every wave too, I may say, far beyond aught that eye can reach. Now go, and leave me alone with God and with the dead!"

They retired a little space and watched him. He never stirred for many minutes; then leaned his elbows on his knees, and his head upon his hands, and so was still again. He remained so long thus, that the pair became anxious, and went towards him. He was asleep, and breathing quick and heavily.

"He will take a fever," said Brimblecombe, "if he sleeps much longer with his head down in the sunshine."

"We must wake him gently, if we wake him at all." And Cary moved forward to him.

As he did so, Amyas lifted his head, and turning it to right and left, felt round him with his sightless eyes.

"You have been asleep, Amyas."

"Have I? I have not slept back my eyes, then. Take up this great useless carcase of mine, and lead me home. I shall buy me a dog when I get to Burrough, I think, and make him tow me in a string, eh? So! Give me your hand. Now march!"

His guides heard with surprise this new cheerfulness.

"Thank God, sir, that your heart is so light already," said good Jack; "it makes me feel quite upraised myself, like."

"I have reason to be cheerful, Sir John; I have left a heavy load behind me. I have been wilful, and proud, and a blasphemer, and swollen with cruelty and pride; and God has brought me low for it, and cut me off from my evil delight. No more Spaniard-hunting for me now, my masters. God will send no such fools as I upon His errands."

"You do not repent of fighting the Spaniards."

"Not I: but of hating even the worst of them. Listen to me, Will and Jack. If that man wronged me, I wronged him likewise. I have been a fiend when I thought myself the grandest of men, yea, a very avenging angel out of heaven. But God has shown me my sin, and we have made up our quarrel for ever."

"Made it up?"

"Made it up, thank God. But I am weary. Set me down awhile, and I will tell you how it befell."

Wondering, they set him down upon the heather, while the bees hummed round them in the sun; and Amyas felt for a hand of each, and clasped it in his own hand, and began,—

"When you left me there upon the rock, lads, I looked away and out to sea, to get one last snuff of the merry sea-breeze, which will never sail me again. And as I looked, I tell you truth, I could see the water and the sky; as plain as ever I saw them, till I thought my sight was come again. But soon I knew it was not so; for I saw more than man could see; right over the ocean, as I live, and away to the Spanish Main. And I saw Barbados, and Grenada, and all the isles that we ever sailed by; and La Guayra in Carraccas, and the Silla, and the house beneath it where she lived. And I saw him walking with her on the barbecu, and he loved her then. I saw what I saw; and he loved her; and I say he loves her still.

"Then I saw the cliffs beneath me, and the Gull-rock, and the Shutter, and the Ledge; I saw them, William Cary, and the weeds beneath the merry blue sea. And I saw the grand old galleon, Will; she has righted with the sweeping of the tide. She lies in fifteen fathoms, at the edge of the rocks, upon the sand; and her men are all lying around her, asleep until the judgment-day."

THE MATE'S STORY

The true story of the disaster which befell a sealing ship in March,
1898, *as told by one of the survivors.*

The sealing steamer *Greenland*, when berthed in Glasgow harbour,
became a vessel of more than usual interest. The terrible disaster
which befell her crew in March, 1898 when, of some 150 men who
were sent out on the ice to "pan" seals, almost a third lost their lives,
excited a great deal of attention.

The reports which appeared in the newspapers gave but a faint
idea of the real nature of the disaster. It felt very different when one
went down to the dock and looked at the blackened, battered, yet
hardy-looking sealer, and talked to the second mate, who shared in the
dangers of the memorable trip, and told so vividly of the storm and
the search for his comrades on the ocean of ice.

The *Greenland*, a wood screw barque, was an ideal sealer. There
was no new-fangled nonsense about her. A steamer, but with sails
enough to make her independent of steam when on the fishing ground,
she reminded one of the vessels described in the stories of adventure
in which we revelled in our schoolboy days.

Ambrose Critch, the second mate, by birth a Newfoundlander, was
the ideal of a sealing fisherman, and gave the impression, which is no
doubt true, that he was more at home on the deck, or even on ice,
than on a city's streets. Bronzed and weather-beaten, yet hardy and
earnest, he spoke seriously, but without restraint, of the terrible three
weeks spent on and among the ice off the coast of Newfoundland.

"You want to hear about the disaster?" he said to a visitor who
boarded the *Greenland*. "I am not sure that I can tell the story very
well. It is too terrible a story.

"We left St. John's on the 10th of March; a Thursday, it was. There
were, I think, 207 of us on board altogether. Steering N.N.E., we made
'The Funks' the following day. About 60 miles, maybe, N.E. of the
island, we struck seals — on the 12th, I think — it was the Saturday,
anyhow. We kept getting seals from then till the 20th — that was a

Sunday, and, as perhaps you may know, we don't seal on Sundays.

"At three o'clock on Monday morning, Captain Barbour sent a watch out on the ice to kill and pan seals. At five he sent two other watches."

(Here Captain Vine, then in command of the *Greenland*, interposed to dispel the notetaker's puzzled look, by explaining that a watch generally consisted of from forty to fifty men, and that to "pan" seals was to gather them into heaps on the ice floes, so that they could be taken to the ship more conveniently.)

"The men were on the ice all day," the mate continued. "About five o'clock at night the storm came on — snow and drift. We could hardly see across the ship. It was like that from five on Monday till three on Tuesday afternoon, and we knew nothing of the poor men who were blindly wandering — perhaps frozen — among the ice and water. We knew the storm had made an opening that they could not get across. The ship was thrown on her beam ends by the wind, and the coal and provisions and seals had to be shifted to right her.

"At three on Tuesday the weather was better, and at five three men were seen on the ice, trying to make for the ship. Those on board were sent to search for the rest. Boats were provisioned and sent out, and before night we had found about eighty of the men. They were frostbitten, all of them, and some so badly injured that they had to be led on board. You see it was smooth ice, not the humpy, loose kind, on which the men could have built huts and sheltered themselves. So they could only stand or lie all the time. They were a mile or so from the ship—"

"A mile from the ship, and on ice?"

"A mile!" the sailor repeated, and he smiled a smile of pity at the ignorance of the man who had never been seal fishing. "Man, we are sometimes a dozen miles from the ship. Ay, a mile!"

Interruptions were few afterwards.

"The men were in extremity, and could not have lasted much longer. We got no bodies on the Tuesday. On Wednesday the drift had cleared, and more searchers were sent out, and on that day many of the dead men were found. Captain Barbour had hoisted flags at half-mast and men from the *Diana* and the *Iceland,* two other sealers, were sent to help us. The *Diana's* men found six bodies, and the *Iceland's* men four. The bodies were found scattered all over the ice, in ones and twos and threes. Many of the men seemed to have been crawling. They would know of the open water that was between them and the ship, and in the blinding drift they would be afraid to walk. One man, who was found alive, was creeping away from the ship. He had lost his mittens, and he had no feeling in his hands.

"The searchers got out the small boats, and hauled them over the ice with ropes. When they found bodies, they put them into the boat and hauled them back to our ship. Our own men did not use boats; they made 'drays' — things like lorries, but without wheels — and hauled them over the ice. We found twenty-four bodies in all."

"Was that the total number lost?"

"Over twenty-four. They must have suffered terribly. I never saw such a storm. It was a wonder how men could have lived at all on the pans. Some of them that the survivors told of actually went mad, and thought the ship was near, and ran into the open water to reach her, and were drowned. There was water all around them, you know.

"There were two boys saved, who had spent fifty-two hours on the ice, in the storm. We found them on the Wednesday, when the storm was over. They had been alone for a while, but they were joined by one of the men, and the three kept together.

"One curious thing there was. It was not the big, hardy-looking men who lived through the storm on the ice. They died, and those who survived were the slight and weak-looking kind.

"The last body we got was found on the Friday, about two miles from the ship. We cruised about for a while, but gave up the search on Saturday, and made for Bay de Verde. The twenty-four bodies were on board here, and I made a pound — a big box, you know — along by this stanchion, and put them all in. I iced them — you have seen salmon iced, a row of fish and a fold of ice — to keep them till we should reach port. We left Bay de Verde on Sunday morning, and

33

after an uneventful voyage, we got to St. John's the same afternoon."

"And the bodies?"

"We saw them buried, of course. I had to take them out of the ice. When I put them in I had put tickets on them, so that we would know them again. No one of us knew them all, but among us we managed to find all their names. It was terrible work taking them out of the ice. The pound was one solid mass. I had to cut each body out in a square piece.

"It was an awful day in St. John's when we arrived. Not many of the lost and dead men belonged there, but there were other ships out, and the folks were frightened. They knew of the disaster, because our captain had telegraphed from Bay de Verde. The Governor did all he could, and the members of council all took part in the work of providing for the suffering, and disposing of the dead. We buried them in the cemeteries of their different churches.

"A relief fund was started, and the Glasgow owners of the ship, as well as the agent in St. John's, contributed handsomely. The crew all belonged to Newfoundland; most of them to Bonavista Bay.

"About the seals? The voyage was abandoned when the disaster happened. It lasted three weeks. We had 14,500 seals on board, and we left as many on the ice as would have loaded the ship. We landed the seals on Tuesday at Harbour Grace, after the bodies were buried, and the ship stayed there until we took on board a cargo of oil and skins for Glasgow.

"You don't often have a sealer in your harbour, I daresay. No, I thought not. We had to come here because the vessel needed a new boiler. No, I don't think I can tell you much more about the disaster. There is plenty more to tell, but somehow I can't tell it. It was terrible."

It was.

THE MARINES' APE

By CAPTAIN BASIL HALL

Captain Basil Hall was one of the earlier writers of sea stories for boys. Here he tells of his experiences while in command of a ten-gun brig in 1816.

I was in command of the *Lyra,* on the homeward voyage from China, after the embassy under Lord Amherst had been concluded. We touched on our way to Calcutta at the Philippine Islands, and, amongst other livestock, laid in a monkey which had seen the world. He was born, they assured us, at Teneriffe, bred at Cadiz, and had afterwards made the voyage across the Pacific Ocean, via Lima and Acapulco, to Manilla. This splendid bay is the chief station of the Spaniards in the eastern world, and has long formed one of those links in the vast colonial chain which enabled that once powerful nation to boast with truth that the sun never set on their dominions. Our extensive traveller had made good use of his time and opportunities, and was destined to see a good deal more of men and manners, indeed almost to make out the circuit of the globe. We brought him with us through the Straits of Malacca to Poolo Penang, and from thence carried him across the Bay of Bengal to Calcutta and Madras. We next visited together the Isle of France; the Cape; and, lastly, St. Helena, at the very time the ex-emperor of the world resided there.

This distinguished monkey differed in one important point from the last, whose adventures have often been related; for he had a particular liking for the marines, who caressed and fed him, and sometimes even ventured to teach him to play off tricks on Jack, which the sailors promised one day to pay back with interest on the soldiers. In so diminutive a vessel as a ten-gun brig, there is but a small party of marines, merely a sergeant's guard, and no commissioned officer, otherwise I hardly think the following trick would have been attempted.

It has been already mentioned, that on Sundays the ship's company are mustered at divisions, ranged on either side of the deck. Every man is then dressed in his very best togs, shaved, and trimmed up as gaily as possible. The marines, of course, sparkle abaft as brightly as polished metal, scarlet cloth, and the eternal pipe-clay, can make them. When all are reported present, the captain walks slowly and solemnly round, eyeing each man from head to foot, to detect a spot of dirt, or a thread opening at a seam, and peering under the breast of every gun to discover some neglected delta of unwashed-away sand; in short, to see that all is right and tight, or 'ship-shape and Bristol fashion'; a term, by the way, of which I know not the origin.

One day, while going these formal rounds, I came to a figure which at first sight puzzled me not a little. This was no other than our great traveller the monkey, rigged out as a marine, and planted like a sentry on the middle step of the short ladder, which, in deep-waisted vessels, is placed at the gangway, and reaches from the deck to the top of the bulwark. The animal was dressed up in a complete suit of miniature uniform, made chiefly of the coloured bunting used for flags, with sundry bits of red baize purloined from the carpenters. His regimental cap was constructed out of painted canvas; and under his lower jaw had been forced a stock of pump-leather, so stiff in itself, and so tightly drawn back, that his head was rendered totally immovable. His chin, and great part of the cheeks, had been shaved with so much care, that only two small curled mustachios and a respectable pair of whiskers remained. His hair behind being tied back tightly into a queue, the poor devil's eyes were almost starting from his head; while the corners of his mouth being likewise tugged towards the ears by the hair-dresser's operations, the expression of his countenance became irresistibly ludicrous. The astonished recruit's elbows were then brought in contact and fastened behind by a lashing, passed round and secured to the middle step of the ladder, so that he could not budge an inch from his position. One of the ship's pistols, fashioned like a musket, and strapped to his shoulder, was tied to his left hand, which had been sewed by the sail-maker to the waistband of his beautifully pipe-clayed trousers; in short, he was rigged up as a complete sea-soldier in full uniform.

As the captain and his train approached, the monkey began to tremble and chatter; but the men, not knowing how their chief might relish the joke, looked rather grave, while, I own, it cost me no small official struggle to keep down a laugh. I did succeed, however, and merely said, in passing, "You should not play these tricks upon travellers; cast him loose immediately." One of the men pulled his knife from his breast, and cutting the cord which fastened the poor Spaniard to the ladder, let him scamper off. Unluckily for the gravity of the officers, however, and that of the crew, Jacko did not run below, or jump into one of the boats out of sight, but made straight for his dear friends the marines, drawn up in line across our little hurricane-house of a poop. Unconscious of the ridicule he was bringing on his military patrons, he took up a position in front of the corps, not unlike a bugleman; and I need hardly say, that even the royals themselves, provoked though they were, joined in the laugh which soon passed along the decks, and was with difficulty suppressed during the remainder of the muster.

A day or two afterwards, and while the monkey was still puzzled to think what was the matter with his chin, he happened to observe the doctor engaged in some chemical process. As his curiosity and desire for information were just such as ought to characterise a traveller of his intelligence, he crept gradually from chest to chest, and from bag to bag, till he arrived within about a yard of Apothecaries' Hall, as that part of the steerage was named by the midshipmen. Poor Mono's delight was very great as he observed the process of pill-making, which he watched attentively while the ingredients were successively weighed, pounded, and formed into a long roll of paste. All these proceedings excited his deepest interest. The doctor then took his spreader, and cut the roll into five pieces, each of which he intended to divide into a dozen pills. At this stage of the process, someone called the pharmacologist's attention to the hatchway. The instant his back was turned, the monkey darted on the top of the medicine-chest, snapped up all the five masses of pill stuff, stowed them hastily away in his pouch, or bag, at the side of his mouth, scampered on deck, and leaped into the main rigging, preparatory to a leisurely feast upon his pilfered treasures.

The doctor's first feeling was that of anger at the abstraction of his medicines; but in the next instant, recollecting that unless immediate steps were taken, the poor animal must inevitably be poisoned, he rushed on deck, without coat or hat, and knife in hand, to the great surprise and scandal of the officer of the watch.

"Lay hold of the monkey, some of you!" roared the doctor to the people. "Jump up in the rigging, and try to get out of his pouch a whole mess of my stuff he has run off with!"

The men only laughed, as they fancied the doctor must be cracked.

"For any sake," cried the good-natured physician, "don't make a joke of this matter. The monkey has now in his jaws more than a hundred grains of calomel, and unless you get it from him, he will die to a certainty!"

Literally, the quantity Jacko had purloined, had it been prescribed, would have been ordered in these terms:

℞Hydrargyri submuriatis, ʒij. (Take of calomel 120 grains!)

This appeal, which was quite intelligible, caused an immediate rush of the men aloft; but the monkey, after gulping down one of the lumps, or twenty-four grains, shot upwards to the top, over the rail of which he displayed his shaven countenance, and, as if in scorn of their impotent efforts to catch him, plucked another lump from his cheek, and swallowed it likewise, making four dozen grains to begin with. The news spread over the ship; and all hands, marines inclusive, most of whom had never been farther in the rigging than was necessary to hang up a wet shirt to dry, were seen struggling aloft to rescue the poor monkey from his sad fate. All their exertions were fruitless; for just as the captain of the maintop seized him by the tail, at the starboard royal yard-arm, he was cramming the last batch of calomel down his throat!

It would give needless pain to describe the effects of swallowing the whole of this enormous prescription. Every art was resorted to within our reach in the shape of antidotes, but all in vain. The sto-

THE MARINES' APE

mach-pump was then, unfortunately, not invented. Poor Jacko's sufferings, of course, were great: first, he lost the use of his limbs, then he became blind, next paralytic; and, in short, he presented, at the end of the week, such a dreadful spectacle of pain, distortion, and rigidity of limb, that I felt absolutely obliged to desire that he might be released from his misery, by being thrown into the sea. This was accordingly done when the ship was going along, for the British Channel, at the rate of seven or eight knots, with a fine fair wind. Very shortly afterwards it fell calm, and next day the wind drew round to the eastward. It continued at that point till we were blown fifty leagues back, and kept at sea so much longer than we had reckoned upon, that we were obliged to reduce our daily allowance of provisions and water to a most painfully small quantity. The sailors unanimously ascribed the whole of our bad luck to the circumstance of the monkey being thrown overboard. I had all my nautical life been well aware that a cat ought never to be so treated; but never knew, till the fate of this poor animal acquainted me with the fact, that a monkey is included in Jack's superstition.

In the same vessel, and on the same voyage to China, the sailors had another pet, of a very singular description; viz. a pig — literally a grunter: nor do I believe there ever was a favourite more deeply cherished, or more sincerely lamented after her singular exit. On our sailing from England, six little sows, of a peculiarly fine breed, had been laid in by my steward. In the course of the voyage, five of these fell under the relentless hands of the butcher; but one of the six, being possessed of a more graceful form than belonged to her sister swine, and kept as clean as any lap-dog, was permitted to run about the decks, amongst the goats, sheep, dogs, and monkeys of our little ark. The occurrence of two or three smart gales of wind off the Cape of Good Hope, and the unceremonious entrance of sundry large seas, swept the decks of most of our livestock, excepting only this one pig, known amongst the crew by the pet name of Jean. During the bad weather off the Bank of Aguilas, her sowship was stowed in the launch of the booms, and never seen, though often enough heard; but when we hauled up to the northward, and once more entered the trade-winds, on our course to the Straits of Sunda, by which entrance we proposed to gain the Java Sea, Miss Jean was again allowed to range about the decks at large, and right happy seemed, poor lady, to exchange the odious confinement of the long-boat for the freedom of the open waist.

In warm latitudes, the men, as I have mentioned before, generally take their meals on deck, and it was Jean's grand amusement, as well as business, to cruise along amongst the messes, poking her snout into every bread-bag, and very often she scalded her tongue in the soup-kids. Occasionally, the sailors, to shew the extent of their regard, amused themselves by pouring a drop of grog down her throat. I never saw her fairly drunk, however, but twice; upon which occasions, as was to be expected, she acted pretty much like a human being in the same hoggish predicament. Whether it was owing to this high feeding, or to the constant scrubbing which her hide received from sand, brushes, and holystones, I know not, but she certainly grew and flourished at a most astonishing rate, and every day waxed more and more impudent and importunate at the dinner-hour. I saw a good deal of this familiarity going on, but had no idea of the estimation Jean was held in, till one day, when we were about half-way across the China Sea, and all our stock of sheep, fowls, and ducks, was expended, I said to the steward, "You had better kill the pig, which, if properly managed, will last till we reach Macao."

The servant stood for some time fumbling with his hair, and shuffling with his feet, muttering something to himself.

"Don't you hear?" I asked. "Kill the pig; and let us have the fry to-day; the head, with plenty of Port wine, as mock-turtle soup, to-morrow; and get one of the legs roasted for dinner on Saturday."

Off he went; but in half an hour returned, on some pretence or other, when he took occasion to ask,

"Did you say Jean was to be killed, sir?"

"Jean! Who is Jean? — Oh, now, I remember; the pig. Yes, certainly. Why do you bother and boggle so about killing a pig?"

"The ship's company, sir—"

"Well; what have the ship's company to say to my pig?"

"They are very fond of Jean, sir."

"The devil they are! Well; what then?"

"Why, sir, they would take it as a great kindness if you would not order her to be killed. She is a great pet, sir, and comes to them when they call her by name, like a dog. They have taught her not to venture abaft the mainmast; but if you only call her, you'll see that what I say is true."

"Indeed! I'll soon try that experiment;" and I seized my hat to go on deck.

"Shall I tell the butcher to hold fast?" asked Capewell.

"Of course!" I exclaimed. "Of course!"

Off shot the steward like an arrow; and I could soon distinguish the effect of the announcement, by the intermission of those horrible screams which ever attend the execution of the pig tribe, all which sounds were instantly terminated on the seizings being cut that tied poor Jean's legs.

On reaching the quarter-deck, I told what had passed to the officer of the watch, who questioned its propriety a little, I thought, by the tone of his answer. I, however, called out "Jean! Jean!" and in a moment the delighted pig came prancing along. So great, in fact, was her anxiety to answer the call, as if to show her sense of the trifling favour I had just conferred upon her, that she dashed towards us, tripped up the officer's heels, and had I not caught him, he would have come souse on the deck. Even as it was, he indulged in a growl, and muttered out,

"You see, sir, what your yielding to such whims brings upon us."

I said nothing, and only took care in future to caution my friends to mind their footing when Jean was summoned aft, which, I allow, was very often; for there was no resisting the exhibition to all strangers of such a patent pet as this. To the Chinese in particular our comical favourite became an object of the highest admiration, for the natives of the celestial empire soon recognised in this happiest of swine the celebrated breed of their own country. Many a broad hint I got as to the acceptable nature of such a present, but I was deaf to them all; for I felt that Jean now belonged more to the ship's company than to myself, and that there was a sort of obligation upon me neither to eat her nor to give her away.

Under this tacit guarantee she gained so rapidly in size, fat, and other accomplishments, that, on our return to China, after visiting Loo Choo and other islands of the Japan Sea, the gentlemen of the factory would hardly credit me that this huge monster was the same animal. In talking of Jean's accomplishments, I must not be understood to describe her as a learned pig; for she could neither play cards, solve quadratic equations, nor perform any of those feats which enchant and astonish the eyes of the citizens of London and elsewhere, where many dogs and hogs are devoutly believed to be vested with a degree of intelligence rather above than below the average range of human intellect. Far from this, honest Jean could do little or nothing more than eat, drink, sleep, and grunt; in which respects she was totally unrivalled, and the effect of her proficiency in these characteristic qualities became daily more manifest. At first, as I have mentioned, when her name was called from any part of the ship, she would caper along, and dash impetuously up to the group by whom she was summoned. But after a time she became so excessively fat and lazy, that it required many a call to get her to move, and the offer of a slice of pineapple, or a handful of lychees, or even the delicious mangosteen, was now hardly enough to make her open her eyes, though in the early stages of the voyage she had been but too thankful for a potato, or the skin of an apple. As she advanced in fatness, she lost altogether the power of walking, and expected the men to bring the good things of their tables to her, instead of allowing her to come for them. This was cheerfully done; and though the only show of gratitude was a grunt, it was taken as a full recompense for all trouble on her account.

At the time of Sir Murray Maxwell's attack on the batteries of Canton, the *Lyra,* under my command, was lying at Macao, and during our stay the brig was visited by many of the Chinese authorities. We were also watched by a fleet of men-of-war junks, and had some reason to suppose that we might have a brush with them. In that event, I think our worst chance would have consisted in the enthusiasm with which the Chinese admiral, captains, and crews, would have fought to have put themselves in possession of such a prize as Jean, an object of infinitely greater attraction to them than anything else we had on board, though by this time sundry of the good dame's faculties had failed her. Both her eyes were bunged up by huge bolsters of fat, which admitted only a slender chink of light between them. As she had long lost the power of locomotion, she generally lay flat on her side all day long, giving out a low sort of grunt for more food about once every hour. At this stage of her happiness, two of her legs only touched the deck, the others being rigged out horizontally; but as she became fatter and fatter, the upper pair of legs gradually formed an angle with the horizon, and eventually assumed the position of 45°. The lower legs next began to leave the deck, as the rotundity of her corporation became greater; till, at length, all four legs were erected towards the heavens, and it became a source of discussion amongst the curious, as to which side she was actually lying upon.

While things were in this interesting position, I received orders to get under weigh, and run up the Canton river to Wampoa. Off we set, escorted by the Chinese fleet of a dozen sail of junks. The wind was against us, but we soon beat up to the Bogue, and passed, unharmed, the batteries, which, to use Lord Nelson's expression, Captain Maxwell had made to look very like a plum-pudding. The water in the enormous river of Canton was as smooth as that in the Pool abreast Rotherhithe. The country on both sides being a dead flat, with the sun bright and hot, though it was mid-winter, we appeared to be navigating amongst rice-fields and cane-brakes, and almost as if we had been towed along a huge canal in a wild and swampy country. There was no wind, so that our sails could avail nothing; but the tide was draining upwards, and, as a number of the Indiamen's boats assisted in towing us, we reached our anchorage before night. During this gentlest of all navigations, even the slight motion caused by bracing the yards about, as the faint puffs of wind came to us over the paddy-fields, seemed to disturb the rest (very nearly being eternal) of poor old Jeany. A hollow, difficult, feeble moan, hardly a grunt, gave token of her impatience when a rope came too near her, or when a party of sailors, running away with the jib-haulyards, tripped over her huge carcass.

We had scarcely anchored at Second Bar, in the midst of the grand fleet of tea ships, when we were boarded by a host of Chinese mandarins and Hong merchants, wearing all the variety of buttons by which ranks are distinguished in that well-classified land. This was not to compliment us, or to offer us assistance, or even to inquire our business. One single object seemed to engage all their thoughts and animate the curiosity of half the province of Quantung. The fame of our fat sow Jean, in short, had far outrun the speed of the *Lyra*, and nothing was heard on every hand but the wondering exclamations of the natives, screaming out in admiration, "High-yaw! High-yaw!"

We had enough to do to clear the ship at night of these our visitors, but we were by no means left in solitude; for the *Lyra's* anchorage was completely crowded with native boats. The motive of all this attention on the part of the Chinese was not merely pure admiration of Jean, as we at first suspected; for when the decks came to be washed next morning, and two or three dead ducks were thrown overboard, a rush of a dozen boats took place towards the spot, and there was a battle royal on the river for the precious property. On inquiry, we found that foreign ships were always surrounded by the boats from Canton, where the state of want appears to be so great, that the people eagerly seek after the smallest morsels of food, and struggle with the keenest avidity to catch dead stock of any kind thrown overboard.

This at once explained the marvellous degree of attention with which we had been honoured; for the acute Chinese, skilled especially in hog's flesh, saw very well that our pet pig was not long for this

45

world, and knowing that if she died a natural death, we should no more think of eating her than one of our own crew; and having guessed also that we had no intention of "killing her to save her life", they very reasonably inferred, that ere long this glorious *bonne bouche* would be at their disposal.

Our men, who soon got wind of this design on the part of the Chinese, became quite outraged against Fukee, as the natives are called, and would hardly permit any visitors to come near their favourite, lest they should accelerate her inevitable fate by poison. At length poor dear Jean gave token of approaching dissolution; she could neither eat, nor drink, nor even grunt; and her breathing was like that of a broken bellows: in short, she died! Every art was taken to conceal the melancholy event from the Chinese; but somehow or other it got abroad, for the other English ships were deserted, and long before sunset a dense mass of boats, like a floating town, was formed astern and on both quarters of the *Lyra*.

The sailors now held a grand consultation as to what was to be done; and after much discussion, and many neat and appropriate speeches, it was unanimously resolved, that the mortal remains of the great sow now no more should be deposited in the mud of the river of Canton, in such a way that the most dexterous and hungry inhabitant of the celestial empire should not be able to fish her up again.

As soon as it was quite dark, and all the Chinese boats sent, as usual, beyond the circle limited by the ship's buoys, the defunct pig's friends set to work to prepare for her obsequies. The chief object was to guard against the ravenous natives hearing the splash as she went overboard; and next, that she should not afterwards float to the surface. The first point was easily accomplished, as will be seen presently; but there was a long debate, in whispers, amongst the men, as to the most expedient plan of keeping the body of their late pet from once more showing her snout above the stream. At length it was suggested by the coxswain of one of the boats which had been sent during the morning to sound the passage, that as the bed of the river where the brig lay consisted of a deep layer of mud, it would be a good thing if Jean's remains could be driven so far into this soft stratum as to lie below the drags and hooks of the Chinese.

This advice was much applauded, and at once acted upon with that happy facility of resource which it is the pride of the profession to have always in store for small as well as for great occasions. The dead sow was first laid on its back, and then two masses of iron ballast, being placed one on each side of the cheek, were lashed securely to the neck and shoulders in such a manner that the ends of the kentledge met across her nose, and formed, as it was very properly called, an extra snout for piercing the mud.

When all was ready, the midship carronade was silently dismounted, the slide unbolted, and the whole removed out of the way. Jean's enormous corporation being then elevated, by means of capstan bars and handspikes, was brought on a level with the port-sill. A slip-rope was next passed between her hind legs, which had been tied together at the feet; and poor Miss Piggy, being gradually pushed over the ship's side, was lowered slowly into the water. When fairly under the surface, and there were no fears of any splash being caused by letting her go, one end of the rope was cast off, upon which the well-loaded carcass shot down perpendicularly at such a rate that there could be no question of its being immersed a fathom deep, at least, in the mud, and, of course, far beyond the reach of the disappointed Chinese!

THE MIDSHIPMAN'S MONGREL

By CAPTAIN BASIL HALL

In 1803, the 50-gun sixth-rate ship of the line, "Leander", was patrolling the coast of the United States, enforcing the blockade. Ships spent months at sea at this time without touching land, and feelings ran high.

During the long winters of our slothful discontent at Bermuda, caused by the Peace of Amiens, the grand resource, both of the idle and the busy, among all classes of the *Leander's* officers, was shooting — that never-ending, still-beginning amusement, which Englishmen carry to the remotest corners of the habitable globe — popping away in all countries, thinking only of the game, and often but too reckless of the prejudices or fears of the natives. This propensity is indulged even in those uninhabited regions of the earth which are visited only once in an age; and if Captain Parry had reached the Pole, he would unquestionably have had a shot at the axis of the earth!

In the meantime, the officers and the young gentlemen of the flagship at Bermuda, in the beginning of 1803, I suppose to keep their hands in for the war which they saw brewing, and hourly prayed for, were constantly blazing away among the cedar groves and orange plantations of those fairy islands, which appeared more and more beautiful after every such excursion. The midshipmen were generally obliged to content themselves with knocking down the blue and the red birds with the ship's pistols, charged with His Majesty's gunpowder, and, for want of small shot, with slugs formed by cutting up His Majesty's musket-bullets. The officers aimed at higher game, and were, of course, better provided with guns and ammunition. Several of these gentlemen had brought from England some fine dogs — highbred pointers; while the middies also, not to be outdone, must needs have a dog of their own: they cared very little of what breed; but some sort of animal they said they must have.

I forget how we procured the strange-looking beast whose services we contrived to engage; but, having once obtained him, we were not slow in giving him our best affections. It is true, he was as ugly as anything could possibly be. His colour was a dirty, reddish yellow; and while one part of his hair became knotted and twisted into curls, another portion hung down, quite straight, almost to the ground. He proved utterly useless for all the purposes of real sport, but was quite good enough to furnish the mids with plenty of fun when they went on shore — in chasing pigs, barking at old white-headed negresses, and other amusements, suited to the exalted taste and habits of the rising generation of officers.

People will differ about the merits of dogs; but we had no doubts as to the great superiority of ours over all the others on board, though the name we gave him certainly implied no such confidence on our part. After a full deliberation, it was decided to call him Shakings. Now, it must be explained that "shakings" is the name given to small fragments of rope-yarns, odds and ends of cordage, bits of oakum, old lanyards, in short, to any kind of refuse arising out of the wear and tear of the ropes. This odd name was perhaps bestowed on our beautiful favourite in consequence of his colour not being very dissimilar to that of well-tarred Russia-hemp; while the resemblance was daily increased by many a dab of pitch, which, in the hot weather, his rough coat imbibed from the seams between the planks of the deck.

If old Shakings was no great beauty, he was at least the most companionable of dogs; and though he dearly loved the midshipmen, and was dearly beloved by them in return, he had enough of the animal in his composition to take a still higher pleasure in the society of his own kind. So that, when the high-bred showy pointers belonging to the officers returned on board, after each shooting excursion, Mr. Shakings lost no time in applying to his fellow-dogs for the news. The pointers, who liked this sort of familiarity very well, gave poor Shakings all sorts of encouragement. Not so their masters, the officers, who could not bear to see "such an abominable cur", as they called our favourite, at once "so cursedly dirty and so utterly useless", mixing with their sleek and well-kept animals. At first their dislike was confined to such insulting expressions as the above; then it came to an occasional kick on the stern, or a knock on the nose with the butt-end of a fowling-piece; and lastly, to a sound cut across the rump with the hunting-whip.

Shakings, who instinctively knew his place, or, at all events, soon learned it, took all this, like a sensible fellow, in good part; while the mids, when out of hearing of the higher powers, uttered curses both loud and deep against the tyranny and oppression exercised towards an animal which, in their fond fancy, was declared to be worth all the showy dogs in the ward-room put together. They were little prepared, however, for the stroke which soon fell upon them, perhaps in consequence of these very murmurs — for bulkheads have ears as well as walls. To their great horror and indignation, one of the lieutenants, provoked at some liberty which Master Shakings had taken with his newly-polished boots, called out, one morning,—

"Man the jolly-boat, and land that infernal, dirty, ugly beast of a dog belonging to the young gentlemen!"

"Where shall I take him to, sir?" asked the strokesman of the boat.

"Oh, anywhere; pull to the nearest part of the shore, and pitch him out on the rocks. He'll shift for himself, I have no doubt." So off went poor dear Shakings!

If a stranger had come into the midshipmen's berth at that moment, he might have thought His Majesty's naval service was about to be broken up. Allegiance, discipline, and subordination, seemed utterly cancelled by this horrible act. Many were the execrations hurled upwards at the offending "nobs", who, we declared, were combining to make our lives miserable. Some of our party voted for writing a letter of remonstrance to the Admiral against this unheard-of outrage; and one youth swore deeply that he would leave the service, unless justice were obtained. But as he had been known to swear the same thing half-a-dozen times every week since he joined the ship, no great notice was taken of this pledge. Another declared, upon his word of honour, that such an act was enough to make a man turn Turk, and fly his country! At last, by general agreement, it was decided that we should not do a bit of duty, or even stir from our seats, till we obtained redress for our grievances.

While we were in the very act of vowing mutiny and disobedience, the hands were turned up to "furl sails!" upon which the whole party, totally forgetting their magnanimous resolution, scudded up the ladders, and jumped into their stations with more than usual alacrity, wisely thinking that the moment for actual revolt had not yet arrived.

A better scheme than throwing up the service, or writing to the Admiral, or turning Mussulman, was afterwards concocted. The midshipmen who went on shore in the next boat easily got hold of poor Shakings, who was howling on the steps of the watering-place. In order to conceal him, he was stuffed, neck and crop, into the captain's cloakbag, brought safely on board, and restored once more to the bosom of his friends.

In spite of all we could do, however, to keep Master Shakings below, he presently found his way to the quarter-deck, to receive the congratulations of the other dogs. There he was soon detected by the higher powers, and very shortly afterwards trundled over the gangway, and again tossed on the beach. Upon this occasion he was honoured by the presence of one of his own masters, a middy, sent upon this express duty, who was specially desired "to land the brute, and not to bring him on board again". Of course, this particular youngster did not bring the dog off; but, before night, somehow or other, old Shakings was snoring away in grand chorus with his more fashionable friends the pointers, and dreaming no evil, before the door of the very officer's cabin whose beautifully-polished boots he had brushed by so rudely in the morning — an offence that had led to his banishment.

This second return of our dog was too much. The whole possé of us were sent for on to the quarter-deck, and in very distinct terms positively ordered not to bring Shakings on board again. These injunctions having been given, this wretched victim, as we termed him, of oppression, was once more landed amongst the cedar-groves. This time he remained a full week on shore; but how or when he found his way off again, no one ever knew; at least no one chose to divulge. Never was there anything like the mutual joy felt by Shakings and his two dozen masters at this meeting. He careered about the ship, barked and yelled with delight, and, in his raptures, actually leaped, with his dirty feet, on the milk-white duck trousers of the disgusted officers, who heartily wished him at the bottom of the anchorage! Thus the poor beast unwittingly contributed to accelerate his hapless fate, by this ill-timed show of confidence in those who were then plotting his ruin. If he had only kept his paws to himself, and stayed quietly in the dark recesses of the cockpit, wings, cable-tiers, and other wild regions, the secrets of which were known only to the inhabitants of our submarine world, all might yet have been well.

We had a grand jollification on the night of Shakings' restoration; and his health was in the very act of being drunk, with three times three, when the officer of the watch, hearing an uproar below, the sounds of which were conveyed distinctly up the windsail, sent down to put our lights out; and we were forced to march off, growling, to our hammocks.

Next day, to our surprise and horror, old Shakings was not to be seen or head of. We searched everywhere, interrogated the coxswains of all the boats, and cross-questioned the marines who had been sentries during the night on the forecastle, gangsways, and poop; but all in vain! — no trace of Shakings could be found.

At length, the idea began to gain ground among us that the poor beast had been put an end to by some diabolical means; and our ire mounted accordingly. This suspicion seemed the more natural, as the officers said not a word about the matter, nor even asked us what we had done with our dog. While we were in this state of excitement and distraction for our loss, one of the midshipmen, who had some drollery in his composition, gave a new turn to the expression of our thoughts.

This gentleman, who was more than twice as old as most of us, say about thirty, had won the affections of the whole of our class, by the gentleness of his manners, and the generous part he always took on our side. He bore among us the pet name of Daddy; and certainly he was as a father to those of us who, like myself, were quite adrift in the ship, without any one to look after them. He was a man of talents and classical education; but he had entered the Navy far too late in life ever to take to it cordially. His habits, indeed, had become so rigid, that they could never be made to bend to the mortifying kind of discipline which it appears essential every officer should run through, but which only the young and light-hearted can brook. Our worthy friend, accordingly, with all his abilities, taste, and acquirements, never seemed at home on board ship; and unless a man can reach this point of liking for the sea, he is better on shore. At all events, our old friend Daddy cared more about his books than about the blocks, and delighted much more in giving us assistance in our literary pursuits, and trying to teach us to be useful, than in rendering himself a proficient in those professional mysteries which he never hoped to practise in earnest himself.

What this very interesting person's early history might have been, we never could find out; nor could we guess why he entered the Navy, nor conjecture how it came, that a man of his powers and accomplishments should have been kept back so long. Indeed, the youngsters never inquired too closely into these matters, being quite contented to have the advantage of his protection against the oppression of some of the other oldsters, who occasionally bullied them. In all cases of difficulty, we never failed to cluster round him, to tell our grievances, great and small, with the certainty of always finding in him that great desideratum in calamity — a patient and friendly listener.

It will easily be supposed, that our kind Daddy took more than usual interest in this affair of Shakings, and that he was applied to by us at every stage of the transaction. He felt, like us, sadly perplexed, when the dog was finally missing; and, for some days afterwards, he could afford us no comfort, nor suggest any mode of revenge which was not too dangerous for his young friends to put in practice. He prudently observed, that as we had no certainty to go upon, it would be foolish to get ourselves into a serious scrape for nothing at all.

"There can be no harm, however," he at last exclaimed, in his dry and slightly sarcastic way, which all who knew him will recollect as well as if they saw him now, drawing his hand slowly across his mouth and chin, "There can be no possible harm, my boys, in putting the other dogs in mourning for their dear departed friend Shakings; for, whatever is become of him, he is lost to them as well as to you, and his memory ought to be duly respected by his old masters."

This hint was no sooner given than a cry was raised for crêpe, and every chest and bag ransacked, to procure badges of mourning. Each of the pointers was speedily rigged up with a large bunch of black, tied in handsome bow upon his left leg just above the knee. The joke took immediately, and even the officers could not help laughing; for, though we considered them little better than fiends at that moment of excitement, these gentlemen showed themselves (except in this instance) the best-natured and most indulgent persons I remember to have sailed with. They ordered the crêpe, however, to be instantly cut off from the dogs' legs; and one of the officers remarked to us, seriously, that "as we had now had our piece of fun, there were to be no more such tricks".

Off we scampered, to consult old Daddy what was to be done next, as we had been positively ordered not to meddle any more with the dogs.

"Put the pigs in mourning!" he said.

All our crêpe had been expended by this time; but this want was soon supplied by men whose trade it is to discover resources in difficulty. With a generous devotion to the memory of the departed Shakings, one of these juvenile mutineers pulled off his black handkerchief, and, tearing it in pieces, gave a portion to each of the circle; and thus supplied, away we all started to put into practice this new suggestion of our director-general of mischief.

The row which ensued in the pig-sty was prodigious, for in those days hogs were allowed a place on board a man-of-war, a custom most wisely abolished of late years, since nothing can be more out of character with any ship than such nuisances. As these matters of taste and cleanliness were nothing to us, we intermitted not our noisy labour till every one of the grunters wore his armlet of such crêpe as we had been able to muster; then, watching our opportunity, we opened the door and let out the whole herd of swine on the main-deck, just at the moment when a group of the officers were standing on the fore part of the quarter-deck. Of course the liberated pigs, delighted with their freedom, passed in review under the very nose of our superiors, each with his mourning-knot displayed, grunting or squealing along, as if it was their express object to attract attention to their domestic sorrow for the loss of Shakings. The officers now became excessively provoked; for they could not help seeing that these proceedings were affording entertainment, at their expense, to the whole crew. The men, of course, took no part in this touch of insubordination; but they (like the middies) were ready enough, in those idle times of the weary, weary peace, to catch at any species of distraction or devilry, no matter what, to compensate for the loss of their wonted occupation of pommelling their enemies.

The matter, therefore, as a point of discipline, necessarily became rather serious; and the whole gang of young culprits being sent for on the quarter-deck, we were ranged in a line, each with his toes at the edge of a plank, according to the orthodox fashion of these gregarious scoldings, technically called "toe-the-line matches". We were then given to understand that our proceedings were impertinent, and, after the orders we had received, highly offensive. It was with much difficulty that either party could keep their countenances during this official lecture, for, while it was going on, the sailors were endeavouring, by the direction of the officers, to remove the bits of silk from the legs of the pigs. If, however, it be difficult — as most difficult we found it — to put a hog into mourning, it is a job ten times more troublesome to take him out again. Such at least is the fair inference from these two experiments, the only ones perhaps on record; for it cost half the morning to undo what we had effected in less than an hour; to say nothing of the unceasing and outrageous uproar which took place along the decks, expecially under the guns, and even under the coppers, forward in the galley, where two or three of the youngest pigs had wedged themselves, apparently resolved to die rather than submit to the degradation of being deprived of their sable badges.

All this was very creditable to the memory of poor Shakings; but, in the course of the day, the real secret of this extraordinary difficulty of taking a pig out of mourning was discoverd. Two of the mids were detected in the very fact of tying on a bit of black bunting to the leg of a sow, from which the seamen declared they had already cut off crêpe and silk enough to have made her a complete suit of black.

On these fresh offences being reported, the whole party of us were ordered to the mast-head as a punishment. Some were sent to sit on the top-mast cross-trees, some on the top-gallant yard-arms, and one small gentleman being perched at the jib-boom end, was very properly balanced abaft by another little culprit at the extremity of the gaff. In this predicament we were hung out to dry for six or eight hours, as old Daddy remarked to us with a grin, when we were called down as the night fell.

Our persevering friend, being rather provoked at the punishment of his young flock, set seriously to work to discover the real fate of Shakings. It soon occurred to him, that if the dog had indeed been made away with, as he shrewdly suspected, the ship's butcher, in all probability, must have had a hand in his murder: accordingly, he sent for the man in the evening, when the following dialogue took place:—

"Well, butcher, will you have a glass of grog to-night?"

"Thank you, sir, thank you. Here's your honour's health!" said the other, after smoothing down his hair, and pulling an immense quid of tobacco out of his mouth.

Old Daddy observed the peculiar relish with which the rogue took his glass: and mixing another, a good deal more potent, placed it before the fellow. He then continued the conversation in these words:

"I tell you what it is, Mr. Butcher — you are as humane a man as any in the ship, I dare say; but if required, you know well that you must do your duty, whether it is upon sheep or hogs?"

"Surely, sir."

"Or upon dogs, either?" suddenly asked the inquisitor.

"I don't know about that," stammered the butcher, quite taken by surprise, and thrown all aback.

"Well — well," said Daddy, "here's another glass for you — a stiff north-wester. Come! Tell us all about it now. How did you get rid of the dog? — of Shakings, I mean."

"Why, sir," said the peaching scoundrel, "I put him in a bag — a bread-bag, sir."

"Well! — what then?"

"I tied up the mouth, and put him overboard, out of the midship lower-deck port, sir."

"Yes — but he would not sink?" said Daddy.

"Oh, sir," cried the fellow, now entering fully into the merciless spirit of his trade, "I put a four-and-twenty pound shot into the bag along with Shakings."

"Did you? — Then, Master Butcher, all I can say, is, you are as precious a rascal as ever went about unhanged. There — drink your grog, and be off with you!"

Next morning when the officers were assembling at breakfast in the ward-room, the door of the captain of marines' cabin was suddenly opened, and that officer, half-shaved, and laughing through a collar of soap-suds, stalked out with a paper in his hand.

"Here," he exclaimed, "is a copy of verses, which I found just now in my basin. I can't tell how they got there, nor what they are about; but you shall judge."

So he read aloud the two following stanzas of doggerel:

"When the Northern Confederacy threatened our shores,
    And roused Albion's Lion, reclining to sleep,
Preservation was taken of all the King's Stores,
    Nor so much as a *Rope Yarn* was launched in the deep.

"But now it is Peace, other hopes are in view,
　And all active service as light as a feather,
　The Stores may be d—d, and humanity too,
　　For SHAKINGS and *Shot* are thrown o'erboard together!"

I need hardly say in what quarter of the ship this biting morsel of cock-pit satire was concocted, nor indeed who wrote it, for there was no one but our good Daddy who was equal to such a flight. About midnight, an urchin — who shall be nameless — was thrust out of one of the after-ports of the lower deck, from which he clambered up to the marine officer's port, and the sash happening to have been lowered down on the gun, the epigram, copied by another of the youngsters, was pitched into the soldier's basin.

The wisest thing would have been for the officers to have said nothing about the matter, and let it blow by. But as angry people are seldom judicious, they made a formal complaint to the captain, who, to do him justice, was not a little puzzled how to settle the affair. The reputed author, however, was called up, and the captain said to him—

"Pray, sir, are you the writer of these lines?"

"I am, sir," he replied, after a little consideration.

"Then, all I can say is," remarked the captain, "they are clever enough, in their way; but take my advice, and write no more such verses."

So the matter ended. The satirist took the captain's hint in good part, and confined his pen to topics less repugnant to discipline.

In the course of a few months the war broke out, and there was no longer time for such nonsense; indeed our generous protector Daddy, some time after this affair of Shakings took place, was sent off to Halifax, in charge of a prize. His orders were, if possible, to rejoin his own ship, the *Leander*, then lying at the entrance of New York harbour, just within Sandy Hook light-house.

Our good old friend, accordingly, having completed his mission, and delivered up his charge to the authorities at Halifax, took his passage in the British packet sailing from thence to the port in which we lay. As this ship sailed past us, on her way to the city of New

York, we ascertained, to our great joy, that our excellent Daddy was actually on board of her. Some hours afterwards, the pilot-boat was seen coming to us, and, though it was in the middle of the night, all the younger mids came hastily on deck to welcome their worthy messmate back again to his home.

It was late in October, and the wind blew fresh from the north-westward, so that the ship, riding to the ebb, had her head directed towards the Narrows, between Staten Land and Long Island: consequently, the pilot-boat (one of those beautiful vessels so well known to every visitor of the American coast) came flying down upon us with the wind nearly right aft. Our joyous party were all assembled on the quarter-deck, looking anxiously at the boat as she swept past. She then luffed round, in order to sheer alongside, at which moment the main-sail jibed, as was to be expected. It was obvious, however, that something more had taken place than the pilot had anticipated, since the boat, instead of ranging up to the gangway, being brought right round on her heel, went off upon a wind on the other tack. The tide carried her out of sight for a few minutes, but she was soon again alongside: when we learned, to our inexpressible grief and consternation, that on the main-boom of the pilot-boat swinging over, it had accidentally struck our poor friend, and pitched him headlong overboard. Being encumbered with his great-coat, the pockets of which, as we afterwards heard, were loaded with his young companions' letters, brought from England by this packet, he in vain struggled to catch hold of the boat, and then sunk to rise no more!

THE WRECKERS

A tale of the bad old days on the Cornish coast when many ships were lured onto the savage rocks by people ashore.

It was a March morning — dark, yet without a drop of rain or breath of wind, that kind of marbly-black, compact sky, which is the sure forerunner of a storm. The night had been a raw and cold one — too cold to sleep with comfort in the open air; yet such was the chamber which a peasant-girl, a native of a little fishing hamlet upon the coast of Cornwall, had chosen for repose. Her couch was a hard and fearful one! The verge of a clift that rose nearly a hundred feet perpendicular from the sea-shore; and yet not the softest couch that ever was spread in hamlet, town, or city, contained a tenant, in form for symmetry — in feature for beauty — excelling the mistress of her who occupied that strange, appalling place of rest! Her slumbers were disturbed, yet deep. Neither the full dawn could break them; nor yet the pressure of a hand that had taken hold of hers; nor the tears that fell upon her face from the eyes of one who was hanging over her — a young man about her own age, or a little older, and who seemed to belong to the profession of the sea.

"And hast thou slept out again all night?" he murmured — his tears still flowing. "And does it grow worse and worse with thy poor wits? And shall I never see the day when I can make thee my wife? They will not let me marry thee, because, as they say, thou art mad, and knowest not what thou dost; but when thy mind was sound, I was loved by thee! Had I married thee then, thou still hadst been my wife! Thou still hadst been cherished and loved! Why must I not marry thee now? I could watch thee, then, at night! My arms would enfold thee, then, and prevent thee from stealing from thy bed to sleep in such a place as this!"

The attachment which united this young man to the being whom he so pathetically apostrophized, was of that pure and steadfast nature, which can never take root, except in the unsophisticated heart. She had lost her reason in consequence of having been witness to a

60

transaction of blood, which made her an orphan. She was to have been married to him; but, in the unfortunate state of her intellects, no clergyman would celebrate the rites. But she did not the less enjoy his protection. Beneath his mother's roof, she lived as sacred as a sister — the object of a passion in which frustration, and almost hopelessness, had only produced increase of strength.

"Kate, Kate," he called. "Rouse thee, Kate — rouse thee. Don't start. Don't be frightened. 'Tis only William. Get up, and come home."

He offered to raise her, but she checked him — looked round, and fixed her eyes, inquiringly, upon the sea.

"Where is it?" she exclaimed — her voice tremulous with intense emotion. "Where is the storm? I see the black sky; but I want the thunder and the wind — the white, white sea, and the big ship, driving upon the reef — or is it all over? No," she added; "'tis coming — 'twill be here! I see it!"

She rose, and passively accompanied her watchful lover to his mother's cottage; where, leaving her under the custody of its mistress, the young man repaired on urgent business to a town at some distance from the hamlet.

That morning the storm came on; three days it continued — it was now the third day. A lee shore, a boiling sea, and on the coast of Cornwall! A wild and fearful offing! Foam, foam, foam, which way soever you looked — nothing but foam. Black reefs of rocks, that even in the highest spring tides were never completely covered, discernible now only by a spot here and there — so quick the breakers flew upon them. The spray flying over the cliffs — fifty, sixty, ay, a hundred feet and more, above the level of the sea, and spreading over the land for acres. And all above pitch black, though at noon-day. Everything seemed to cower before the spirit of the storm — everything except man. The shore — which consisted partly of huge masses of rock, partly of shingle — was lined with human beings — some in groups — some alone — promiscuously furnished with boathooks, gaffs, grapples, hatchets, and knives — ready to dispute with the waves the plunder of the fated ship that might be driven within the jaws of that inhospitable bay. Expectation glistened in their eyes, that kept eagerly prowling backward and forward, far and near, over the waste of waters — they were wreckers! Not a few women, as well as children, were among them; nor were these unprovided against the approach of the wished-for prey — all seemed to have their appropriated places; from which, if they stirred, it was only a step or two, to be the next minute retraced. Little was spoken.

At one and the same moment almost every head was turned toward the cliff, at a wild and shrill halloo that rung from it.

"'Tis only Kate," cried one, here and there, as the maniac rapidly descended by a crevice, which few of the lookers-on would have attempted, and that with wary feet.

"The crazy slut will break her neck," carelessly remarked one to another. But she was safe in her recklessness or unconsciousness of danger, and in a second or two stood among them.

"A lovely day; a fair, lovely day," she exclaimed to the first she came up to. "Good luck to you! Anything yet? No, no," she continued, replying to herself, "white to the north — white to the west — white to the south — all white! Not a speck upon the water! But 'tis coming — 'tis coming — 'tis coming!" she reiterated, dropping her voice to its lowest pitch; "I saw it here last night; a big, black hull — one mast standing out of three — cannons and stores overboard — rising and sinking — rocking and reeling — driving full bump upon the reef where the *William and Mary* was wrecked seven years ago! I saw it," she repeated, eyeing the standers-by with a look that dared incredulity; then, all at once, her voice sinking into a whisper. "Hist, hist!" she added; "'twill be a handful or two for you; and a load for you; and more than you can carry for you;" addressing this person and that successively, "casks, cases, chests, gear, and gold! But what will it be for Black Norris? It will be a brighter day for him than for any of you! When do they say his time is out?"

"Whose time?" inquired one among the group she was addressing.

"One — two — three;" she went on without noticing the question, until she had counted seven; "his seven years were out last May; he was transported three years before his hopeful son murdered my father."

"Hush, you crazy wench," exclaimed those around her; "if Norris hears you, you may chance to take a swim in the creek where he is standing."

"Crazy!" she echoed. "Yes; bless heaven that made me so! It knows best what it does! I saw my father murdered, though his murderer saw not me! They were struggling which should keep possession of the prey. Old Norris's knife decided it! I was powerless with fright! I could not speak! I could not stir! I became mad, and the judge would not believe me! I could tell my story better now, but it would be of no use; for they say I am crazy still. There she is!" vociferated she, pointing toward the offing at the southern extremity of the bay.

"Where — where — where?" inquired her auditors.

"No, no," she resumed, after a minute or two of silence, during which her eye-balls kept straining in the direction toward which she had pointed. "No," she resumed, dropping her hand; "but she is coming; and Black Norris will neither want roof nor board, gold nor gear, to welcome back the father that bred him up to his own trade. But where is he?" inquired she; "where, but upon the long reef, where I saw him?" Saying this, she proceeded to the southern extremity of the bay.

A stalwart figure, in advance of the regular line, sat stationed upon the landward-end of a huge reef of rocks, that gradually dipped into the sea. His hair black and lank, thrown back from a swarthy, ill-favoured visage hung halfway down his shoulders; his eye dark, small, and glistening bright, directed toward the sea, in quick and restless motion, was everywhere at once. A long boat-hook, clenched with both his hands, rested across his knees; and, in a belt, which encircled his waist, were stuck a clasp-knife of more than ordinary size, and a hatchet. The wave repeatedly washed more than halfway up his lower extremities, but he paid no more heed than if he were part of the rock that scattered it into mist.

"A lovely day — a fair, lovely day," cried the maniac, approaching him.

"How beest thou, Black Norris? Nay, I am good, now," continued she, in a deprecating tone: "don't look angry, I'll never say ain that it was you."

The wrecker moved his hand towards his knife,

"Stop, stop, Black Norris," cried she, coaxingly and hurriedly, laying her hand upon his arm, "keep it for other work. You'll want it to-day: before night there will be a hull ashore. There will be need of knife, axe, hook and all — for the storm is lively yet — the sea shows no signs of going down — the breakers keep tumbling upon the shore. Mark how they sweep the shingles up and back again. By-and-by they will have something else to roll. 'Tis coming, Black Norris; 'tis coming. A huge, black hull — one mast standing out of three — cannons and stores overboard — rising and sinking — rocking and reeling — driving full bump upon the reef where the *William and Mary* was wrecked — the very reef on which you stand, Black Norris; ay, and the very spot."

"Silence, jade!" exclaimed the wrecker, looking from beneath his hand, which, with the rapidity of lightning, was raised to his brow, and placed there horizontally, and leaning eagerly forward.

"In the south?"

"Yes."

"Just clear of the point?"

"Yes; the looming of something: 'tis a sloop! I see but one mast."

"'Tis a ship, Black Norris. The other two have been cut away."

"Peace, jade! What know'st thou of the matter?"

"'Tis a ship," she continued. "I told you so! There is the huge black hull!"

"'Tis there, indeed!" exclaimed the wrecker. "Art thou a witch as well as crazed? 'Tis there, indeed! She is driving right into the bay, coming broadside on!"

A huge black hull it was, high out of the water, as if every article of weight that could be spared had been thrown overboard. Reeling and pitching she came on, staggering every now and then at the stroke of some wave that broke over her. Fast was she nearing the shore.

"Now, now, now!" ever and anon exclaimed the wreckers; but she was floating still, so much had those on board lightened her. At length she was fairly among the breakers. She touched and touched; yet went on — at last she struck, a long-continued crash came undulating upon the ears of the lookers-on, accompanied with halloos and shrieks. The shore was now all astir.

"That does for her!" exclaimed several voices all at once, as an enormous wave towering, as if charged with her doom, came foaming toward her. In another minute it broke upon her in a fury that sent the spray to the clouds, and totally hid her from the shore. When she became visible again, the whole of her larboard broadside was stove in. In a moment, men, women, and children were up to their middle in the surf. Another billow — she was gone! Planks, pulleys, spars, and cordage now came floating in, and everyone went to work — everyone but Black Norris.

He kept his station upon the reef — a post which common consent seemed to have yielded up to him. No one ventured to dispute his right to it. In advance of him stood the maniac, constantly looking in one direction — a kind of cove produced by a forking in the reef. Thence she never took her eye, except to throw a glance at Black Norris whenever he made a movement, as if about to quit the stand which he had chosen.

"'Twill be here," she kept repeating; "'twill be here: that which will be worth the hull to thee, were it high and dry, and all thine own; wait for it, 'tis sent to thee; 'twill be here. Did I not tell you of the huge black hull, and came it not? As surely that will come, which in that hull was sent to thee. Be ready with thy boat-hook. The minutes are counted. The wave that is to bring it, is rolling in. There it is! I know it! Here, take my place and be ready. Here it is — a body — hook it by the clothes; keep it clear of the rocks. Round — round — round here, into this nook. Look if it does not lie there as if it were made for it. What think you now, Black Norris? What think you now

3

of crazy Kate? Softly, softly;" she continued, as the wrecker, substituting his hands for the instrument, began to draw the body up to the beach. "Softly, the pockets are full. Softly, lest anything should drop from them. That will do! That will do!"

Scarcely was the body clear of the surf when the wrecker began to strip it. The pockets were full! One of them was speedily emptied, when a laugh from the maniac, who, squatting, sat gibbering at the head, arrested Black Norris in the act of examining the contents.

"What laugh'st thou at, jade?" he inquired.

"Go on," she replied: "'tis a fair, lovely day, as I told thee; is it not, Black Norris?"

"Peace, jade!" exclaimed the wrecker. "Jewels!" he ejaculated, closing a small case which he had opened. The maniac laughed again.

"Wilt thou stop thy cursed mouth," vociferated the wrecker.

"Go on," murmured the maniac. "Go on, Black Norris. You should not be angry with me. Did I not tell you it was coming? Go on. 'Tis a fair, lovely day. Isn't it, Black Norris?"

"Gold!" exclaimed he to himself, as he emptied into his hand a portion of the contents of a purse, which he had taken from the other pocket; "broad, heavy, yellow pieces!" — another laugh from the maniac.

"Silence!" again cried; "I tell thee what, mad Kate," roared out the wrecker, "take to thy heels, or abide the consequence if thou utterest that sound again."

"Softly! — softly!" whispered Kate, "he hears you!"

"Who, jade?" cried the wrecker, starting from his knees.

"The owner of the diamonds and the gold. His lids have been moving for the last minute, and now they are wide open!"

The wrecker just glanced at the face of the shipwrecked man.

"Get thee away, good Kate!" said he, in a conciliatory tone. "Go, Kate; leave me by myself, and I'll never be angry with thee again. Go, good Kate; go."

The maniac looked at the wrecker for a moment — smiled — nodding her head significantly, and rose.

"I am gone, Black Norris!" she cried, "a good day to you! and a good fair day it is! And a lovely day! Isn't it, Black Norris! I'll leave you by yourself. I'll not stay! I am gone!" and starting toward a pathway which led up the cliff, and the commencement of which was sheltered by a screen of rock, she was quickly out of sight.

The wrecker now began to reconnoitre all around him. Everyone was engrossed with his own occupation, securing such portions of the wreck, or such articles of property as were brought within his reach. His hand approached his knife — grasped it — half drew the weapon from his belt; but suddenly replaced it, and now fastened on the axe — the counterpoise to the blade of which was a wedge-like piece of iron, broad, and flattened at the end. In a second the instrument swung by his side. Once again he reconnoitered toward the beach; then turned toward the prostrate man. He thought the body moved — he trembled from head to foot. He advanced a single step, but stopped — the fingers were in motion! A low sound — half voice, half breath — issued from the throat — which now evidently began to work! He advanced another step, though a tottering one! — Another! He was now within a foot or two of the head — he sank, or rather dropped upon one knee. The eyes of the seaman moved — they turned to the right and to the left, and at last glared back upon the wrecker! Both hands now clenched the axe! Slowly 'twas lifted, the edge averted, and the blunt end suspended over the forehead of him that lay. 'Twas raised! It hovered a moment or two, then fell with a short, dull crash — a pause for a moment or two more — limb, eye, everything were still — the wrecker threw his weapon behind him, and wiped from his brow the drops that stood thick upon it.

"Ah! Ha! You have done it!"

The wrecker turned and beheld the maniac standing behind him with the hatchet in her hand, her eyes flashing.

"Nay, move not, Black Norris!" she continued, "unless you would have me give the corpse a fellow! Let me get farther from thee without forcing me to do thee a mischief, and I will tell thee something!" She retreated about twenty paces, without turning her back;

the wrecker now perfectly unnerved, not daring to move. "Black
Norris," she resumed, "did I not tell you that this was a fair, lovely
day! And a fair, lovely day it is! And a bonny one, too! — And know
you not why, Black Norris? This day you have done — what you have
done! — And this day seven years was the day — the fair, lovely day
when you murdered my father! Black Norris! Now follow me out,
but goodbye!"

She fled. The wrecker had not power to follow!

By the fire of a miserable hut, was seated upon a stool a female,
of youthful but haggard appearance. She had an infant at her breast,
and was endeavouring to lull it, rocking to and fro, with a low melancholy hum. Every now and then, she paused and listened, and after
a second or two, resumed her maternal task.

"Be quiet, Shark; be quiet," she would occasionally cry, as a lean,
black, rough-coated dog, between the Newfoundland and the mas-
tiff, which was stretched across the hearth, would raise his head,
and turning it in the direction of the door, keep howling amidst the
gusts of the storm, which was slowly and fitfully subsiding.

At length the infant fell asleep, and was transferred from its
mother's lap to a wretched pallet in an adjoining room. Her charge
being thus disposed of, she returned into the outer apartment. A
cooking vessel was on the fire. She lifted the lid. The steam faintly
rose from the contents.

"Will it never grow hot!" she impatiently exclaimed; and resorting
assiduously, but almost in vain, to urge the sluggish fuel. "He'll brain
me, if he comes home and nothing ready," she cried to herself, in a
querulous under-tone. "Heaven send him luck, and I shall have peace
for a day or two," continued she. "But for my baby, I wish I had
never seen the face of Black Norris."

"Let me in!" cried the wrecker at the door.

"Thank heaven, he has met with luck!" ejaculated the wretched
wife. She let him in. He had a trunk upon his shoulder, and under his
arms he carried a bundle of clothes.

"Good luck, Norris?" tremulously, and doubtingly she inquired.

"Yes!" was his sullen reply. "Why do you ask with such a face as that?"

"I was afraid you had not met with any."

"Why?" demanded he, sternly.

"From your looks," timidly responded she.

"Curse thee!" muttered the ruffian; "what business hast thou to mind my looks? Here! Lend a hand, and help this load from my back."

The trunk was deposited upon the floor. "What! Nothing ready? Hast thou not victuals in the house? Hast thou not fire? Hast thou not hands? And why is not my dinner ready? Bestir thee! I have something to do in the next room. On thy life let me not be interrupted till I have done. Haste! Give me the key of the big chest."

"Don't wake the baby," entreatingly enjoined the wife. "He has not slept the whole morning, and is only just now dropped off."

"Curse the child," cried the wrecker, "thou thinkest of nothing but the child. Look to my dinner!" He went into the next apartment, shut the door after him, and bolted it.

He examined the jewels again. He emptied the purse of its contents and counted them. He then applied the key, and hastily began to deposit them in the chest. In the progress of his work, he started and stopped short, at a shuffling of feet he heard in the outer apartment, accompanied by the sound of voices, as of persons speaking in a low key. Muttering a curse, he proceeded.

"Norris, Norris!" whispered his wife at the door. He replied not, but went on.

"Norris!" she whispered again. "You are wanted!" He answered not, but listened anxiously. All was silent.

"Norris!" she repeated.

"Silence! and confound thee," was the ruffian's reply.

"I cannot help it, Norris," rejoined she, still whispering. "You are wanted, husband. O come! Do come!"

"Presently," he vociferated.

The last article was put in. He locked the chest, and unbolting the door, threw it open.

"Well! Is my dinner ready?" he noisily demanded, entering the outer apartment, and looking toward the table — which had been constructed out the fragments of a wreck — with a corpse stretched upon it. At the head and at the foot was a group of his neighbours. He stood for a moment or two transfixed.

"What means this?" at length he boldly inquired, with a loud voice, striving to conceal a cowering heart.

"Merciful powers!" exclaimed one, lifting the rifled trousers, which the wrecker had thrown upon the floor. "Merciful powers! If it is not your father's body, Norris, that you have been stripping."

"My father's body," echoed Black Norris; the blood utterly forsaking his cheeks.

"Yes! There it is, stretched upon the table."

Black Norris did not attempt to speak. He looked at the body — at the bystanders — at his wife — at the body again — with an expression of perfect vacuity in his countenance. He then approached the table, half seated himself on a corner of it, his back to the corpse, and with one leg upon the floor, kept swinging the other, looking wildly around him. His wife, who had dropped upon the stool on which she had been nursing her child, sat the image of horror. The rest kept silence.

"It can't be helped," at last exclaimed Black Norris. "The dead have no use for clothes. We'll bury him tomorrow, and wake him tonight."

His auditors looked at one another, but made no remark. Pipes, tobacco, and spirits, were speedily procured and placed upon the same table with the corpse, which was now covered with a sheet. Black Norris seated himself at the head. His neighbours, whose numbers were now increased by occasional droppers-in, accommodating themselves as they could, with stools, empty kegs placed on end, and pieces of plank converted into temporary forms, sat ranged around. The room waxed merry, save where the wrecker's wife sat crouching near the fire, her head supported by the wall. At length the first supply of spirits was out.

"I'll bring you better," cried the wrecker. "What we have been drinking was watered. I'll bring it you as pure as from the still."

He disappeared; and, after the lapse of about ten or fifteen minutes, returned with a fresh supply. He opened the door unobserved, but stopped short upon remarking that the place which he had just quitted, was occupied by three or four who were intently employed in examining the head of the dead body, from which the sheet had been partially removed. The rest of the company were leaning forward, apparently absorbed in what was passing.

"'Tis an ugly mark," said one.

"No rock could do that," observed another.

"No," interposed a third; "'tis more like the blunt end of an axe-head. See! Here is the regular mark of the edge, all round. I would not be Black Norris for all he has got by this day's work."

"Why not?" vociferated the wrecker, springing forward and confronting the speaker.

Every eye was turned toward the wrecker, in whose countenance desperation and gathering fury were fearfully depicted. No answer was returned to his question.

"Why not," echoed the young man, recovering from temporary surprise. "Why, who was it stove your father's forehead in, Black Norris?" added he, after a pause.

He had scarcely time to duck his head. The vessel which the wrecker carried, flew over it, and in the next moment the young man's throat was in the ruffian's grip.

"Loose your hold of him," cried several all at once. Black Norris paid no heed to them. Three or four of the strongest and boldest rushed together upon him at once; overpowered him and rescued his almost suffocated victim. The wrecker drew his knife and brandished it. They rushed upon him again before he had time to make a stroke with it, and wrenched it from him. His wife, who, it appeared, had retired into the inner apartment during the interval of her husband's absence, now burst from it, sank on her knees before him, and, clasping him round the legs with one arm, while with the other she supported her infant, implored him to be calm. A blow levelled child and mother to the earth! With horror of the savage act, the spectators stood a while, as if bereft of the power of speech or motion. For a second or two the wrecker glared around him like a fiend, then suddenly rushed into the inner room. He searched here and there, blaspheming all the time, cursing this thing and that thing, as anything came to his hand except what he wanted. At length, however, he succeeded in finding his pistols. Then a pouch filled with slugs, and last of all, a powder-horn, presented themselves. Hastily he loaded and primed the weapons, and proceeding to the door with one in each hand, advanced a pace into the outer apartment.

"Now!" roared the wrecker, "now, who is the man to come on?" No one stirred. "I give you just as much time," continued he, "as it will take you to clear the house. When that is expired, I fire at the man that remains."

A wild, shrill, piercing laugh was the answer to his menace. It came from the head of the corpse. The maniac was standing there. The wrecker's axe was in her hand; the blunt end resting on the mark in the dead man's forehead.

"Ha! ha!" she cried, exultingly; "there is your father, Black Norris! a corpse upon the plank of wood, to get possession of which, you murdered my father; and here is your axe upon the mark which you made in your father's forehead when I told you, as you were rifling him on the beach, that his eyes were moving, and you coaxed me to leave you alone with him. See how nicely it fits. But I knew you, and stole back. I did, Black Norris. And I saw the blow; and heard the crash; and snatched up your hatchet when you threw it behind you; and ran away with it. Give you joy of your diamonds and your gold, Black Norris. A fair day. Is it not? A fair, lovely day — a fair lovely bonny day."

The wrecker had been gradually raising his right arm. It was now nearly brought to a level. He fired; but the charge perforated the roof. His arm was struck up by someone, and at the same moment he felt himself powerfully pinioned. He looked round; he found himself in the hands of four of the preventive guard, accompanied by Kate's lover, with the staff of a boarding-pike in his grasp.

That day, having completed the business which called him from home, had the young man returned. His first inquiry was for Kate. She had been at her usual pranks, and had stolen away. He sought her in all her haunts — she was nowhere to be found — dispirited and fatigued, too; for he had walked upward of thirty miles since morning; he was repairing home when he received, from a group, returning from the wreck, and of whom he made inquiries after her, an account of her appearance among the wreckers, and her wild, mysterious prophecy, which had so strangely been fulfilled. Pondering what he had heard, he lifted the latch of his mother's door, and entered; but stopped short. A female, almost naked to the zone, was sitting with her back toward him; her skin of so pure a whiteness, that it fairly shone. The waist and shoulders of such a mould, as of itself apprises the beholder of the presence of surprising richness: although unrefined, uninformed, he is utterly at a loss to tell in what it lies. A moment he stood; then, abashed, confounded — he was on the point of retiring, when the female turned suddenly round.

"Kate!" burst in astonishment from the young man's lips.

The next moment the maniac, unconscious of her situation, was hanging upon his neck. Wildly she kissed him: straining him to her bosom and laughing.

"He had done it! He had done it!" she almost schrieked. "He had murdered his own father. Here is the hatchet with which he beat his forehead in," added she, springing from him to the other end of the room, and snatching up the instrument and flourishing it; her sun-burnished hands and neck forming an extraordinary contrast with the snow which had never been before revealed to the eyes of her lover, whose mother now entering from an adjoining room with some articles of apparel upon her arm, hastily retired again, drawing the poor, half-resisting girl along with her. The former presently returned.

"She had been down on the shore all day. There has been a wreck," said she. "About a quarter of an hour ago she came in inquiring for you, that you might take Black Norris, as she said, and hang him; for he had murdered his father. She was wet to the skin with the spray and the rain, and I was making her change herself when you came in. Hist! she is here!"

Kate entered. Her lover looked at her. Nothing appeared now but the hue, that was the child of the weather. The hatchet was in her hand. Exultation and impatience were painted in her looks.

"Come! come!" she cried; and opening the door, at once led the way to Black Norris's. Scarcely had they got fifty yards from the house, when, at a turn in the road, they came upon four privates of the preventive service. The men were on duty. Kate instantly accosted them, related the transaction which had taken place upon the reef, and commanded them to accompany her. They looked — and obeyed.

Three weeks after there was a trial and an execution. Black Norris was the criminal. Among the spectators at the latter were a young man and a young woman. As soon as the body swung in the air, a shrill peal of laughter arose from one of the crowd. It was from the female who, the next moment, lay fainting in the arms of her companion. Kate was conveyed home. She was restored to consciousness; but her mind, so highly excited before, seemed now to have sunk into a state of infantile imbecility. Thus she remained for several days, nay weeks. A gloom seemed to have overspread her lover's mind, which threatened consequences similar to those under which the being whom he so tenderly loved had laboured. He avoided society — he would hardly exchange a word even with his mother. He was continually wandering about the cliff and the shore alone.

One day, when he had thrown himself upon the very spot where, as we related in the beginning, he had intruded upon the slumbers of the maniac — pondering the cause which now utterly absorbed his mind and soul, and lost to external consciousness — he was startled by something falling upon his face. He looked up, and saw the loved one hanging over him. The tear-drop stood trembling upon her lid — the light of reason beamed from her eye. She pronounced his name, talked to him of her father's death, informed him that she believed his murderer had suffered the penalty of his crime, but knew not when, or by what means. He drew her softly toward him — encouraged her to speak on — questioned her — found of all that had passed since her wits had gone astray, the only circumstance which had left an impression upon her memory, was the fate of Black Norris. He now endeavoured to ascertain the state of her heart with respect to him. An eye at once cast down — a burning cheek — lips that made soundless motion, confirmed the dearest hopes, and crowned the most ardent wishes of his soul. Reason was perfectly reinstated — love had never lost its seat. He urged the soft confession — and her face was buried in his bosom. In a week she was his wife, and along with his mother, accompanied him to a distant part of the country, lest old and painful recollections might be recalled by the presence of scenes, alas! but too familiar.

THE ALBATROSS

An amazing story of how an albatross carried an S.O.S. from the survivors of a French barque wrecked on the desolate Crozet Rocks, close to the Antarctic ice.

Early in 1888 an extraordinary and romantic story went the rounds of the means successfully employed by some shipwrecked sailors to inform the world of their perilous plight on a little island almost within sight of Antarctic ice. The story came from official sources in France, and was to the effect that the French Government had been informed, by the British Ambassador in Paris, word had been received from the Governor of West Australia that on 22nd September last a dead albatross had been found on the beach at Freemantle, around whose neck was fastened a small piece of metal, on which had been scratched in French: — "Thirteen shipwrecked men took refuge upon the Crozet Islands. — 4th August, 1887."

The story excited some incredulity. The Crozet Islands are hundreds of miles south of Madagascar, far out of the ordinary track of ships. Whalers are about the only vessels that visit this vast southern waste of waters. It was indeed a wonderful series of fortunate events if castaways on those far-off islands had found a winged messenger which, unconsciously exerting on their behalf his far-famed powers of endurance on the wing, had carried their tidings over thousands of miles of sea with few opportunities to rest on the way, and had finally dropped dead, probably of exhaustion, on the shores of a civilised land.

Considering the source from which the information was derived, the French Government promptly decided that there could be no doubt that this albatross, with its important message, had been found at Freemantle, which is one of the largest towns in south-western Australia. The French Minister of Marine at once sent orders to the commander of the naval division of the Indian Ocean to despatch the transport *Meurthe* as soon as possible to the Crozets to search for the castaways.

The strange story was published in the Paris newspapers, and the next day a communication came from the commercial house of Bordes & Son, of Bordeaux, saying they had reasons to fear that the thirteen sailors on the Crozets were the crew of their three-master *Tamaris*, which had sailed many months before for New Caledonia, in the Pacific. She was some time overdue. Her owners had expected her to take a course not far from the Crozet Islands, and her crew numbered thirteen persons.

This information gave additional interest and probability to the story. The British Government decided to take part also in the search, and Her Majesty's ship *Thalia*, which was about to leave England for Australia, was ordered to go out of her course to call at the Crozet Islands. But the sequel of this romance of the sea was made known by the French vessel.

The *Meurthe*, returning from her search early in the year, reached the bay of Diego Suarez, in North Madagascar, 6th January. That day her commander wrote a report of his voyage. He said that the first of the four Crozet Islands at which he touched was the little Island of Cochous. He found no human beings there, but plenty of evidence that the island had recently been occupied. Traces of recent camp fires and biscuit boxes, and other *débris,* comparatively fresh in appearance, were scattered around.

A heap of stones had been piled up to attract attention, and in this heap was a sheet of paper on which this communication had been written in French with a lead pencil: "The iron ship *Tamaris*, of Bordeaux, with thirteen men in the crew, went ashore on the Island of Cochous during a heavy fog. Some time after she got clear and floated off, but three hours later she filled and sank. The crew escaped in two small boats to the island, taking with them a large quantity of biscuits. The crew have lived on Cochous Island nine months, and, their food being exhausted, they are about to set out for Possession Island. — 30th September, 1887."

Possession Island, which is also one of the Crozet group is eighty miles from Cochous. The *Meurthe* at once went to that island, but found no trace whatever of the shipwrecked men. Then she went to East Island, another island of the group, where she found some American whalers who had been there for some weeks. They had neither seen nor heard anything of the castaways. All the other islands in those waters were visited without result. It is firmly believed that the unfortunate men were lost in the perilous passage by small boats to Possession Island, though there is a bare chance that they were picked up by some American whaler.

Of course the two hundred and thirty pounds of biscuit with which the men reached Cochous Island were only a small part of the provision they required during their nine months' sojourn there. At least one other crew has been shipwrecked on the Crozets, and it subsisted until rescued on penguin flesh, eggs, and fish. In this way doubtless the men in the *Tamaris* eked out their food resources, and it is not probable they would have starved had their patience held out a little longer until relief came.

They probably thought that at Possession Island the chances would be better that some whaler would discover them. They knew there was not one chance in many thousands that the "man o' war" bird to whom they entrusted their brief message would carry it safely and quickly thousands of miles to the civilised world. They little dreamed that eight days before they set out from the desolate rock where they had lived so forlornly the bird they sent skimming over the waters had finished his wonderful flight, and had told the world of their unhappy situation.

Few stories of the animal kingdom equal in pathetic interest that of this strong-winged bird, whose happy fulfilment of the mission entrusted to him set two nations at work to rescue men in sore distress.

THE PLAGUE SHIP

By HERMAN MELVILLE

*"Redburn", published in 1849, is Herman Melville's story of his own
first voyage to sea. He sailed from New York in 1837, as a boy of
seventeen, aboard the barque "Highlander", outward bound for Liverpool. He had run away to sea with, as he said, "the devil in his heart".*

"MAMMY! mammy! come and see the sailors eating out of little
troughs, just like our pigs at home." Thus exclaimed one of the
steerage children, who at dinner-time was peeping down into the forecastle, where the crew were assembled, helping themselves from the
"kids", which, indeed, resemble hog-troughs not a little.

"Pigs, is it?" coughed Jackson, from his bunk, where he sat presid-
ing over the banquet, but not partaking, like a devil who had lost his
appetite by chewing sulphur.—"Pigs, is it?—And the day is close by,
ye spalpeens, when you'll want to be after taking a sup at our
troughs!"

This malicious prophecy proved true.

As day followed day without glimpse of shore or reef, and head-
winds drove the ship back, as hounds a deer; the improvidence and
shortsightedness of the passengers in the steerage, with regard to their
outfits for the voyage, began to be followed by the inevitable results.

Many of them at last went aft to the mate, saying that they had
nothing to eat, their provisions were expended, and they must be
supplied from the ship's stores, or starve.

This was told to the captain, who was obliged to issue a ukase from
the cabin, that every steerage passenger, whose destitution was demon-
strable, should be given one sea-biscuit and two potatoes a day; a sort
of substitute for a muffin and a brace of poached eggs.

But this scanty ration was quite insufficient to satisfy their hunger:
hardly enough to satisfy the necessities of a healthy adult. The consequence was, that all day long, and all through the night, scores of
the emigrants went about the decks, seeking what they might devour.

79

They plundered the chicken-coop; and disguising the fowls, cooked them at the public galley. They made inroads upon the pig-pen in the boat, and carried off a promising young shoat: *him* they devoured raw, not venturing to make an incognito of his carcass; they prowled about the cook's caboose, till he threatened them with a ladle of scalding water; they waylaid the steward on his regular excursions from the cook to the cabin; they hung round the forecastle, to rob the bread-barge; they beset the sailors, like beggars in the streets, craving a mouthful in the name of the Church.

At length, to such excesses were they driven, that the Grand Russian, Captain Riga, issued another ukase, and to this effect: Whatsoever emigrant is found guilty of stealing, the same shall be tied into the rigging and flogged.

Upon this, there were secret movements in the steerage, which almost alarmed me for the safety of the ship; but nothing serious took place, after all; and they even acquiesced in, or did not resent, a singular punishment which the captain caused to be inflicted upon a culprit of their clan, as a substitute for a flogging. For no doubt he thought that such rigorous discipline as *that* might exasperate five hundred emigrants into an insurrection.

A head was fitted to one of the large deck-tubs—the half of a cask; and into this head a hole was cut; also, two smaller holes in the bottom of the tub. The head—divided in the middle, across the diameter of the orifice—was now fitted round the culprit's neck; and he was forthwith coopered up into the tub, which rested on his shoulders, while his legs protruded through the holes in the bottom.

It was a burden to carry; but the man could walk with it; and so ridiculous was his appearance, that in spite of the indignity, he himself laughed with the rest at the figure he cut.

"Now, Pat, my boy," said the mate, "fill that big wooden belly of yours, if you can."

Compassionating his situation, our old "doctor" used to give him alms of food, placing it upon the cask-head before him; till at last, when the time for deliverance came, Pat protested against mercy, and would fain have continued playing Diogenes in the tub for the rest of this starving voyage.

Although fast-sailing ships, blest with prosperous breezes, have frequently made the run across the Atlantic in eighteen days; yet, it is not uncommon for other vessels to be forty, or fifty, and even sixty, eighty, and ninety days, in making the same passage. Though in these cases, some signal calamity or incapacity must occasion so great a detention. It is also true, that generally the passage out from America is shorter than the return; which is to be ascribed to the prevalence of westerly winds.

We had been outside of Cape Clear upward of twenty days, still harassed by head-winds, though with pleasant weather upon the whole, when we were visited by a succession of rain-storms, which lasted the greater part of a week.

During the interval, the emigrants were obliged to remain below; but this was nothing strange to some of them; who, not recovering, while at sea, from their first attack of seasickness, seldom or never made their appearance on deck, during the entire passage.

During the week, now in question, fire was only once made in the public galley. This occasioned a good deal of domestic work to be done in the steerage, which otherwise would have been done in the open air. When the lulls of the rain-storms would intervene, some unusually cleanly emigrant would climb to the deck, with a bucket of slops, to toss into the sea. No experience seemed sufficient to instruct some of these ignorant people in the simplest, and most elemental principles of ocean-life. Spite of all lectures on the subject, several would continue to shun the leeward side of the vessel, with their slops. One morning, when it was blowing very fresh, a simple fellow pitched over a gallon or two of something to windward. Instantly it flew back in his face; and also, in the face of the chief mate, who happened to be standing by at the time. The offender was collared, and shaken on the spot; and ironically commanded, never, for the future, to throw anything to windward at sea, but fine ashes and scalding hot water.

During the frequent hard blows we experienced, the hatchways on the steerage were, at intervals, hermetically closed; sealing down in their noisome den, those scores of human beings. It was something to be marvelled at, that the shocking fate, which, but a short time ago, overtook the poor passengers in a Liverpool steamer in the Channel, during similar stormy weather, and under similar treatment, did not overtake some of the emigrants of the *Highlander*.

Nevertheless, it was, beyond question, this noisome confinement in so close, unventilated, and crowded a den: joined to the deprivation of sufficient food, from which many were suffering; which, helped by their personal uncleanliness, brought on a malignant fever.

The first report was, that two persons were affected. No sooner was it known, than the mate promptly repaired to the medicine-chest in the cabin: and with the remedies deemed suitable, descended into the steerage. But the medicines proved of no avail; the invalids rapidly grew worse; and two more of the emigrants became infected.

Upon this, the captain himself went to see them; and returning, sought out a certain alleged physician among the cabin-passengers; begging him to wait upon the sufferers; hinting that, thereby, he might prevent the disease from extending into the cabin itself. But this person denied being a physician; and from fear of contagion — though he did not confess that to be the motive — refused even to enter the steerage.

The cases increased: the utmost alarm spread through the ship: and scenes ensued, over which, for the most part, a veil must be drawn; for such is the fastidiousness of some readers, that, many times, they must lose the most striking incidents in a narrative like mine.

Many of the panic-stricken emigrants would fain now have domiciled on deck; but being so scantily clothed, the wretched weather — wet, cold, and tempestuous — drove the best part of them again below. Yet any other human beings, perhaps, would rather have faced the most outrageous storm, than continued to breathe the pestilent air of the steerage. But some of these poor people must have been so used to the most abasing calamities, that the atmosphere of a lazar-house almost seemed their natural air.

The first four cases happened to be in adjoining bunks; and the emigrants who slept in the farther part of the steerage, threw up a barricade in front of those bunks; so as to cut off communication. But this was no sooner reported to the captain, than he ordered it to be thrown down; since it could be of no possible benefit; but would only make still worse, what was already direful enough.

It was not till after a good deal of mingled threatening and coaxing, that the mate succeeded in getting the sailors below, to accomplish the captain's order.

The sight that greeted us, upon entering, was wretched indeed. It was like entering a crowded jail. From the rows of rude bunks, hundreds of meagre, begrimed faces were turned upon us; while seated upon the chests, were scores of unshaven men, smoking tea-leaves, and creating a suffocating vapour. But this vapour was better than the native air of the place, which from almost unbelievable causes, was fetid in the extreme. In every corner, the females were huddled together, weeping and lamenting; children were asking bread from their mothers, who had none to give; and old men, seated upon the floor, were leaning back against the heads of the water-casks, with closed eyes and fetching their breath with a gasp.

At one end of the place was seen the barricade, hiding the invalids; while — notwithstanding the crowd — in front of it was a clear area, which the fear of contagion had left open.

"That bulkhead must come down," cried the mate, in a voice that rose above the din. "Take hold of it, boys."

But hardly had we touched the chests composing it, when a crowd of palefaced, infuriated men rushed up; and with terrific howls, swore they would slay us, if we did not desist.

"Haul it down!" roared the mate.

But the sailors fell back, murmuring something about merchant seamen having no pensions in case of being maimed, and they had not shipped to fight fifty to one. Further efforts were made by the mate who at last had recourse to entreaty; but it would not do; and we were obliged to depart, without achieving our object.

About four o'clock that morning, the first four died. They were all men; and the scenes which ensued were frantic in the extreme. Certainly, the bottomless profound of the sea, over which we were sailing, concealed nothing more frightful.

Orders were at once passed to bury the dead. But this was unnecessary. By their own countrymen, they were torn from the clasp of their wives, rolled in their own bedding, with ballast-stones, and with hurried rites, were dropped into the ocean.

At this time, ten more men had caught the disease; and with a degree of devotion worthy all praise, the mate attended them with his medicines; but the captain did not again go down to them.

It was all-important now that the steerage should be purified; and had it not been for the rains and squalls, which would have made it madness to turn such a number of women and children upon the wet and unsheltered decks, the steerage passengers would have been ordered above, and their den have been given a thorough cleansing. But, for the present, this was out of the question. The sailors peremptorily refused to go among the defilements to remove them; and so besotted were the greater part of the emigrants themselves, that though the necessity of the case was forcibly painted to them, they would not lift a hand to assist in what seemed their own salvation.

The panic in the cabin was now very great; and for fear of contagion to themselves, the cabin passengers would fain have made a prisoner of the captain, to prevent him from going forward beyond the mainmast. Their clamours at last induced him to tell the two mates that for the present they must sleep and take their meals elsewhere than in their old quarters, which communicated with the cabin.

On land, a pestilence is fearful enough; but there, many can flee from an infected city; whereas, in a ship, you are locked and bolted in the very hospital itself. Nor is there any possibility of escape from it; and in so small and crowded a place, no precaution can effectually guard against contagion.

Horrible as the sights of the steerage now were, the cabin, perhaps, presented a scene equally despairing. Many, who had seldom prayed before, now implored the merciful heavens, night and day, for fair winds and fine weather. Trunks were opened for Bibles; and at last, even prayer-meetings were held over the very table across which the loud jest had been so often heard.

Strange, though almost universal, that the seemingly nearer prospect of that death which anybody at any time may die, should produce these spasmodic devotions, when an everlasting Asiatic Cholera is forever thinning our ranks; and die by death we all must at last.

On the second day, seven died, one of whom was the little tailor; on the third, four; on the fourth, six, of whom one was the Greenland sailor, and another, a woman in the cabin, whose death, however, was afterward supposed to have been purely induced by her fears. These last deaths brought the panic to its height; and sailors, officers, cabin-passengers, and emigrants — all looked upon each other like lepers. All but the only true leper among us — the mariner Jackson, who seemed elated with the thought, that for *him* — already in the deadly clutches of another disease — no danger was to be apprehended from a fever which only swept off the comparatively healthy. Thus, in the midst of the despair of the healthful, this incurable invalid was not cast down; not, at least, by the same considerations that appalled the rest.

And still, beneath a gray, gloomy sky, the doomed craft beat on; now on this tack, now on that; battling against hostile blasts, and drenched in rain and spray; scarcely making an inch of progress toward her port.

On the sixth morning, the weather merged into a gale, to which we stripped our ship to a storm-stay-sail. In ten hours' time, the waves ran in mountains; and the *Highlander* rose and fell like some vast buoy on the water. Shrieks and lamentations were driven to leeward and drowned in the roar of the wind among the cordage; while we gave to the gale the blackened bodies of five more of the dead.

But as the dying departed, the places of two of them were filled in the rolls of humanity, by the birth of two infants, whom the plague, panic, and gale had hurried into the world before their time. The first cry of one of these infants, was almost simultaneous with the splash of its father's body in the sea. Thus we come and we go. But, surrounded by death, both mothers and babes survived.

At midnight, the wind went down; leaving a long, rolling sea; and, for the first time in a week, a clear, starry sky.

In the first morning-watch, I sat with Harry on the windlass, watching the billows; which, seen in the night, seemed real hills, upon which fortresses might have been built; and real valleys, in which villages, and groves, and gardens, might have nestled. It was like a landscape in Switzerland; for down into those dark, purple glens, often tumbled the white foam of the wavecrests, like avalanches; while the seething and boiling that ensued, seemed the swallowing up of human beings.

By the afternoon of the next day this heavy sea subsided; and we bore down on the waves, with all our canvas set; stun'-sails alow and aloft; and our best steersman at the helm; the captain himself at his elbow;— bowling along, with a fair, cheering breeze over the taffrail.

The decks were cleared, and swabbed bone-dry; and then, all the emigrants who were not invalids, poured themselves out on deck, snuffing the delightful air, spreading their damp bedding in the sun, and regaling themselves with the generous charity of the captain, who of late had seen fit to increase their allowance of food. A detachment of them now joined a band of the crew, who proceeding into the steerage, with buckets and brooms, gave it a thorough cleansing, sending on deck, I know not how many bucketsful of defilements. It was more like cleaning out a stable than a retreat for men and women. This day we buried three; the next day one, and then the pestilence left us, with seven convalescent; who, placed near the opening of the hatchway, soon rallied under the skilful treatment, and even tender care of the mate.

But even under this favorable turn of affairs, much apprehension was still entertained, lest in crossing the Grand Banks of Newfoundland, the fogs, so generally encountered there, might bring on a return of the fever. But, to the joy of all hands, our fair wind still held on; and we made a rapid run across these dreaded shoals, and south-ward steered for New York.

Our days were now fair and mild, and though the wind abated, yet we still ran our course over a pleasant sea. The steerage-passengers — at least by far the greater number — wore a still, subdued aspect, though a little cheered by the genial air, and the hopeful thought of soon reaching their port. But those who had lost fathers, husbands, wives, or children, needed no crêpe, to reveal to others who they were. Hard and bitter indeed was their lot; for with the poor and desolate, grief is no indulgence of mere sentiment, however sincere, but a gnaw-ing reality, that eats into their vital beings; they have no kind condo-lers, and bland physicians, and troops of sympathizing friends; and they must toil, though to-morrow be the burial and their pallbearers throw down the hammer to lift up the coffin.

How, then, with these emigrants, who, three thousand miles from home, suddenly found themselves deprived of brothers and husbands, with but a few pounds, or perhaps but a few shillings, to buy food in a strange land?

As for the passengers in the cabin, who now so jocund as they, drawing nigh, with their long purses and goodly portmanteaus to the promised land, without fear of fate? One and all were generous and gay, the jelly-eyed old gentleman, before spoken of, gave a shilling to the steward.

One lady who had died, was an elderly person, an American, re-turning from a visit to an only brother in London. She had no friend or relative on board, hence, as there is little mourning for a stranger dying among strangers, her memory had been buried with her body.

But the thing most worthy of note among these now light-hearted people in feathers, was the gay way in which some of them bantered others, upon the panic into which nearly all had been thrown.

And since, if the extreme fear of a crowd in a panic of peril, proves grounded on causes sufficient, they must then indeed come to perish; — therefore it is, that at such times they must make up their minds either to die, or else survive to be taunted by their fellow-men with their fear. For except in extraordinary instances of exposure, there are few living men, who, at bottom, are not very slow to admit that any other living men have ever been very much nearer death than themselves. Accordingly, *craven* is the phrase too often applied to anyone who, with however good reason, has been appalled at the prospect of sudden death, and yet lived to escape it. Though, should he have perished in conformity with his fears, not a syllable of *craven* would you hear. This is the language of one, who more than once has beheld the scenes, whence these principles have been deduced. The subject invites much subtle speculation; for in every being's ideas of death, and his behavior when it suddenly menaces him, lies the best index to his life and his faith. Though the Christian era had not then begun, Socrates died the death of the Christian; and though Hume was not a Christian in theory, yet he, too, died the death of the Christian — humble, composed, without bravado; and thought the most skeptical of philosophical skeptics, yet full of that firm, creedless faith, that embraces the spheres. Seneca died dictating to posterity; Petronius lightly discoursing of essences and love-songs; and Addison, calling upon Christendom to behold how calmly a Christian could die; but not even the last of these three, perhaps, died the best death of the Christian.

The cabin passenger who had used to read prayers while the rest knelt against the transoms and settees, was one of the merry young sparks, who had occasioned such agonies of jealousy to the poor tailor, now no more. In his rakish vest, and dangling watch-chain, this same youth, with all the awfulness of fear, had led the earnest petitions of his companions, supplicating mercy, where before he had never solicited the slightest favour. More than once had he been seen thus engaged by the observant steersman at the helm: who looked through the little glass in the cabin bulk-head.

But this youth was an April man; the storm had departed; and now he shone in the sun, none braver than he.

One of his jovial companions ironically advised him to enter into holy orders upon his arrival in New York.

"Why so?" said the other, "have I such an orotund voice?"

"No;" profanely returned his friend — "but you are a coward — just the man to be a parson, and pray."

However this narrative of the circumstances attending the fever among the emigrants on the *Highlander* may appear; and though these things happened so long ago; yet just such events, nevertheless, are perhaps taking place to-day. But the only account you obtain of such events, is generally contained in a newspaper paragraph, under the shipping-head. *There* is the obituary of the destitute dead, who die on the sea. They die, like the billows that break on the shore, and no more are heard or seen. But in the events, thus merely initialized in the catalogue of passing occurrences, and but glanced at by the readers of news, who are more taken up with paragraphs of fuller flavour; what a world of life and death, what a world of humanity and its woes, lies shrunk into a three-worded sentence!

You see no plague-ship driving through a stormy sea; you hear no groans of despair; you see no corpses thrown over the bulwarks; you mark not the wringing hands and torn hair of widows and orphans: — all is a blank. And one of these blanks I have but filled up, in recounting the details of the *Highlander*'s calamity.

THE GREAT CARRACK

The Knights Hospitallers of St. John, who had been expelled from Palestine at the close of the crusade in 1291 and then taken refuge temporarily in Cyprus, had found sanctuary in their great fortress on the island of Rhodes. In 1507 they faced the mounting threat of a Turkish invasion and were at their wits' end preparing to defend their fortress to the death.

This was the occasion of Campson's desiring leave of Bajazet to supply himself with timber out of the forests of Cilicia. Whilst his artificers were employed in these kinds of work, the grand seigneur put to sea a fleet consisting of a great number of galiots, flutes and other sorts of vessels, with a body of land-forces on board, under the command of a famous corsair called Camali, to whom the rest of the corsairs had joined themselves in this expedition, and who had all of them orders, as we have said, to make descents on the isles belonging to the knights, and destroy all with fire and sword. But they were prevented by the care and vigilance of the grand master: several detachments of cavalry, with the bravest knights at their head, were posted along the coast of the isle of Rhodes to guard it; so that the corsairs attempting to make a descent, the troops which they put on shore were surrounded by the Rhodians as soon as they advanced into the country. The greatest part of them were cut to pieces, and Camali gathering together as many as he could of those that escaped the sword of the knights, set sail again and fell upon the isles of Simia, Tilo and Nissaro, but with no better success than he had at Rhodes. He was in hopes however of repairing these miscarriages by the conquest of the isle of Lango; in this view he stood away for that coast, and was not far from it when he was informed that the grand master had put a considerable body of knights in it, under the command of brother Raimond de Balaguer, an old knight, dreaded over all those seas for his valour and experience.

All this expedition ended in a descent on the isle of Lero, which does not so much deserve the name of an island, as of a rock or shelf;

Camali landed 500 Turks, who began to batter the castle with all the cannon of their vessels.

The govenor of this little place was an old knight, of the language of Italy, who being extremely ill at that time, left the care of defending it to a young knight of Piedmont, scarce eighteen years old, Paul Simeoni by name. This young knight having no garrison nor soldiers, but only some poor inhabitants that cultivated the least rocky places of the isle, put a good face upon the matter, and fired briskly on the infidels that battered the place; but as their artillery had beat down a great panel of the wall of his castle, he, to intimidate the enemy and prevent their making an assault, dressed the inhabitants of the island, and also their wives, in the habit of knights, with the white cross: this new militia, by his orders, lined the breach in great numbers. The Turks taking them to be really knights, and imagining that they were a reinforcement which had been sent on the noise of their cannon, and landed in the isle by night, raised the siege with precipitation, for fear of being surprised by the galleys of the order, which owed the preservation of this fort to the resolution and adress of young Simeoni. The Sultan of Egypt, pursuant to the treaty which he had made with Bajazet, had sent seven flutes into those seas; which are a sort of long vessels with a low deck, and provided with oars as well as sails. These flutes had land-forces on board, and the commodore's design was to make an attempt on the isle of Lango. Two of these vessels, that were a sort of van to the rest, advancing a good way before them in order to reconnoitre, were discovered by the sentinels of the castle. The governor immediately ordered two galleys to sail out of the port, who after having put out to sea, turned back upon the flutes, and cut off their retreat. The Saracens not thinking themselves strong enough to fight them, and not able to get back to their squadron, made for the coast of Lango, ran their ships aground, got on shore, fled and hid themselves in the island. The knights knowing they could not escape being taken, lost no time in pursuing them, but towed off the two flutes, put Christian soldiers and seamen on board them, with two knights, and set the same course which the infidels had held before. The other five flutes that came quietly on, seeing the two others that preceded them, came up with them without mistrusting anything; but they were strangely surprised to see themselves attacked: they were still more so, when they saw to two galleys of the order appear from behind a cape of the island, and lay them aboard. The infidels, after a smart attack, were forced to strike, and were all made slaves in the galleys, as well as those that had fled to the island, where they were soon discovered and taken prisoner.

This little advantage was succeeded by an enterprise much more considerable, that was executed by one of the vessels of the order.

There went every year from Alexandria a great carrack laden with silks, spices, and all sorts of merchandise, which the Sultan's subjects brought from the Indies by the way of the Red Sea, and were carried in this vessel from Egypt into Africa, and Tunis, and up as far as Constantinople. This ship was of so extraordinary a bulk, that they say the top of the highest mast of the largest galleon was not near the height of the prow of this prodigious machine. Six men were scarce able to clasp the mast about.

This vessel had seven stories, two of which were lower than the surface of the water; it was able to carry, besides its freight, and the merchants and seamen necessary for the working of it, a thousand soldiers for its defence; it was a sort of floating castle, mounted with above an hundred pieces of cannon; the Saracens called this carrack the "Queen of the Sea".

The knights, during the government of Aubusson, had attempted several times to come up with it and attack it, but never could carry their point. The order was more lucky under his successor. Advice being brought that it was at sea, the grand master ordered the Chevalier de Gastineau, commander of Limoges, to go on board the admiral galley of the order, and endeavour to meet the carrack and engage it, but to make use of artifice rather than force in the taking of it, and to be particularly careful neither to burn nor sink it. The commander, pursuant to his orders, set sail, steering his course for

Candia, and cruising a little beyond that island to wait the coming up of the prize. The carrack soon appeared, and discovered the Christian caper; but the Saracens presuming on their own force, and the superiority of their fire and artillery, would not change their course; so far from that; they looked on their enemy with contempt, and thought it a rashness in the Christian to put himself in their way, as if he had a mind to be taken, and surrender himself up into his hands.

The knight however still kept on his course, and seeing himself within cannon shot, sent one of his officers in his long-boat to summon the captain of the carrack to deliver up his ship. The Saracen replied that the ship belonged to the Sultan his master; that he had by his orders commanded her several years, without having met with any enemy in those seas daring enough to attack him, and required him to tell his commander that he had a number of brave Mussulmen on board who would lose their lives rather than lose their honour and their liberty. The knight, upon receiving this answer and as if he had a mind to make up this affair by way of treaty, sent his officer back to the Saracen, to represent to him that his superiors had given him express orders to attack him whether strong or weak; that he could not help obeying them, and therefore could only offer them, if they would surrender, to give them good quarter; but that in case they would not, he would either burn or sink them.

By means of these parleys, and the time spent in dispatching the Christian officer backwards and forwards, the commander, who had no design but to amuse them, was still advancing forwards, and was come almost insensibly up close to the carrack; so that the Saracens having threatened the envoy to throw him into the sea if he returned any more with such proposals. He was no sooner got on board the galley of the order, but the commander let fly a broadside of his cannon laden with cartridges, which killed the Saracen captain, with most of the officers, as well as soldiers and seamen that were upon the deck. The merchants, soldiers and sea-

94

men that were left in the carrack, frightened at the terrible havoc made by this volley, and seeing them preparing to fire a second broadside, struck and offered to yield. The commander obliged the leader of them to come on board his galley, and at the same time sent a party of his own officers and seamen on board their vessel, to take the management of it. It would be impossible to relate the immense wealth that was found in this prize, besides vast sums of money and precious stones belonging to the merchants.

The Sultan sent several bales of pepper, ginger, cinnamon, cloves, and a great quantity of rich tapestry, camlets, and various sorts of commodities of great value for the ransom of the merchants and his other subjects. The vessels of the order took likewise, a few days after, near the coast of Cyprus, three ships of the Saracens, and sent the merchandise on board them to be sold in France, the produce of the sale being laid out in cannon, arms, and ammunition, which the agents of the order sent to Rhodes.

The Sultan, incensed at these losses, resolved to augment his naval force, and to have always a certain number of galleys in the Mediterranean and Red Sea. That prince sent five and twenty vessels of different bulk into the Gulf of Ajazzo, to transport the timber which he had caused to be cut and ready framed there, and designed to make use of for the building of new vessels.

The grand master having certain advice of the arrival of this Egyptian fleet in the gulf, and that this new armament was designed against a Christian prince, resolved to oppose it. He proposed the matter to the council. Several of the grand cross thought the enterprise dangerous by reason of the forces of the Sultan; but as the order was stronger at sea than that prince, and besides, the council was persuaded of the wisdom and prudence of the grand master, his opinion prevailed, and they allowed him to draw out of the treasury the money necessary for this expedition. He gave orders for equipping the great carrack, and they fitted out at the same time four galleys of the order, and eighteen vessels of several sizes.

As the king of Portugal's interest was chiefly concerned in this war, the grand master gave the command of the galleys to Andrew d'Amaral, a Portuguese, of the language of Castile, commander of the Vera Cruz, a brave knight, and well skilled in naval affairs, but proud, conceited, and too much prepossessed in favour of his own valour and capacity.

The ships were under the command of the chevalier de Villiers de l'Isle-Adam: the grand master chose him for this employment, on account of the esteem and reputation he had in the order, which he had merited by his valour and wise conduct in commanding.

The galleys sailing out of the port of Rhodes, came up to the isle of Cyprus, and went coasting up and down the island. But the commander de l'Isle-Adam, to avoid being becalmed, kept out to sea; and both, according to appointment, came by different ways to cape St. Andre, which is on the east of the kingdom of Cyprus. When the whole fleet of the order was joined, they held a council of war upon the manner of their attacking the infidels. The two chieftains, I mean d'Amaral and l'Isle-Adam, were of different opinions. The Frenchman proposed to wait, and surprise the ships when they should be at sea with the timber on board; d'Amaral was for going to attack them in the bottom of the gulf, without considering that they might be defended by batteries erected on the shore; and pretended to make his opinion pass for a law, at the same time that he rejected that of l'Isle-Adam with contempt. The debate grew very hot; the two generals were on the point of fighting; but the Frenchman having more moderation, and fearing that the quarrel might cause the enterprise to miscarry, sacrificed his resentment to the common good of the order, and submitted to d'Amaral's opinion.

The whole fleet then showed itself, and entered full sail into the gulf. The commodore of the Saracens was the Sultan's nephew: the young prince, who wanted no courage, seeing the Rhodian fleet, put what land-forces he had on board his ship, weighed anchor, advanced to meet the knights, and offered them battle. There were in the Christian fleet excellent pilots used to those seas, who, by working their ships, got the wind of the enemy; the infidels however were not daunted at it, but fought on with the same courage. The artillery was played equally well on both sides, and the generals fought themselves, and obliged their soldiers to fight like men that would not outlive their defeat. The continual fire of the cannon and small arms, the crash and havoc of the shipping, the shooting down of masts, and sinking of several vessels, all this lost abundance of men on both sides; and after an obstinate engagement for three hours together, it was scarce discernible on what side the victory inclined: and in all probability, if they had continued firing and cannonading only at a distance, the battle would not have been so soon ended; but the knights, by order of their generals, endeavoured to board them, and following their example, leaped most of them sword in hand into the enemies' vessels. This soon changed the face of the combat; and as, when they came to grapple, a knight had a great advantage over a Saracen soldier both in courage and address, the Egyptians lost several ships. Most of the infidels got into their long-boats, whilst others threw themselves into the sea to swim to the shore. Such as were lucky enough to get thither, fled into the woods and mountains; only their general chose rather to die honourably fighting, than either abandon his ship or surrender.

The knights in this engagement took eleven ships and four galleys, and sunk the rest. They afterwards landed some troops that pursued the fugitives, and took most of them, and made them slaves; and after setting fire to the timber, which the Egyptians had framed, they returned to Rhodes, and came back into the port with the ships and galleys they had taken from the enemy, and a great number of prisoners that they had taken in this expedition.

4

THE EMPEROR'S VISIT

By HERMAN MELVILLE

During his seven years at sea, the basis on which he wrote his famous books, Herman Melville served a term in a warship of the United States Navy. This is his tale of the visit paid to his ship by the Emperor of Brazil. It is an episode from his book "White-Jacket" which was first published in 1850.

While we lay in Rio, we sometimes had company from shore; but an unforeseen honour awaited us. One day, the young emperor, Don Pedro II, and suite — making a circuit of the harbour, and visiting all the men-of-war in rotation — at last condescendingly visited the *Neversink*.

He came in a splendid barge, rowed by thirty African slaves, who, after the Brazilian manner, in concert rose upright to their oars at every stroke; then sank backward again to their seats with a simultaneous groan.

He reclined under a canopy of yellow silk, looped with tassels of green, the national colours. At the stern waved the Brazilian flag, bearing a large diamond figure in the centre, emblematical, perhaps, of the mines of precious stones in the interior; or, it may be, a magnified portrait of the famous "Portuguese diamond" itself, which was found in Brazil, in the district of Tejuco, on the banks of the Rio Belmonte.

We gave them a grand salute, which almost made the ship's live-oak *knees* knock together with the tremendous concussions. We manned the yards, and went through a long ceremonial of paying the emperor homage. Republicans are often more courteous to royalty than royalists themselves. But doubtless this springs from a noble magnanimity.

At the gangway, the emperor was received by our commodore in person, arrayed in his most resplendent coat and finest French epaulets. His servant had devoted himself to polishing every button that morning with rottenstone and rags — your sea air is a sworn foe to metallic glosses; whence it comes that the swords of sea-officers have, of late, so rusted in their scabbards that they are with difficulty drawn.

It was a fine sight to see this emperor and commodore complimenting each other. Both wore *chapeaux-de-bras,* and both continually waved them. By instinct, the emperor knew that the venerable personage was as much a monarch afloat as he himself was ashore. Did not our commodore carry the sword of state by his side? For though not borne before him, it must have been a sword of state, since it looked far too lustrous to have been his fighting sword. *That* was naught but a limber steel blade, with a plain, serviceable handle, like the handle of a slaughter-house knife.

Who ever saw a star when the noon sun was in sight? But you seldom see a king without satellites. In the suite of the youthful emperor came a princely train; so brilliant with gems, that they seemed just emerged from the mines of the Rio Belmonte.

You have seen cones of crystallized salt? Just so flashed these Portuguese barons, marquises, viscounts, and counts. Were it not for their titles, and being seen in the train of their lord, you would have sworn they were eldest sons of jewellers all, who had run away with their fathers' cases on their backs.

Contrasted with these lamp-lustres of barons of Brazil, how waned the gold lace of our barons of the frigate, the officers of the gun-room! And compared with the long, jewel-hilted rapiers of the marquises, the little dirks of our cadets of noble houses — the middies — looked like gilded tenpenny nails in their girdles.

But there they stood! Commodore and emperor, lieutenants and marquises, middies and pages! The brazen band on the poop struck up; the marine guard presented arms; and high aloft, looking down on this scene, all the people vigorously hurrahed. A top-man next me on the main-royal-yard removed his hat, and diligently manipulated his head in honour of the event; but he was so far out of sight in the clouds, that this ceremony went for nothing.

A great pity it was, that in addition to all these honours, that admirer of Portuguese literature, Viscount Strangford, of Great Britain — who, I believe, once went out Embassador Extraordinary to the Brazils — it was a pity that he was not present on this occasion, to yield his tribute of "A Stanza to Braganza!" For our royal visitor was an undoubted Braganza, allied to nearly all the great families of Europe. His grandfather, John VI, had been King of Portugal; his own sister, Maria, was now its queen. He was, indeed, a distinguished young gentleman, entitled to high consideration, and that consideration was most cheerfully accorded him.

He wore a green dress-coat, with one regal morning-star at the breast, and white pantaloons. In his chapeau was a single, bright, golden-hued feather of the Imperial Toucan fowl, a magnificent, omnivorous, broad-billed bandit bird of prey, a native of Brazil. Its perch is on the loftiest trees, whence it looks down upon all humbler fowls, and, hawk-like, flies at their throats. The Toucan once formed part of the savage regalia of the Indian caciques of the country, and, upon the establishment of the empire, was symbolically retained by the Portuguese sovereigns.

His Imperial Majesty was yet in his youth; rather corpulent, if anything, with a care-free, pleasant face, and a polite, indifferent, and easy address. His manners, indeed, were entirely unexceptionable.

Now here, thought I, is a very fine lad, with very fine prospects before him. He is supreme emperor of all these Brazils; he has no stormy nightwatches to stand; he can lay abed of mornings just as long as he pleases. Any gentleman in Rio would be proud of his personal acquaintance, and the prettiest girl in all South America would deem herself honoured with the least glance from the acutest angle of his eye.

Yes: this young emperor will have a fine time of this life, even so long as he condescends to exist. Every one jumps to obey him; and see, as I live, there is an old nobleman in his suite — the Marquis d'Acarty they call him, old enough to be his grandfather — who, in the hot sun, is standing bareheaded before him, while the emperor carries his hat on his head.

"I suppose that old gentleman, now," said a young New England tar beside me, "would consider it a great honour to put on his Royal Majesty's boots; and yet, White-Jacket, if yonder emperor and I were to strip and jump overboard for a bath, it would be hard telling which was of the blood royal when we should once be in the water. Look you, Don Pedro II," he added, "how do you come to be emperor? Tell me that. You cannot pull as many pounds as I on the main-topsail-halyards; you are not as tall as I; your nose is a pug, and mine is a cut-water; and how do you come to be a 'brigand' with that thin pair of spars? A *brigand*, indeed!"

"*Braganza*, you mean," said I willing to correct the rhetoric of so fierce a republican, and, by so doing, chastise his censoriousness.

"Braganza! *bragger* it is," he replied; "and a bragger, indeed. See that feather in his cap! See how he struts in that coat! He may well wear a green one, top-mates — he's a green-looking swab at the best."

"Hush, Jonathan," said I; "there's the *First Luff* looking up. Be still! The emperor will hear you;" and I put my hand on his mouth.

"Take your hand away, White-Jacket," he cried; "there's no law up aloft here. I say, you emperor — you green-horn in the green coat, there — look you, you can't raise a pair of whiskers yet; and see what a pair of homewardbounders I have on my jowls. *Don Pedro*, eh? What's that, after all, but plain Peter — reckoned a shabby name in my country. Damm me, White-Jacket, I wouldn't call my dog Peter!"

"Clap a stopper on your jaw-tackle, will you?" cried Ringbolt, the sailor on the other side of him. "You'll be getting us all into darbies for this."

"I won't trice up my red rag for nobody," retorted Jonathan. "So you had better take a round turn with yours, Ringbolt, and let me alone, or I'll fetch you such a swat over your figure-head, you'll think a Long Wharf truckhorse kicked you with all four shoes on one hoof! You emperor — you counterjumping son of a gun — cock your weather eye up aloft here, and see your betters! I say, top-mates, he ain't any emperor at all — *I'm* the rightful emperor. Yes, by the commodore's boots! They stole me out of my cradle here in the palace at Rio, and put that green-horn in my place. Aye, you timberhead, you, I'm Don Pedro II, and by good rights you ought to be a main-top-man here, with your fist in a tar-bucket! Look you, I say, that crown of yours ought to be on my head; or, if you don't believe *that,* just heave it into the ring once, and see who's the best man."

"What's this hurrah's nest here aloft?" cried Jack Chase, coming up the t'-gallant rigging from the top-sail yard. "Can't you behave your-self, royal-yard-man, when an emperor's on board?"

"It's this here Jonathan," answered Ringbolt; "he's been black-guarding the young nob in the green coat, there. He says Don Pedro stole his hat."

"How?"

"Crown, he means, noble Jack," said a top-man.

"Jonathan don't call himself an emperor, does he?" asked Jack.

"Yes," cried Jonathan; "that green-horn, standing there by the commodore, is sailing under false colours; he's an impostor, I say; he wears my crown."

"Ha! ha!" laughed Jack, now seeing into the joke, and willing to humour it; "though I'm born a Briton, boys, yet, by the mast! these Don Pedros are all Perkin Warbecks. But I say, Jonathan, my lad, don't pipe your eye now about the loss of your crown; for, look you, we all wear crowns, from our cradles to our graves, and though in *double-darbies* in the *brig,* the commodore himself can't unking us."

"A riddle, noble Jack."

"Not a bit; every man who has a sole to his foot has a crown to his head. Here's mine;" and so saying, Jack, removing his tarpaulin, ex-hibited a bald spot, just about the bigness of a crown-piece, on the summit of his curly and classical head.

I beg their Royal Highnesses' pardon all round, but I had almost forgotten to chronicle the fact, that with the emperor came several other royal princes — kings for aught we knew — since it was just after the celebration of the nuptials of a younger sister of the Brazilian monarch to some European royalty. Indeed, the emperor and his suite formed a sort of bridal party, only the bride herself was absent.

The first reception over, the smoke of the cannonading salute having cleared away, and the martial outburst of the brass band having also rolled off to leeward, the people were called down from the yards, and the drum beat to quarters.

To quarters we went; and there we stood up by our iron bull-dogs, while our royal and noble visitors promenaded along the batteries, breaking out into frequent exclamations at our warlike array, the extreme neatness of our garments, and, above all, the extraordinary polish of the bright-work about the great guns, and the marvellous whiteness of the decks.

"Que gosto!" cried a marquis, with several dry goods samples of ribbon, tallied with bright buttons, hanging from his breast.

"Que gloria!" cried a crooked, coffee-coloured viscount, spreading both palms.

"Que alegria!" cried a little count, mincingly circumnavigating a shot-box.

"Que contentamento he o meu!" cried the emperor himself, complacently folding his royal arms, and serenely gazing along our ranks.

Pleasure, Glory, and *Joy* — this was the burden of the three noble courtiers. *And very pleasing indeed* — was the simple rendering of Don Pedro's imperial remark.

"Aye, aye," growled a grim rammer-and-sponger behind me; "it's all devilish fine for you nobs to look at; but what would you say if you had to holy-stone the deck yourselves, and wear out your elbows in polishing this cursed old iron, besides getting a dozen at the gangway, if you dropped a grease-spot on deck in your mess? Aye, aye, devilish fine for you, but devilish dull for us!"

In due time the drums beat the retreat, and the ship's company scattered over the decks.

Some of the officers now assumed the part of cicerones, to show the distinguished strangers the bowels of the frigate, concerning which several of them showed a good deal of intelligent curiosity. A guard of honour, detached from the Marine Corps, accompanied them, and they made the circuit of the berthdeck, where, at a judicious distance, the emperor peeped down into the cable-tier, a very subterranean vault.

The captain of the main-hold, who there presided, made a polite bow in the twilight, and respectfully expressed a desire for His Royal Majesty to step down and honour him with a call; but, with his handkerchief to his Imperial nose, his Majesty declined. The party then commenced the ascent to the spar-deck; which, from so great a depth in a frigate, is something like getting up to the top of Bunker Hill Monument from the basement.

While a crowd of the people was gathered about the forward part of the booms, a sudden cry was heard from below; a lieutenant came running forward to learn the cause, when an old sheet-anchor-man, standing by, after touching his hat, hitched up his waistbands, and replied, "I don't know, sir, but I'm thinking as how one o' them 'ere kings has been tumblin' down the hatchway."

And something like this it turned out. In ascending one of the narrow ladders leading from the berth-deck to the gun-deck, the Most Noble Marquis of Silva, in the act of elevating the Imperial coat-tails, so as to protect them from rubbing against the newly painted combings of the hatchway, this Noble Marquis's sword, being an uncommonly long one, had caught between his legs, and tripped him head over heels down into the fore-passage.

"Onde ides?" (where are you going?) said his royal master, tranquilly peeping down toward the falling marquis; "and what did you let go of my coat-tails for?" he suddenly added, in a passion, glancing round at the same time, to see if they had suffered from the unfaithfulness of his train-bearer.

"Oh, Lord!" sighed the captain of the fore-top, "who would be a Marquis of Silva?"

Upon being assisted to the spar-deck, the unfortunate marquis was found to have escaped without serious harm; but, from the marked coolness of his royal master, when the marquis drew near to apologize for his askwardness, it was plain that he was condemned to languish for a time under the royal displeasure.

Shortly after, the Imperial party withdrew, under another grand national salute.

4*

THE DESTRUCTION OF LAGOS

By G. A. HENTY

On Boxing Day, 1851, the Royal Navy attacked the town of Lagos in West Africa, It was the capital of Akitoye, the reigning chieftain, who had asked the British consul to help him to defend his port against aggression by his brother. After the first attempt to aid the chief had failed, another small squadron was sent out.

The first expedition against Lagos having failed solely from want of sufficient force to keep possession of the town, Commodore Bruce sent one of ample strength, and thoroughly organized, to drive the slave-dealing chief Kosoko from his stronghold.

The squadron appeared off Lagos by the 24th December. The boats of the *Sampson* and *Bloodhound* were for some time employed in ascertaining the position of the enemy's fortifications. The *Bloodhound* and *Teazer* at this time got on shore, and while they were being hove off, their people were exposed to a very hot fire from the negroes, who soon proved that they were no contemptible antagonists.

As the fire from jingalls, petrals, and muskets continued from the ditch and embankment abreast of the ship, and as the enemy were observed trying to bring their guns into position, at half-past two, Lieutenant Thomas Saumarez, with the boats of the *Sampson,* accompanied by Lieutenant E. M. Arthur, R.M.A., in command of the Marine Artillery, was despatched to attempt a landing and to spike the guns. They did all that men could do; but it was found impossible to make their way through the showers of musketry opened against them. Mr. Richards, a gallant young midshipman, was mortally wounded, and ten men were severely wounded; while so hot was the fire, that there seemed every prospect of the whole party being cut off. Still they bravely persevered. While undaunted efforts were being made to get on shore, Mr. William J. Stivey, carpenter of the *Sampson,* setting a noble example which others followed, leaped on shore, and, axe in hand, hewed manfully away at the stakes to make a passage for the boats to go through them. All, however, was in vain; their numbers were thinning rapidly; and at length Lieutenant Saumarez himself, being hit in three places, reluctantly, but very properly, gave the signal for return. The remainder of the day was spent in throwing shot and shell, as circumstances required, so as to prevent any guns being moved against the steamer. The nearest shot passed about ten yards astern of her.

The *Teazer* still continuing on shore, it became evident that before the tide rose the enemy would destroy her, unless the guns which were annoying her were captured. It was resolved, therefore, at once to effect this.

All being ready, the boats pulled in towards the stockade, where the best place for landing appeared to exist, keeping up all the time a continued fire of spherical grape and canister shot. As the boats touched the shore, they received a discharge directly in their faces of some 1500 muskets; but notwithstanding this, the men undauntedly landed, and, forming on the beach, after some severe fighting forced their way into the stockade, driving out the enemy, who fled into the thick bush close to the rear of it. Among those who landed and charged with Captain Lyster were Mr. Walling and Mr. Sproule, surgeons of the *Penelope,* and who afterwards exposed themselves equally in their attendance on the wounded under fire. Scarcely had the blacks retreated, than Lieutenant Corbett rushed ahead and spiked all the guns in the fort.

This object being accomplished, Captain Lyster issued orders for the re-embarkation of the party; but scarcely had he done so, when it was discovered that the enemy, having made a desperate rush at the first lifeboat, had succeeded in getting hold of her, and were tracking her along the beach towards the spot where the guns were posted which had first opened on the *Teazer.* On seeing this, the British, headed by their gallant leader, Captain Lyster, hurried down to the shore for the purpose of retaking her; but some delay occurred in consequence of having to divide her crew of sixty men among the other boats, which somewhat crowded them. The enemy, on seeing this, rushed back from their concealment in the woods by swarms, and poured in a destructive, crushing fire on the boats at pistol range. On this occasion a gallant young officer, Mr. F. R. Fletcher, midshipman in command of the second cutter, and who had charge of the boats while on shore, was shot through the head and killed. Several officers and men had before been wounded on shore, among whom was Lieutenant Williams, of the Marine Artillery, who, though hit in three places, had continued at the head of his men till they returned to the boats. Commander Hillyar was also wounded, and very many of the men were killed. Among the latter was James Webb, gunner's mate, belonging to the first lifeboat. When he saw that she was likely to fall into the hands of the blacks, he made a desperate attempt to spike her gun; but while thus engaged, he was cut down by the enemy, and mortally wounded. While Commander Hillyar was arranging the boats so that they might keep up their fire as they retreated to the *Teazer*, some of the kroomen on board Mr. Beecroft's *Victoria* let go her anchor, and there she lay exposed entirely to the fire of the blacks. On seeing this, Captain Lyster pulled back to her to learn what was the matter. "What has occurred now?" he asked of Mr. Bligh, the boatswain. "The kroomen let go the anchor without orders," he replied. "Then slip your cable, and get out of this," exclaimed Captain Lyster. "It's a chain cable, clenched to the bottom, and we can't unshackle it," replied Mr. Bligh. On hearing this disheartening intelligence, Captain Lyster jumped on board to see what assistance he could render. Just then Lieutenant Corbett staggered up towards the stern, exclaiming, "I have done it, and am alive!" In truth, he had cut the chain cable with a cold chisel, and in so doing, while leaning over the bows of the boat, had received five different wounds, which, with the addition of a severe one received on shore, rendered him almost helpless. His right arm was hanging to his side, but he still with his left worked away, and assisted in getting the *Victoria* off to the *Teazer*. While Captain Lyster was leaving the *Victoria* to get into his own boat, he was shot in the back with a musket-ball. On account of the hot fire to which they were still exposed, and the number of men already killed and wounded, he judged that he should not be justified in attempting to recover the lifeboat on that occasion. Leaving her, therefore, on the beach, the party returned to the *Teazer*. The people who had at first got possession of the lifeboat had afterwards abandoned her; but they now returned, and some forty or fifty got into her, intending to carry her off. Seeing this, Mr. Balfour, acting mate, assisted by Mr. Dewar, gunner, pulling back to the shore in the first cutter, threw a rocket towards her, and so well directed was it that it entered her magazine and blew it up. As soon as the party got back to the *Teazer* (having now pretty well silenced the fire of the enemy), they set to work to get all the provisions out of her, and then, having thrown overboard all her coals with the exception of ten tons, they contrived to shore her up, to await the rising of the tide. At length their exertions were crowned with success, and at sunset they succeeded in heaving her off. Then, getting up the steam, they anchored out of gunshot for the night.

On this unfortunate occasion there were no less than thirteen men killed belonging to H.M.S. *Penelope*, besides Mr. Fletcher and Mr. H. M. Fillham, master's assistant, who afterwards died of his wounds; while Captain Lyster, Commander Hillyar, Lieutenant Corbett, and First Leutenant of Marines J. W. C. Williams were wounded severely, together with fifty-seven men of the *Penelope* and two of the *Teazer,* most of them also very severely wounded. Crowded together in so small a vessel during the night, the poor fellows suffered greatly, though the medical officers of the expedition, Mr. R. Carpenter, senior surgeon, Mr. Walling, assistant surgeon of the *Penelope,* Dr. Barclay, acting surgeon, and Dr. Sproule, assistant surgeon, exerted themselves to their very utmost in the performance of their duty to the wounded. During the day they had never flinched from exposing their own lives, as, in the midst of the fire, they stepped from boat to boat to alleviate the sufferings of the wounded and dying.

Soon after seven o'clock in the morning the *Teazer* was got under weigh, and, finding the right channel, steamed up towards the *Bloodhound*, with the squadron of boats in her company. As soon as she was seen from the *Bloodhound,* Captain Jones ordered that the guns of the *Bloodhound's* gunboats should open a deliberate flanking fire on the west part of the enemy's defences; and he then sent a boat under Mr. Bullen, his clerk, who was acting as his aide-de-camp, to point out to Captain Lyster the position in which he wished the *Teazer* to be anchored. At ten minutes past eight, the *Teazer* having anchored, Captain Jones pulled on board her, to consult further with Captain Lyster on the plan of proceeding. The rocket-boats were then ordered to take up a position to the northward of the *Bloodhound.* This was quickly done, and Lieutenant Marshall threw some rockets with beautiful effect, setting fire to several houses, among which, to the satisfaction of all, was that of the Prime Minister Tappis. When this was seen, a hearty and spontaneous cheer ran through the whole squadron for the crew of the rocket-boat, who had thus punished the chief instigator of the former attack on the British boats. After this, the rocket-boat shifted her position ahead of the *Teazer,* and a general but deliberate fire was opened from the whole force. At forty-five minutes past ten, Lieutenant Marshall threw a rocket which struck the battery below Tappis' house, and at the same time a shot from the *Teazer* capsized the gun. The firing became still more rapid; an awful explosion ensued; a magazine of the enemy's had blown up. And from this moment the fate of Lagos was decided; house after house caught fire, and the whole town was shortly in a general blaze. More ships-of-war now came in, and Kosoko, finding his case hopeless, took to flight, and Akitoye was reinstated.

The only portion of the British forces landed was a small body under Commander Coote, who went on shore to spike guns.

The next morning, he and Commander Gardner, with the boats' crews of the *Sampson* and *Penelope,* were employed in a similar way. They returned in the afternoon, having by extraordinary exertions embarked or destroyed fifty-two pieces of ordnance.

Captain Jones in his despatch especially mentions Captain Lyster and Commander Hillyar, neither of whom, though severely wounded, would return on board till they had seen the success of their exertions.

He speaks also in high terms of Lieutenants Marshall, Rich, Corbett, and Saumarez; of Mr. J. Cook, gunner of the *Sampson*; of Charles Blofield, boatswain's mate, who commanded the pinnace when there remained no officer to put into her; of George Yule, gunner of Royal Marine Artillery, who served a twenty-four-inch howitzer in the first lifeboat with admirable precision; of Mr. Donelly, the surgeon of the *Sampson*, who nearly lost his life in coming to the assistance of the wounded; of Mr. Hacking, purser; and of Mr. Robert H. Bullen, who acted as his secretary and aide-de-camp, and "than whom," he observes, "no lieutenant could have done better."

Lagos has now been erected into a British province.

THE "PEQUOD" MEETS THE "ROSEBUD"

By HERMAN MELVILLE

"Moby Dick" is the best of all Herman Melville's books. In it the mad Captain Ahab hunts in frenzy the White Whale, the unconquered monarch of the deep sea. In this story the whole spirit of old-time whaling is told in a way never since equalled.

It was a week or two after the last whaling scene recounted, and when we were slowly sailing over a sleepy, vapory, mid-day sea, that the many noses on the *Pequod*'s deck proved more vigilant discoverers than the three pairs of eyes aloft. A peculiar and not very pleasant smell was smelt in the sea.

"I will bet something now," said Stubb, "that somewhere hereabouts are some of those drugged whales we tickled the other day. I thought they would keel up before long."

Presently, the vapors in advance slid aside; and there in the distance lay a ship, whose furled sails betokened that some sort of whale must be alongside. As we glided nearer, the stranger showed French colours from his peak; and by the eddying cloud of vulture sea-fowl that circled, and hovered, and swooped around him, it was plain that the whale alongside must be what the fishermen call a blasted whale, that is, a whale that has died unmolested on the sea, and so floated an unappropriated corpse. It may well be conceived, what an unsavory odor such a mass must exhale; worse than an Assyrian city in the plague, when the living are incompetent to bury the departed. So intolerable indeed is it regarded by some, that no cupidity could persuade them to moor alongside of it. Yet are there those who will still do it; notwithstanding the fact that the oil obtained from such subjects is of a very inferior quality, and by no means of the nature of attar-of-rose.

Coming still nearer with the expiring breeze, we saw that the

Frenchman had a second whale which seemed even more of a nose-gay than the first. In truth, it turned out to be one of those proble-matical whales that seem to dry up and die with a sort of prodigious dyspepsia, or indigestion; leaving their defunct bodies almost entirely bankrupt of anything like oil. Nevertheless, in the proper place we shall see that no knowing fisherman will ever turn up his nose at such a whale as this, however much he may shun blasted whales in general.

The *Pequod* had now swept so nigh to the stranger, that Stubb vowed he recognised his cutting spade-pole entangled in the lines that were knotted round the tail of one of these whales.

"There's a pretty fellow, now," he banteringly laughed, standing in the ship's bows, "there's a jackal for ye! I well know that these Crappoes of Frenchmen are but poor devils in the fishery; sometimes lowering their boats for breakers, mistaking them for Sperm Whale spouts; yes, and sometimes sailing from their port with their hold full of boxes of tallow candles, and cases of snuffers, foreseeing that all the oil they will get won't be enough to dip the Captain's wick into; aye, we all know these things; but look ye, here's a Crappo that is content with our leavings, the drugged whale there, I mean; aye, and is content too with scraping the dry bones of that other precious fish he has there. Poor devil! I say, pass round a hat, someone, and let's make him a present of a little oil for dear charity's sake. For what oil he'll get from that drugged whale there, wouldn't be fit to burn in a jail; no, not in a condemned cell. And as for the other whale, why, I'll agree to get more oil by chopping up and drying out these three masts of ours, than he'll get from that bundle of bones; though, now that I think of it, it may contain something worth a good deal more than oil; yes, ambergris. I wonder now if our old man has thought of that. It's worth trying. Yes, I'm in for it;" and so saying he started for the quarter-deck.

By this time the faint air had become a complete calm; so that whether or no, the *Pequod* was now fairly entrapped in the smell, with no hope of escaping except by its breezing up again. Issuing from the cabin, Stubb now called his boat's crew, and pulled off for the stranger. Drawing across her bow, he perceived that in accordance with the fanciful French taste, the upper part of her stem-piece was carved in the likeness of a huge drooping stalk, was painted green, and for thorns had copper spikes projecting from it here and there; the whole terminating in a symmetrical folded bulb of a bright red colour. Upon her head-boards, in large gilt letters, he read *"Bouton de Rose,"* — Rose-button, or Rose-bud; and this was the romantic name of this aromatic ship.

Though Stubb did not understand the *Bouton* part of the inscription, yet the word *rose,* and the bulbous figure-head put together sufficiently explained the whole to him.

"A wooden rose-bud, eh?" he cried with his hand to his nose, "that will do very well; but how like all creation it smells!"

Now in order to hold direct communication with the people on deck, he had to pull round the bows to the starboard side, and thus come close to the blasted whale; and so talk over it.

Arrived then at this spot, with one hand still to his nose, he bawled— "Bouton-de-Rose, ahoy! Are there any of you Bouton-de-Roses that speak English?"

"Yes," rejoined a Guernsey-man from the bulwarks, who turned out to be the chief-mate.

"Well, then, my Bouton-de-Rose-bud, have you seen the White Whale?"

"*What* whale?"

"The *White* Whale — a Sperm Whale — Moby-Dick, have ye seen him?"

"Never heard of such a whale. Cachalot Blanche! White Whale — no."

"Very good, then; good-bye now, and I'll call again in a minute."

Then rapidly pulling back towards the *Pequod,* and seeing Ahab leaning over the quarter-deck rail awaiting his report, he moulded his two hands into a trumpet and shouted — "No, Sir! No!" Upon which Ahab retired, and Stubb returned to the Frenchman.

He now perceived that the Guernsey-man, who had just got into the chains, and was using a cutting-spade, had slung his nose in a sort of bag.

"What's the matter with your nose, there?" said Stubb. "Broke it?"

"I wish it was broken, or that I didn't have any nose at all!" answered the Guernsey-man, who did not seem to relish the job he was at very much. "But what are you holding *yours* for?"

"Oh, nothing! It's a wax nose; I have to hold it on. Fine day, ain't it? Air rather gardenny, I should say; throw us a bunch of posies, will ye, Bouton-de-Rose?"

"What in the devil's name do you want here?" roared the Guernsey-man, flying into a sudden passion.

"Oh! keep cool-cool? Yes, that's the word; why don't you pack those whales in ice while you're working at 'em? But joking aside, though; do you know, Rose-bud, that it's all nonsense trying to get any oil out of such whales? As for that dried up one, there, he hasn't a gill in his whole carcase."

"I know that well enough; but, d'ye see, the Captain here won't believe it; this is his first voyage; he was a Cologne manufacturer before. But come aboard, and mayhap he'll believe you, if he won't me; and so I'll get out of this dirty scrape."

"Anything to oblige ye, my sweet and pleasant fellow," rejoined Stubb, and with that he soon mounted to the deck. There a queer scene presented itself. The sailors, in tasselled caps of red worsted, were getting the heavy tackles in readiness for the whales. But they worked rather slow and talked very fast, and seemed in anything but a good humour. All their noses upwardly projected from their faces like so many jib-booms. Now and then pairs of them would drop their work, and run up to the mast-head to get some fresh air. Some thinking they would catch the plague, dipped oakum in coal tar, at intervals held it to their nostrils. Others having broken the stems of their pipes almost short off at the bowl, were vigorously puffing tobacco smoke, so that it constantly filled their olfactories.

Stubb was struck by a shower of outcries and anathemas proceeding from the Captain's round-house abaft; and looking in that direction saw a fiery face thrust from behind the door, which was held ajar from within. This was the tormented surgeon, who, after in vain remonstrating against the proceedings of the day, had betaken himself to the Captain's round-house (*cabinet* he called it) to avoid the pest; but still, could not help yelling out his entreaties and indignations at times.

Marking all this, Stubb argued well for his scheme, and turning to the Guernsey-man had a chat with him, during which the stranger mate expressed his detestation of his Captain as a conceited ignoramus, who had brought them all into so unsavory and unprofitable a pickle. Sounding him carefully, Stubb further perceived that the Guernsey-man had not the slightest suspicion concerning the ambergris. He therefore held his peace on that head, but otherwise was quite frank and confidential with him, so that the two quickly concocted a little plan for both circumventing and satirizing the Captain, without his at all dreaming of distrusting their sincerity. According to this little plan of theirs, the Guernsey-man, under cover of an interpreter's office, was to tell the Captain what he pleased, but as coming from Stubb; and as for Stubb, he was to utter any nonsense that should come uppermost in him during the interview.

By this time their destined victim appeared from his cabin. He was a small and dark, but rather delicate looking man for a sea-captain, with large whiskers and moustache, however; and wore a red cotton velvet vest with watch-seals at his side. To this gentleman, Stubb was now politely introduced by the Guernsey-man, who at once ostentatiously put on the aspect of interpreting between them.

"What shall I say to him first?" said he.

"Why," said Stubb, eyeing the velvet vest and the watch and seals, "you may as well begin by telling him that he looks a sort of babyish to me, though I don't pretend to be a judge."

"He says, Monsieur," said the Guernsey-man, in French, turning to his captain, "that only yesterday his ship spoke to a vessel, whose captain and chief mate, with six sailors, had all died of a fever caught from a blasted whale they had brought alongside."

Upon this the captain started, and eagerly desired to know more. "What now?" said the Guernsey-man to Stubb.

"Why, since he takes it so easy, tell him that now I have eyed him carefully, I'm quite certain that he's no more fit to command a whale-ship than a St. Jago monkey. In fact, tell him from me he's a baboon."

"He vows and declares, Monsieur, that the other whale, the dried one, is far more deadly than the blasted one; in fine, Monsieur, he conjures us, as we value our lives, to cut loose from these fish."

Instantly the captain ran forward, and in a loud voice commanded his crew to desist from hoisting the cutting-tackles, and at once cast loose the cables and chains confining the whales to the ship.

"What now?" said the Guernsey-man, when the Captain had returned to them.

"Why, let me see; yes, you may as well tell him now that—that—in fact, tell him I've diddled him, and" (aside to himself) "perhaps somebody else."

"He says, Monsieur, that he's very happy to have been of any service to us."

Hearing this, the captain vowed that they were the grateful parties (meaning himself and mate) and concluded by inviting Stubb down into his cabin to drink a bottle of Bordeaux.

"He wants you to take a glass of wine with him," said the interpreter.

"Thank him heartily; but tell him it's against my principles to drink with the man I've diddled. In fact, tell him I must go."

"He says, Monsieur, that his principles won't admit of his drinking; but that if Monsieur wants to live another day to drink, then Monsieur had best drop all four boats, and pull the ship away from these whales, for it's so calm they won't drift."

By this time Stubb was over the side, and getting into his boat, hailed the Guernsey-man to this effect, — that having a long tow-line in his boat, he would do what he could to help them, by pulling out the lighter whale of the two from the ship's side. While the Frenchman's boats, then, were engaged in towing the ship one way, Stubb benevolently towed away at his whale the other way, ostentatiously slacking out a most unusually long towline.

Presently a breeze sprang up; Stubb feigned to cast off from the whale; hoisting his boats, the Frenchman soon increased his distance, while the *Pequod* slid in between him and Stubb's whale. Whereupon Stubb quickly pulled to the floating body, and hailing the *Pequod* to give notice of his intentions, at once proceeded to reap the fruit of his unrighteous cunning. Seizing his sharp boat-spade, he commenced an excavation in the body, a little behind the side fin. You would almost have thought he was digging a cellar there in the sea; and when at length his spade struck against the gaunt ribs, it was like turning up old Roman tiles and pottery buried in fat English loam. His boat's crew were all in high excitement, eagerly helping their chief, and looking as anxious as gold-hunters.

And all the time numberless fowls were diving, and ducking, and screaming, and yelling, and fighting around them. Stubb was beginning to look disappointed, especially as the horrible nosegay increased, when suddenly from out the very heart of this plague, there stole a faint stream of perfume, which flowed through the tide of bad smells without being absorbed by it, as one river will flow into and then along with another, without at all blending with it for a time.

"I have it, I have it," cried Stubb, with delight, striking something in the subterranean regions, "a purse! a purse!"

Dropping his spade, he thrust both hands in, and drew out handfuls of something that looked like ripe Windsor soap, or rich mottled old cheese; very unctuous and savory withal. You might easily dent it with your thumb; it is of a hue between yellow and ash colour. And this, good friends, is ambergris, worth a gold guinea an ounce to any druggist. Some six handfuls were obtained; but more was unavoidably lost in the sea, and still more, perhaps, might have been secured were it not for impatient Ahab's loud command to Stubb to desist, and come on board, else the ship would bid them good-bye.

Now this ambergris is a very curious substance, and so important as an article of commerce, that in 1791 a certain Nantucket-born

Captain Coffin was examined at the bar of the English House of Commons on that subject. For at that time, and indeed until a comparatively late day, the precise origin of ambergris remained, like amber itself, a problem to the learned. Though the word ambergris is but the French compound for grey amber, yet the two substances are quite distinct. For amber, though at times found on the seacoast, is also dug up in some far inland soils, whereas ambergris is never found except upon the sea. Besides, amber is a hard, transparent, brittle, odourless substance, used for mouth-pieces to pipes, for beads and ornaments; but ambergris is soft, waxy, and so highly fragrant and spicy, that it is largely used in perfumery, in pastils, precious candles, hair-powders, and pomatum. The Turks use it in cooking, and also carry it to Mecca, for the same purpose that frankincense is carried to St. Peter's in Rome. Some wine merchants drop a few grains into claret, to flavour it.

Who would think, then, that such fine ladies and gentlemen should regale themselves with an essence found in the inglorious bowels of a sick whale! Yet so it is. By some, ambergris is supposed to be the cause, and by others the effect, of the dyspepsia in the whale. How to cure such a dyspepsia it were hard to say, unless by administering three or four boat-loads of Brandreth's pills, and then running out of harm's way, as labourers do in blasting rocks.

I have forgotten to say that there were found in this ambergris, certain hard, round, bony plates, which at first Stubb thought might be sailors' trousers buttons; but it afterwards turned out that they were nothing more than pieces of small squid bones embalmed in that manner.

Now that the incorruption of this most fragrant ambergris should be found in the heart of such decay; is this nothing? Bethink thee of that saying of St. Paul in Corinthians, about corruption and incorruption; how that we are sworn in dishonour, but raised in glory. And likewise call to mind that saying of Paracelsus about what it is that maketh the best musk. Also forget not the fact that of all things of ill-savour, Cologne-water, in its manufacturing stages, is the worst.

I should like to conclude the chapter with the above appeal, but cannot, owing to my anxiety to repel a charge often made against whalemen, and which, in the estimation of some already biased minds, might be considered as indirectly substantiated by what has been said of the Frenchman's two whales. Elsewhere in this volume the slanderous aspersion has been disproved, that the vocation of whaling is throughout a slatternly, untidy business. But there is another thing to rebut. They hint that all whales always smell bad. Now how did this odious stigma originate?

I opine, that it is plainly traceable to the first arrival of the Greenland whaling ships in London, more than two centuries ago. Because those whalemen did not then, and do not now, try out their oil at sea as the Southern ships have always done; but cutting up the fresh blubber in small bits, thrust it through the bung holes of large casks, and carry it home in that manner; the shortness of the season in those Icy Seas, and the sudden and violent storms to which they are exposed, forbidding any other course. The consequence is, that upon breaking into the hold, and unloading one of these whale cemeteries, in the Greenland dock, a savour is given forth somewhat similar to that arising from excavating an old city graveyard, for the foundations of a Lying-in Hospital.

I partly surmise also, that this wicked charge against whalers may be likewise imputed to the existence on the coast of Greenland, in former times, of a Dutch village called Schmerenburgh or Smeerenberg, which latter name is the one used by the learned Fogo Von Slack, in his great work on Smells, a text-book on that subject. As its name imports (smeer, fat; berg, to put up), this village was founded in order to afford a place for the blubber of the Dutch whale fleet to be tried out, without being taken home to Holland for that purpose. It was a collection of furnaces, fat-kettles, and oil sheds; and when the works were in full operation certainly gave forth no very pleasant savour. But all this is quite different with a South Sea Sperm Whaler; which in a voyage of four years perhaps, after completely filling her hold with oil, does not, perhaps, consume fifty days in the business of boiling out; and in the state that it is casked, the oil is nearly scentless. The truth is, that living or dead, if but decently treated, whales as a species are by no means creatures of ill odour; nor can whalemen be recognised, as the people of the middle ages affected to detect a Jew in the company, by the nose. Nor indeed can the whale possibly be otherwise than fragrant, when, as a general thing, he enjoys such high health; taking abundance of exercise; always out of doors; though, it is true, seldom in the open air. I say, that the motion of a Sperm Whale's flukes above water dispenses a perfume, as when a musk-scented lady rustles her dress in a warm parlour. What then shall I liken the Sperm Whale to for fragrance, considering his magnitude? Must it not be to that famous elephant, with jewelled tusks, and redolent with myrrh, which was led out of an Indian town to do honour to Alexander the Great?

CAPTURE AND RECAPTURE

By CAPTAIN MARRYAT

"The King's Own" is probably Marryat's first work of fiction, al-
though it was published a year later than "Frank Mildmay". In this
story the young heroes take a leading part in recapturing the ship
from the French prize-crew.

The gales of wind in the tropical climates are violent while they
last, but are seldom of long duration. Such was the case in the present
instance: for it subsided in a few hours after daylight; and the schooner, that had been propelled before it, was now sheltered under the
lee of the island of St. Domingo, and, with all her canvas spread, was
gliding through a tranquil sea. Again they were collected round the
dinner-table, to a more quiet repast than they had hitherto enjoyed
since they came on board. Paul had not quite recovered his spirits,
although, when he went on deck, just before the dinner was announced, he was delighted at the sudden change which had taken
place; but the mirth of his companions at his expense was not received
in very good part.

After dinner, finding himself in a better humour, he turned to
Peter, and addressed him, — "I say, Peter, I made no answer to your
remarks last night, when we expected to go down; but I have since had
time deliberately to weigh your arguments, and I should like you to
explain to me where the *comfort* was that you so strenuously pointed
out, for hang me if I can discover it."

Seymour again had charge of the first watch; and, notwithstanding
that the order for the prisoners to remain below after dark had been
communicated to them, he observed that, on one pretence or other,
they occasionally came on deck, and repeatedly put their heads above
the hatchway. This conduct reminded him of the conversation which
he had overheard, and again it was the subject of his thoughts. Captain M— had one day observed to him, that if there was no duty going
on, he could not employ himself in a more useful manner, when he

was walking the deck, than by placing himself, or the ship, in difficult situations, and reflecting upon the most elegible means of relief. "Depend upon it," observed Captain M——, "the time will come, when you will find it of use to you; and it will create for you a presence of mind, in a sudden dilemma, which may be the salvation of yourself and the ship you are in."

Seymour, remembering this injunction, reflected upon what would be the most advisable steps to take, in case of the French prisoners attempting a recapture during his watch on deck. That there were but six, it was very true; but, at the same time, during the night-watches there were but five English seamen, and the officer of the watch, on deck. Should the Frenchmen have the boldness to attempt to regain possession of the vessel, there was no doubt that, if the watch could be surprised, the hatches would be secured over those below. What should be the steps, in such a case, that he ought to take?

Such were the cogitations of Seymour, when midnight was reported, and Jerry was summoned to relieve the deck — which he did not do, relying upon our hero's good-nature, until past one bell. Up he came, with his ready apology — "I really beg your pardon, my dear fellow, but I had not a wink of sleep last night."

"Never mind, Jerry, I am not at all sleepy. I had been thinking about these French prisoners — I cannot get their conversation out of my head."

"Why, I did not like it myself, when I heard of it," replied Jerry. "I hope they won't attempt it in my watch; it would not give them much trouble to launch me over the quarter — I should skim away, 'flying light', like a lady's bonnet."

"What would you do, Jerry, if you perceived them rushing aft to retake the vessel?" inquired Seymour, who was aware of his ready invention.

"Skin up the rigging like a lamp-lighter, to be sure. Not that it would be of much use, if they gained the day — except to say a few prayers before I went astern."

"Well, that was my idea; but I thought that if one had a musket and ammunition up there, a diversion might be created in favour of those below — for the prisoners have no firearms."

"Very true," replied Jerry; "we might puzzle them not a little."

"Now, Jerry, suppose we were to take that precaution, for I do not like their manoeuvres during my watch. It will do no harm, if it does no good. Suppose you fetch two muskets and cartouch-boxes from the cabin — I'll take one, and secure it in the fore-cross-trees, and you do the same at the main: for Courtenay is too proud to keep an armed watch."

Jerry agreed to the proposal, and brought up the muskets and ammunition Seymour gave him and a stout *fox* to lash the musket; and taking another himself, they both ascended the rigging at the same time, and were busy securing the muskets up and down at the head of the lower masts, when they heard a sudden rush upon deck, beneath them.

It was dark, though not so dark but they could distinguish what was going on, and they perceived that their thoughts had but anticipated the reality. "The French are up!" roared the man at the wheel, to rouse those below, as well as the watch, who were lying about the decks but, to the astonishment of the youngsters aloft, as well as of the men on deck, not six but about twenty Frenchmen, armed with cutlasses, made their appearance. The hatches were over and secured in a minute; and the unarmed English on deck were then attacked by the superior force. It was with agonised feelings that Seymour and Jerry heard the scuffle which took place; it was short; and plunge after plunge into the water, alongside, announced the death of each separate victim. The man at the wheel struggled long — he was of an athletic frame — but, overpowered by numbers, he was launched over the taffrail.

The French, supposing that the remainder of the crew were below, placed sentries over the hatches, that they might not be forced, and then collected together abaft, altering the course of the vessel for St. Domingo.

It will be necessary to explain the sudden appearance of so many

Frenchmen. When the captain of the privateer was occupied, during the night previous to the attack, with several plans of defence, he also arranged one for the recapture of the vessel, in case of their being overpowered. With this in view, he had constructed a platform in the hold, on which a tier of casks was stowed, and under which there was sufficient space for fifteen or twenty men to lie concealed. When the privateer's men had been driven below, and the hatches secured over them, fifteen, armed with cutlasses, concealed themselves in this place, with the hopes of recapturing the vessel from the prize-master, after she should have parted company with the frigate. The prisoners who had been sent on board to assist in navigating the schooner to Jamaica, had communicated with them, unperceived, after dark. As all the English were fatigued, from having been on deck during the previous night, the middle watch was proposed for the attempt, which had thus far been attended with success.

Seymour and Jerry remained quiet at the mast-heads; for although they did not attempt to communicate with each other, for fear of discovery, they both rightly judged that it would be best to remain till daylight; by which time, some plans would have been formed by the party below, which their situation would enable them materially to assist. Nearly four hours elapsed previous to the dawning of the day, during which interval Jerry had ample time to say some of those prayers which he spoke of, and which it was to be supposed that they both did not fail to offer up in their perilous situation.

As soon as the day began to break, Jerry, who had not yet loaded his musket, lest he might be heard, thought it time to prepare for action. He primed and put in his cartridge, in the ramming down of which a slight ringing of the ramrod against the muzzle attracted the notice of one of the Frechmen, who, looking up, after a short time, exclaimed:—

"*Diable! C'est monsieur misère qui est là!*"

Jerry levelled with a steady aim, and the bullet passed through the broad chest of the Frenchman, who rolled upon the deck.

"Now, they may chant your *miserere*," cried the youngster.

A second shot from the fore-cross-trees laid another Frenchman alongside of his companion.

"*Comment! diable! Nous serons abimés par ces enfants-là; il faut monter.*"

The muskets were again loaded, and again each boy brought down his bird, before the Frenchmen could decide upon their operations. It was a case of necessity that the youngsters should be attacked; but it was a service of no little danger, and of certain destruction to one, who must fall a sacrifice, that the other might be able to secure the youngster before he had time to reload his musket. Two of the most daring flew to the main rigging, one ascending to windward, and the other to leeward. Seymour, who perceived their intentions, reserved his fire until he saw the one in the weather rigging fall by Jerry's musket; he then levelled at the one to leeward, who dropped into the lee-chains, and from thence into the sea. Thus had six Frenchmen already fallen by the coolness and determination of two boys, one but fourteen, and the other not sixteen years old.

A short consultation ended in the Frenchmen resorting to the only measures likely to be attended with success. Leaving three to guard the hatchways, the remaining twelve, divided into four parties, began to mount both fore and main-rigging, to windward and to leeward, at the same time. The fate of Jerry and Seymour now appeared to be decided. They might each kill one man more, and then would have been hurled into the sea. But during the consultation Seymour, who anticipated this movement, and had a knife in his pocket, divided the lanyards of the lee top-mast-rigging, and running up the weather side with his musket and ammunition, as soon as he had gained the mast cross-trees, hauled up the lee rigging after him; thus gaining a position that would admit but one person mounting up to him at a time. He called to Jerry, pointing out what he had done, that he might do the same; but infortunately Jerry had no knife, and could not. He contented himself with climbing up to the top-mast cross-trees, to which he was followed by two of the Frenchmen. Jerry levelled his musket, and passed his bullet through the skull of one of his pur-

127

suers, whose heavy fall on the deck shook the schooner fore and aft: and then, aware that nothing more could be done, pitched his musket overboard, that they might not gain possession of it, and climbing, with a nimbleness suited to the occasion, up to the mast-head, descended by the top-gallant-stay to the fore-topmast cross-trees, and joined Seymour, in the presence of the exasperated Frenchmen, who now, unable to reach either of them, were at a non plus. "I say, monsieur, no catchee, no habbee," cried Jerry, laughing, and putting his hand to his side from loss of breath.

But we must now acquaint the reader with what is going on below. The surprise of Courtenay, when he found the hatches down, and the deck in possession of the French, was removed, when the men who had been secured with him stated that, as they lay in their hammocks, they had been awakened by a large body of men running up the hatch-way. He now perceived that there must have been men concealed in the hold of the vessel. The struggle on deck, the splashing in the water, all had been plainly heard below; they were aware of the fate of their shipmates, and did not expect to see daylight again, until they were handed up as prisoners in a French port.

The feelings of Courtenay were not enviable. He upbraided himself for having, by his want of prudence, lost the vessel, and sacrificed the lives of the two midshipmen and five seamen who had the watch on deck. The party below consisted of Courtenay, Peter and Paul, Billy Pitts, and five seamen; and a consultation was held as to their proceedings. To regain the vessel and avenge the death of their shipmates, or to perish in the attempt, was the determination of the lieutenant.

He was aware that the French had no firearms; and, amply supplied as they were, he would have cared little for their numbers if once on deck; but how to get on deck was the problem. To set fire to the vessel, and rush up in the flames, — to scuttle her, — or to blow her up, and all go down together, were each proposed and agitated.

Peter's plan was considered as the most feasible. He suggested, that one half of the cabin table, which was divided in two, should be placed upon the other, so as to raise it up to the combings of the skylight-hatch; on the upper table, to place a pound or two of powder, which, from the ascending principle of explosion, would blow off the skylight and grating without injuring the vessel below. Then, with their muskets loaded and bayonets fixed, to jump on the table, and from thence, if possible, gain the deck.

This was agreed to, and the preparations were well forward, when the report of Jerry's musket was heard — another succeeded, and they were perplexed. Had the Frenchmen firearms? — and if so, what could they be firing at? The falling of the bodies on deck, and the indistinct curses of the Frenchmen, puzzled them even more. "What can it be?" observed Courtenay.

"I recollect now," said Paul, "as I lay awake, I saw a young *devilskin* pass my bed with a musket — I wondered what it was for."

"Then, probably, he has gained the rigging with it, and is safe," cried Courtenay, intuitively. "Be quick! Where's the powder? Take that candle further off."

The train was laid as the muskets continued to be discharged; they removed from the cabin; — it was fired, and the skylight was blown up, killing the Frenchman who guarded the hatchway, at the very moment that the Frenchmen were in the rigging, puzzled with the manœuvres of Seymour and the escape of Jerry.

Courtenay and his party rushed into the cabin, mounted the table, and were on deck before the smoke had cleared away; and the Frenchmen, who had not had time to descend the rigging, were at their mercy.

Mercy they were not entitled to. They had shown none to the unarmed English, whom they had wantonly thrown into the sea when they had overpowered them, and were now thirsting for the blood of the two boys. No mercy was shown to them. As they dropped one by one from the rigging, wounded or dead, they were tossed into the wave, as an expiatory sacrifice to the *manes* of the murdered Englishmen. In a few minutes the carnage was over. Seymour and Jerry descended from their little *fortalice* aloft, and were warmly greeted by their friends as they reached the deck.

5

THE KRAKEN

By FRANK T. BULLEN

"The Cruise of the Cachalot", from which this story is taken, is one of the finest tales of whaling ever written. It also deals with the mysterious and exciting subject of sea monsters.

It has often been a matter for considerable surprise to me, that while the urban population of Great Britain is periodically agitated over the great sea-serpent question, sailors, as a class, have very little to say on the subject. During a considerable sea experience in all classes of vessels, except men-of-war, and in most positions, I have heard a fairly comprehensive catalogue of subjects brought under dog-watch discussion; but the sea-serpent has never, within my recollection, been one of them.

The reasons for this abstinence may vary a great deal, but chief among them is — sailors, as a class, "don't believe in no such a pusson." More than that, they do believe that the mythical sea-serpent is "boomed" at certain periods, in the lack of other subjects, which may not be far from the fact. But there is also another reason, involving a disagreeable, although strictly accurate, statement. Sailors are, again taken as a class, the least observant of men. They will talk by the hour of trivialities about which they know nothing; they will spin interminable "cuffers" of debaucheries ashore all over the world; pick to pieces the reputation of all the officers with whom they have ever sailed; but of the glories, marvels, and mysteries of the mighty deep you will hear not a word. I can never forget when on my first voyage to the West Indies, at the age of twelve, I was one night smitten with awe and wonder at the sight of a vast halo round the moon, some thirty or forty degrees in diameter. Turning to the man at the wheel, I asked him earnestly "what *that* was." He looked up with an uninterested eye for an instant in the direction of my finger, then listlessly informed me, "That's what they call a sarcle." For a long time I wondered what he could mean, but it gradually dawned upon me that it was his Norfolk pronunciation of the word "circle". The definition was a typical one, no worse than would be given by the great majority of seamen of most of the natural phenomena they witness daily. Very few seamen could distinguish between one whale and another of a different species, or give an intelligible account of the most ordinary and often-seen denizens of the sea. Whalers are especially to be blamed for their blindness. "Eyes and no Eyes; or the Art of Seeing" has evidently been little heard of among them. To this day I can conceive of no more delightful journey for a naturalist to take than a voyage in a southern whaler, especially if he were allowed to examine at his leisure such creatures as were caught. But on board the *Cachalot* I could get no information at all upon the habits of the strange creatures we met with, except whales, and very little about them.

I have before referred to the great molluscs upon which the sperm-whale feeds, portions of which I so frequently saw ejected from the stomach of dying whales. Great as my curiosity naturally was to know more of these immense organisms, all my inquiries on the subject were fruitless. These veterans of the whalefishery knew that the sperm whale lived on big cuttlefish; but they neither knew, nor cared to know, anything more about these marvellous molluscs. Yet, from the earliest dawn of history, observant men have been striving to learn something definite about the marine monsters of which all old legends of the sea have something to say.

As I mentioned in the last chapter, we were gradually edging across the Indian Ocean towards Sumatra, but had been checked in our course by a calm lasting a whole week. A light breeze then sprang up, aided by which we crept around Achin Head, the northern point of the great island of Sumatra. Like some gigantic beacon, the enormous mass of the Golden Mountain dominated the peaceful scene. Pulo Way, or Water Island, looked very inviting, and I should have been glad to visit a place so well known to seamen by sight, but so little known by actual touching at. Our recent stay at the Cocos, however, had settled the question of our calling anywhere else for some time decidedly in the negative, unless we might be compelled by accident;

moreover, even in these days of law and order, it is not wise to go poking about among the islands of the Malayan seas unless you are prepared to fight. Our mission being to fight whales, we were averse to running any risks, except in the lawful and necessary exercise of our calling.

It would at first sight appear strange that, in view of the enormous traffic of steamships through the Malacca Straits, so easily "gallied" a creature as the cachalot should care to frequent its waters; indeed, I should certainly think that a great reduction in the numbers of whales found there must have taken place. But it must also be remembered, that in modern steam navigation certain well-defined courses are laid down, which vessels follow from point to point with hardly any deviation therefrom, and that consequently little disturbance of the sea by their panting propellers takes place, except upon these marine pahways; as, for instance, in the Red Sea, where the examination of thousands of log-books proved conclusively that, except upon straight lines drawn from point to point between Suez to Perim, the sea is practically unused to-day.

The few Arab dhows and loitering surveying ships hardly count in this connection, of course. At any rate, we had not entered the straits, but were cruising between Car Nicobar and Junkseylon, when we "met up" with a full-grown cachalot, as ugly a customer as one could wish. From nine a.m. till dusk the battle raged — for I have often noticed that unless you kill your whale pretty soon, he gets so wary, as well as fierce, that you stand a gaudy chance of being worn down yourselves before you settle accounts with your adversary. This affair certainly looked at one time as if such would be the case with us; but along about five p.m., to our great joy, we got him killed. The ejected food was in masses of enormous size, larger than any we had yet seen on the voyage, some of them being estimated to be of the size of our hatch-house, viz. 8 feet × 6 feet × 6 feet. The whale having been secured alongside, all hands were sent below, as they were worn out with the day's work. The third mate being ill, I had been invested with the questionable honour of standing his watch, on account of my sea experience and growing favour with the chief. Very bitterly did I resent the privilege at the time, I remember, being so tired and sleepy that I knew not how to keep awake. I did not imagine that anything would happen to make me prize that night's experience for the rest of my life, or I should have taken matters with a far better grace.

At about eleven p.m. I was leaning over the lee rail, gazing steadily at the bright surface of the sea, where the intense radiance of the tropical moon made a broad path like a pavement of burnished silver. Eyes that saw not, mind only confusedly conscious of my surroundings, were mine; but suddenly I started to my feet with an exclamation, and stared with all my might at the strangest sight I ever saw. There was a violent commotion in the sea right where the moon's rays were concentrated, so great that, remembering our position, I was at first inclined to alarm all hands; for I had often heard of volcanic islands suddenly lifting their heads from the depths below, or disappearing in a moment, and, with Sumatra's chain of active volcanoes so near, I felt doubtful indeed of what was now happening. Getting the night-glasses out of the cabin scuttle, where they were always hung in readiness, I focussed them on the troubled spot, perfectly satisfied by a short examination that neither volcano nor earthquake had anything to do with what was going on; yet so vast were the forces engaged that I might well have been excused for my first supposition. A very large sperm whale was locked in deadly conflict with a cuttle-fish, or squid, almost as large as himself, whose interminable tentacles seemed to enlace the whole of his great body. The head of the whale especially seemed a perfect net-work of writhing arms — naturally, I suppose, for it appeared as if the whale had the tail part of the mollusc in his jaws, and, in a business-like, methodical way, was sawing through it. By the side of the black columnar head of the whale appeared the head of the great squid, as awful an object as one could well imagine even in a fevered dream. Judging as carefully as possible, I estimated it to be at least as large as one of our pipes, which contained three hundred and fifty gallons; but it may have been, and probably was, a good deal larger. The eyes were very remarkable from their size and blackness, which, contrasted with the livid whiteness of the head, made their appearance all the more striking. They were, at least, a foot in diameter, and, seen under such conditions, looked decidedly eerie and hobgoblin-like. All around the combatants were numerous sharks, like jackals round a lion, ready to share the feast, and apparently assisting in the destruction of the huge cephalopod. So the titanic struggle went on, in perfect silence as far as we were concerned, because, even had there been any noise, our distance from the scene of conflict would not have permitted us to hear it.

Thinking that such a sight ought not to be missed by the captain, I overcame my dread of him sufficiently to call him, and tell him of what was taking place. He met my remarks with such a furious burst of anger at my daring to disturb him for such a cause, that I fled precipitately on deck again, having the remainder of the vision to myself, for none of the others cared sufficiently for such things to lose five minutes' sleep in witnessing them. The conflict ceased, the sea resumed its placid calm, and nothing remained to tell of the fight but a strong odour of fish, as of a bank of seaweed left by the tide in the blazing sun. Eight bells struck, and I went below to a troubled sleep, wherein all the awful monsters that an over-excited brain could conjure up pursued me through the gloomy caves of ocean, or mocked my pigmy efforts to escape.

The occasions upon which these gigantic cuttlefish appear at the sea surface must, I think, be very rare. From their construction, they appear fitted only to grope among the rocks at the bottom of the ocean. Their mode of progression is backward, by the forcible ejection of a jet of water from an orifice in the neck, besides the rectum or cloaca. Consequently their normal position is head-downward, and with tentacles spread out like the ribs of an umbrella — eight of them at least; the two long ones, like the antennæ of an insect, rove unceasingly around, seeking prey.

The imagination can hardly picture a more terrible object than one of these huge monsters brooding in the ocean depths, the gloom of his surroundings increased by the inky fluid (sepia—which he se-cretes in copious quantities) every cup-shaped disc, of the hundreds with which the restless tentacles are furnished, ready at the slightest touch to grip whatever is near, not only by suction, but by the great claws set all round within its circle. And in the centre of this net-work of living traps is the chasm-like mouth, with its enormous parrot beak, ready to rend piecemeal whatever is held by the tentaculæ. The very thought of it makes one's flesh crawl. Well did Michelet term them "the insatiable nightmares of the sea".

Yet, but for them, how would such great creatures as the sperm whale be fed? Unable, from their bulk, to capture small fish except by accident, and, by the absence of a sieve of baleen, precluded from subsisting upon the tiny crustacea which support the *Mysticetæ*, the cachalots seem to be confined for their diet to cuttlefish, and, from their point of view, the bigger the latter are the better. How big they may become in the depths of the sea, no man knoweth; but it is un-likely that even the vast specimens seen are full-sized, since they have only come to the surface under abnormal conditions, like the one I have attempted to describe, who had evidently been dragged up by his relentless foe.

Creatures like these, who inhabit deep waters, and do not need to come to the surface by the exigencies of their existence, necessarily present many obstacles to accurate investigation of their structure and habits; but, from the few specimens that have been obtained of late years, fairly comprehensive details have been compiled, and may be studied in various French and German works, of which the Natural History Museum at South Kensington possesses copies. These, through the courtesy of the authorities in charge, are easily accessible to stu-dents who wish to prosecute the study of this wonderful branch of the great mollusca family.

When we commenced to cut in our whale next morning, the sea was fairly alive with fish of innumerable kinds, while a vast host of sea-birds, as usual, waited impatiently for the breaking-up of the huge carcass, which they knew would afford them no end of a feast.

An untoward accident, which happened soon after the work was started, gave the waiting myriads immense satisfaction, although the unfortunate second mate, whose slip of the spade was responsible, came in for a hurricane of vituperation from the enraged skipper. It was in detaching the case from the head—always a work of difficulty, and requiring great precision of aim. Just as Mr. Cruce made a powerful thrust with his keen tool, the vessel rolled, and the blow, missing the score in which he was cutting, fell upon the case instead, piercing its side. For a few minutes the result was unnoticed amidst the wash of the ragged edges of the cut, but presently a long streak of white, wax-like pieces floating astern, and a tremendous commotion among the birds, told the story. The liquid spermaceti was leaking rapidly from the case, turning solid as it got into the cool water. Nothing could be done to stop the waste, which, as it was a large whale, was not less than twenty barrels, or about two tuns of pure spermaceti. An accident of this kind never failed to make our skipper almost unbearable in his temper for some days afterwards; and, to do him justice, he did not discriminate very carefully as to who felt his resentment besides its immediate cause.

Therefore we had all a rough time of it while his angry fit lasted, which was a whole week, or until all was shipshape again. Meanwhile we were edging gradually through the Malacca Straits and around the big island of Borneo, never going very near the land on account of the great and numerous dangers attendant upon coasting in those localities to any but those continually engaged in such a business.

Indeed, navigation in those seas in sailing vessels is dangerous, and requires the greatest care. Often we were obliged at a minute's notice to let go the anchor, although out of sight of land, some rapid current being found carrying us swiftly towards a shoal or race, where we might come to grief. Yet there was no fuss or hurry, the same leisurely old system was continued, and worked as well as ever. But it was not apparent why we were threading the tortuous and difficult waters of the Indian Archipelago. No whales of any kind were seen for at least a month, although, from our leisurely mode of sailing, it was evident that the captain was on the lookout for them and was hopeful of success in his search.

An occasional native craft came alongside, desirous of bartering fish, which we did not want, being able to catch all we needed as readily almost as they were. Fruit and vegetables we could not get at such distances from land, for the small canoes that lie in wait for passing ships do not of course venture far from home.

RUNNING AWAY TO SEA

By R. M. BALLANTYNE

Ballantyne's book "Martin Rattler" remains a thrilling story of young adventure. In this extract he tells of how Martin came to run away to sea and of the disasters which quickly followed.

Martin was now fourteen, broad and strong, and tall for his age. He was the idol of the school — dashing, daring, reckless, and good-natured. There was almost nothing that he would not attempt, and there were very few things that he could not do. He never fought, however — from principle; and his strength and size often saved him from the necessity. But he often prevented other boys from fighting, except when he thought there was good reason for it; then he stood by and saw fair play. There was a strange mixture of philosophical gravity, too, in Martin. As he grew older he became more enthusiastic and less boisterous.

Bob Croaker was still at the school, and was, from prudential motives, a fast friend of Martin. But he bore him a secret grudge, for he could not forget the great fight.

One day Bob took Martin by the arm and said, "I say, Rattler, come with me to Bilton and have some fun among the shipping."

"Well, I don't mind if I do," said Martin. "I'm just in the mood for a ramble, and I'm not expected home till bedtime."

In little more than an hour the two boys were wandering about the dockyards of the seaport town, and deeply engaged in examining the complicated rigging of the ships. While thus occupied, the clanking of a windlass and the merry, "Yo, heave ho! and away she goes," of the sailors, attracted their attention.

"Hallo! There goes the *Firefly*, bound for the South Seas", cried Bob Croaker; "come, let's see her start. I say, Martin, isn't your friend, Barney O'Flannagan, on board?"

"Yes, he is. He tries to get me to go out every voyage, and I wish I could. Come quickly; I want to say good-bye to him before he starts."

"Why don't you run away, Rattler?" inquired Bob, as they hurried round the docks to where the vessel was warping out.

"Because I don't need to. My aunt has given me leave to go if I like; but she says it would break her heart if I do, and I would rather be screwed down to a desk for ever than do that, Bob Croaker."

The vessel, upon the deck of which the two boys now leaped, was a large, heavy-built barque. Her sails were hanging loose, and the captain was giving orders to the men, who had their attention divided between their duties on board and their mothers, wives, and sisters, who still lingered to take a last farewell.

"Now, then, those who don't want to go to sea had better go ashore," roared the captain.

There was an immediate rush to the side.

"I say, Martin," whispered Barney, as he hurried past, "jump down below for'ard; you can go out o' the harbour mouth with us, and get ashore in one o' the shore-boats alongside. They'll not cast off till we're well out. I want to speak to you—"

"Man the fore-top-sail halyards," shouted the first mate.

"Ay, ay, sir-r-r!" and the men sprang to obey. Just then the ship touched on the bar at the mouth of the harbour, and in another moment she was aground.

"There now, she's hard and fast!" roared the captain, as he stormed about the deck in a paroxysm of rage. But man's rage could avail nothing. They had missed the passage by a few feet, and now they had to wait the fall and rise again of the tide ere they could hope to get off.

In the confusion that followed, Bob Croaker suggested that Martin and he should take one of the punts, or small boats, which hovered round the vessel, and put out to sea, where they might spend the day pleasantly in rowing and fishing.

"Capital!" exclaimed Martin. "Let's go at once. Yonder's a little fellow who will let us have his punt for a few pence. I know him. — Hallo, Tom!"

"Ay, ay," squeaked a boy who was so small that he could scarcely lift the oar, light though it was, with which he sculled his punt cleverly along.

"Shove alongside, like a good fellow; we want your boat for a little to row out a bit."

"It's a-blowin' too hard," squeaked the small boy, as he ranged alongside. "I'm afeared you'll be blowed out."

"Nonsense!" cried Bob Croaker, grasping the rope which the boy threw to him. "Jump on board, youngster; we don't want you to help us, and you're too heavy for ballast. Slip down the side, Martin, and get in while I hold on to the rope. All right? Now I'll follow. Here, shrimp, hold the rope till I'm in, and then cast off. Look alive!"

As Bob spoke, he handed the rope to the little boy, but in doing so let it accidentally slip out of his hand.

"Catch hold o' the main chains, Martin — quick!"

But Martin was too late. The current that swept out of the harbour whirled the light punt away from the ship's side and carried it out seaward. Martin instantly sprang to the oar, and turned the boat's head round. He was a stout and expert rower, and would soon have regained the ship; but the wind increased at the moment, and blew in a squall off shore, which carried him farther out despite his utmost efforts. Seeing that all further attempts were useless, Martin stood up and waved his hand to Bob Croaker, shouting as he did so, "Never mind, Bob; I'll make for the South Point. Run round and meet me, and we'll row back together."

The South Point was a low cape of land which stretched a considerable distance out to sea, about three miles to the southward of Bilton harbour. It formed a large bay, across which, in ordinary weather, a small boat might be rowed in safety. Martin Rattler was well known at the seaport as a strong and fearless boy, so that no apprehension was entertained for his safety by those who saw him blown away. Bob Croaker immediately started for the Point on foot, a distance of about four miles by land; and the crew of the *Firefly* were so busied with their stranded vessel that they took no notice of the doings of the boys.

But the weather now became more and more stormy. Thick clouds gathered on the horizon. The wind began to blow with steady violence and shifted a couple of points to the southward, so that Martin found it impossible to keep straight for the Point. Still he worked perseveringly at his single oar, and sculled rapidly over the sea; but as he approached the Point, he soon perceived that no effort of which he was capable could enable him to gain it. But Martin's heart was stout. He strove with all the energy of hope until the Point was passed; and then, turning the head of his little boat towards it, he strove with all the energy of despair, until he fell down exhausted. The wind and tide swept him rapidly out to sea, and when his terrified comrade reached the Point, the little boat was but a speck on the seaward horizon.

Well was it then for Martin Rattler that a friendly heart beat for him on board the *Firefly*. Bob Croaker carried the news to the town, but no one was found daring enough to risk his life out in a boat on that stormy evening. The little punt had been long out of sight ere the news reached them, and the wind had increased to a gale. But Barney O'Flannagan questioned Bob Croaker closely, and took particular note of the point of the compass at which Martin had disappeared; and when the *Firefly* at length got under way, he climbed to the foretop cross-trees and stood there scanning the horizon with an anxious eye.

It was getting dark, and a feeling of despair began to creep over the seaman's heart as he gazed round the wide expanse of water, on which nothing was to be seen except the white foam that crested the rising billows.

"Starboard, hard!" he shouted suddenly.

"Starboard it is!" replied the man at the wheel, with prompt obedience.

In another moment Barney slid down the backstay and stood on the deck, while the ship rounded to, and narrowly missed striking a small boat that floated keel up on the water. There was no cry from the boat; and it might have been passed as a mere wreck, had not the lynx-eye of Barney noticed a dark object clinging to it.

"Lower away a boat, lads," cried the Irishman, springing over-board, and the words had scarcely passed his lips when the water closed over his head.

The *Firefly* was hove to, a boat was lowered and rowed towards Barney, whose strong voice guided his shipmates towards him. In less than a quarter of an hour the bold sailor and his young friend Martin Rattler were safe on board, and the ship's head was again turned out to sea.

It was full half an hour before Martin was restored to conscious-ness in the forecastle, to which his deliverer had conveyed him.

"Musha, lad, but ye're booked for the blue wather now, an' no mis-take!" said Barney, looking with an expression of deep sympathy at the poor boy, who sat staring before him quite speechless. "The cap-tain'll not let ye out o' this ship till ye git to the Gold Coast, or some sich place. He couldn't turn back av he wanted iver so much; but he doesn't want to, for he needs a smart lad like you, an' he'll keep you now, for sartin."

Barney sat down by Martin's side and stroked his fair curls, as he sought in his own quaint fashion to console him. But in vain. Martin grew quite desperate as he thought of the misery into which poor Aunt Dorothy Grumbit would be plunged, on learning that he had been swept out to sea in a little boat, and drowned, as she would natur-ally suppose. In his frenzy he entreated and implored the captain to send him back in the boat, and even threatened to knock out his brains with a handspike if he did not; but the captain smiled, and told him that it was his own fault. He had no business to be putting to sea in a small boat in rough weather; and he might be thankful he wasn't drowned. He wouldn't turn back now for fifty pounds twice told.

At length Martin became convinced that all hope of returning home was gone. He went quietly below, threw himself into one of the sailors' berths, turned his face to the wall, and wept long and bitterly.

Time reconciles a man to almost anything. In the course of time Martin Rattler became reconciled to his fate, and went about the ordinary duties of a cabin-boy on board the *Firefly* just as if he had been appointed to that office in the ordinary way — with the consent of the owners and by the advice of his friends. The captain, Skinflint by name, and as surly an old fellow as ever walked a quarter-deck, agreed to pay him wages "if he behaved well". The steward, under whose immediate authority he was placed, turned out to be a hearty good-natured young fellow, and was very kind to him. But Martin's great friend was Barney O'Flannagan, the cook, with whom he spent many an hour in the night watches, talking over plans, and prospects, and retrospects, and foreign lands.

As Martin had no clothes except those he wore, which fortunately happened to be new and good, Barney gave him a couple of blue striped shirts, and made him a jacket, pantaloons, and slippers of canvas; and, what was of much greater importance, taught him how to make and mend the same for himself.

"Ye see, Martin, lad," he said, while thus employed one day, many weeks after leaving port, "it's a great thing, intirely, to be able to help yerself. For my part, I niver travel without my work-box in my pocket."

"Your work-box!" said Martin, laughing.

"Jist so. An' it consists of a sailmaker's needle, a ball o'twine, and a clasp-knife. Set me down with these before a roll o' canvas and I'll make ye a'most anything."

"You seem to have a turn for everything, Barney," said Martin. "How came you to be a cook?"

"That's more nor I can tell ye, lad. As far as I remimber, I began with murphies, when I was two foot high, in my father's cabin in ould Ireland. But that was on my own account intirely, and not as a purfession; and a sorrowful time I had of it, too, for I was for iver burnin' my fingers promiskiously, and fallin' into the fire ivery day more or less—"

"Stand by to hoist top-gallant-sails!" shouted the captain. "How's her head?"

"South and by east, sir," answered the man at the wheel.

"Keep her away two points. Look alive, lads. — Hand me the glass."

The ship was close-hauled when these abrupt orders were given, battling in the teeth of a stiff breeze, off the coast of South America. About this time several piratical vessels had succeeded in cutting off a number of merchantmen near the coast of Brazil. They had not only taken the valuable parts of their cargoes, but had murdered the crews under circumstances of great cruelty. The ships trading to these regions were, consequently, exceedingly careful to avoid all suspicious craft as much as possible. It was therefore with some anxiety that the men watched the captain's face as he examined the strange sail through the telescope.

"A Spanish schooner," muttered the captain, as he shut up the glass with a bang. "I won't trust her. Up with the royals and rig out stun-sails, Mr. Wilson" (to the mate). "Let her fall away, keep her head nor'west, d'ye hear?"

"Ay, ay, sir."

"Let go the lee braces and square the yards. Look sharp, now, lads. If that blackguard gets hold of us, ye'll have to walk the plank, every man of ye."

In a few minutes the ship's course was completely altered; a cloud of canvas spread out from the yards, and the *Firefly* bounded on her course like a fresh race-horse. But it soon became evident that the heavy barque was no match for the schooner, which crowded sail and bore down at a rate that bade fair to overhaul them in a few hours. The chase continued till evening, when suddenly the look-out at the masthead shouted, "Land, ho!"

"Where away?" cried the captain.

"Right ahead," sang out the man.

"I'll run her ashore sooner than be taken," muttered the captain, with an angry scowl at the schooner, which was now almost within range on the weather quarter, with the dreaded black flag flying at her peak. In a few minutes breakers were descried ahead.

"D'ye see anything like a passage?" shouted the captain.

"Yes, sir; two points on the weather bow."

At this moment a white cloud burst from the schooner's bow, and a shot, evidently from a heavy gun, came ricochetting over the sea. It was well aimed, for it cut right through the barque's main-top-mast, and brought the yards, sails, and gearing down upon the deck. The weight of the wreck, also, carried away the fore-top-mast, and in a single instant the *Firefly* was completely disabled.

"Lower away the boats," cried the captain. "Look alive, now; we'll give them the slip yet. It'll be dark in two minutes."

The captain was right. In tropical regions there is little or no twilight. Night succeeds day almost instantaneously. Before the boats were lowered and the men embarked it was becoming quite dark. The schooner observed the movement, however, and, as she did not dare to venture through the reef in the dark, her boats were also lowered, and the chase was recommenced.

The reef was passed in safety, and now a hard struggle took place, for the shore was still far distant. As it chanced to be cloudy weather, the darkness became intense, and progress could only be guessed at by the sound of the oars; but these soon told too plainly that the boats of the schooner were overtaking those of the barque.

"Pull with a will, lads," cried the captain; "we can't be more than half a mile from shore; give way, my hearties."

"Surely, captain, we can fight them; we've most of us got pistols and cutlasses," said one of the men, in a sulky tone.

"Fight them!" cried the captain; "they're four times our number, and every man armed to the teeth. If ye don't fancy walking the plank or dancing on nothing at the yardarm, ye'd better pull away and hold your jaw."

By this time they could just see the schooner's boats in the dim light, about half-musket range astern.

"Back you' oars," shouted a stern voice in broken English, "or I blow you out de watter in one oder moment — black-guards!"

This order was enforced by a musket shot, which whizzed over the boat within an inch of the captain's head. The men ceased rowing, and the boats of the pirate ranged close up.

"Now then, Martin," whispered Barney O'Flannagan, who sat at

145

the bow oar, "I'm goin' to swim ashore; jist you slip arter me as quiet as ye can."

"But the sharks!' suggested Martin.

"Bad luck to them," said Barney, slipping over the side; "they're welcome to me. I'll take my chance. They'll find me mortal tough, anyhow. Come along, lad, look sharp!"

Without a moment's hesitation Martin slid over the gunwale into the sea, and, just as the pirate boats grappled with those of the barque, he and Barney found themselves gliding as silently as otters towards the shore. So quietly had the manoeuvre been accomplished, that the men in their own boat were ignorant of their absence. In a few minutes they were beyond the chance of detection.

"Keep close to me, lad," whispered the Irishman. "If we separate in the darkness, we'll niver forgather again. Catch hould o'my shoulder if ye get blowed, and splutter as much as ye like. They can't hear us now, and it'll help to frighten the sharks."

"All right," replied Martin; "I can swim like a cork in such warm water as this. Just go a little slower, and I'll do famously.'

Thus encouraging each other, and keeping close together, lest they should get separated in the thick darkness of the night, the two friends struck out bravely for the shore.

SAVED BY A SHARK

The strange tale of how a shark brought justice to a slaver and saved the career of the naval officer who captured the terrible death-ship "Artemoza".

It is a good many years ago, since the incident I am about to relate happened, but it is as fresh in my mind as if it had occurred but yesterday. I, Lieutenant Richard Beaulyne, was then temporary commander of the sloop *Terror,* of the Royal Navy.

We were bound for Port Royal, in Jamaica, and were about fifty miles to the south-east of that port when the lookout aloft cried, "Sail-ho!" "Where away, my lad?" I shouted. "Southwest, sir," he replied, and, seizing my glass, I swung myself into the rigging, and swept the waters in search of the vessel. At last I focussed it, and soon made her out to be a large top-sail schooner, built like a slaver, running on a course nearly parallel to our own.

As I have said, the schooner had the build and rig of a slaver, which were common in those days. Here was my opportunity. I was a young officer, with nothing but my pay and a small command, and it was a proverb in the service, that a lieutenant placed in that position seldom obtained anything better. If I could only capture this boat, and bring her captain to justice, it would be a great thing for me. Visions of promotion and prize money flashed rapidly through my mind, and, leaping down, I gave orders for spreading more canvas, and the ship's course was altered so as to head off the slaver.

The *Terror* was a fast little vessel, although I have a prejudice against sloops, and for a craft of her rig was rather large. So, although the schooner undoubtedly was a fast sailer, I hoped that we should catch her. Her skipper did not apparently notice us until we were within some four miles of her, when he quickly spread a cloud of canvas and altered his course a couple of points.

I was very much excited, and equally so were my small crew. Tinsley, my midshipman, was fairly crazy at the prospects of a brush with the enemy. After some considerable time, during which we reduced

147

the distance between us by more than half, I had the long nine-pound-er loaded, and sent a shot in the schooner's wake as a polite intima-tion for her to heave to. But the vessel kept on, and we fired again. This time the shot struck the slaver's stern, and through the glass I saw a small shower of splinters fly up. It soon became evident that we were overhauling her, as the wind was just right for us, while it did not seem to suit the schooner.

Presently our "Long Tom" spoke again, and the ball just shaved the mainmast, without apparently doing any damage. The slaver now put his helm hard down, and for some unaccountable reason tried to stand across our course, and get to windward of the sloop. "The man must be mad," I muttered; then raising my voice, I exclaimed, "Noakes, train the gun on her spars. Fire!" The smoke cleared away, and then we saw the ball go skipping along, and strike the mainmast, which swayed, and then went over the side with a clash.

"Hurrah, lads, she's won!" I shouted, for the crippled schooner now lay to, rocking on the swell. The *Terror* approached to within a cable's length, and then, with a well-armed boat's crew, I went aboard. As we rowed towards the ship I saw a man throw something over-board from the stern, but at the time I took no particular notice of the occurrence.

The slaver captain met me at the gangway, and though in my time I have seen a good many ugly faces, I do not remember ever having beheld a physiognomy so utterly villainous as was this man's. He was a Portuguese half-breed, with a dark, sallow face, ornamented with a hideous scar. "Well, senor," he cried, as I jumped on the deck, "what does this mean? You have fired on a peaceful merchant, and you shall suffer."

"We shall see," I replied, lightly. "Now, my man, I am Lieutenant Beaulyne, of His Majesty's sloop *Terror,* and I must search this craft!' "Search my ship," he screeched, for that is the only way of correctly describing the sounds which came from his throat. "You shall not. The law I will have upon you. I am one peaceful trader. You shall not."

"We shall see," I replied again, and rashly calling on him to follow me, I went below. If I had had more experience of this kind of work, I should have made the slaver precede me, but I have since learnt to be more careful.

While we were talking, my men had secured the crew, who were about equal to their captain in looks and manner. As we descended the companion way I heard a slight clink as of metal behind me, and looking round, was just in time to seize the wrist of the slaver, who held a long knife in his hand. Together we fell to the bottom of the steps, where, thanks to my old public-school wrestling experience, I soon had him down, and bound with his own sash and neckerchief. Meanwhile he glared at me like a wild beast, and if a look could have killed me, I should have been annihilated there and then.

This done, I proceeded to search the hold. It was divided into compartments in the approved fashion for stowing slaves, and in the forehold was a store of rice for feeding the poor wretches, but slaves there were none. Somewhat dissatisfied at the result of my chase, I entered the captain's cabin, and began to ransack it for the ship's papers. But they, like the slaves, were missing.

In a rather discontented frame of mind I returned to the captain. "Well," he grinned, "Mistare Inglese, you are too clever. I will have——."

"Where are the ship's papers?" I said, cutting short his vapourings. He shook his head, and resolutely refused me any information. Annoyed at my want of success, I went on deck, had the slaver's men sent below and secured, and, leaving a small prize crew, commanded by Tinsley, on board, we sailed in company for Port Royal, which we reached next morning.

I was rather puzzled about what had become of the ship's papers. Evidently they were in the bundle I had seen the rascal throw into the sea, but that could not be proved, and as the case stood, I did not quite know what the law would say about the matter. However, sailors are always bad reasoners, being more given to act than to think, and so I gave up cogitating about the subject, and devoted myself to other affairs.

Next morning, as I have said, we reached Port Royal, the naval station of Jamaica. After seeing to the mooring of the *Terror* and her prize, I went ashore to report myself to the port admiral. He was an old friend of my late father, Captain Beaulyne, and in his heart had, I believe, a sneaking fondness for me. But that is beside my story. He listened with a smile on his face until I told him about my search of the slaver, and then he frowned.

"It may be all right," he said, "but I suppose you know that you may get into no end of a bother if there is no evidence against him. There is not the least doubt that he *is* a slaver; but you cannot *prove* it without his papers, and, if he gets off and chooses to be revengeful, he can have you up for unlawfully boarding him on the high seas and putting him and his crew under arrest."

I listened ruefully to the admiral's remarks, but still I hoped for the best. On my returning to the sloop, the prisoners were sent to the town jail.

In a few days the trial came on, and I had to go up and give my evidence. After much examination and cross examination, the proceedings were adjourned for a week, in order that a final search might be made for the missing papers. I had been plainly told that if they were not forthcoming, the slaver would certainly be acquitted.

Too well I knew what that meant. An act of indiscretion means much to a young naval officer, and my blunder — if blunder it was — would be counted a very grave offence. Numerous friends on board other warships in the harbour came to cheer me up and sympathise with me, but all agreed that the outlook was very black.

Thus things went on till the morning of the trial, and the ship's papers had not been discovered. I was sitting brooding over the situation in my cabin, when a tapping at the door aroused me, and the boatswain entered.

"Someone to see you, sir," he said, pulling his forelock; "very important business, he says."

"Show him down," I replied.

Presently a heavy step was heard, and a tall, finely built man entered the cabin. He was dressed in the uniform of a merchant skipper.

"Good morning, sir," I said, rising to my feet, "to what do I owe the honour of this visit?"

Returning my greeting, he remarked, "No doubt you wonder what business brought me here. I am Captain Crosse of the *Somerset* barque, of London. On arriving at the port yesterday, I heard of the capture of the slaver, and that her skipper was now on trial. What is the name of your prize, may I ask?"

"The *Artemoza*," I replied, surprised and somewhat excited.

"Then I can help you," said the captain. "Calm yourself, and I will explain. When we were about forty miles south-east of this port, a shark came alongside. The men having obtained permission, succeeded in capturing and killing it. On ripping open the stomach, we found this box."

Here the officer placed a small tin box on the table. My excitement now became intense, but without heeding it, the captain continued, "I took possession of the box, and on opening it, I found within the papers of a ship called the *Artemoza*. If you will read them, you will see that your prize is an out-and-out slaver. I will come to the court with you, and we shall have the satisfaction of seeing him put away for a time."

Hastily perusing the documents, I read sufficient to confirm the captain's story. "Oh, how can I thank you!" I exclaimed; "you have extricated me from a terrible predicament."

"Pshaw," he said with a laugh, "come along; it is time for the trial," and together we made our way to the court.

On Captain Crosse being called to give his evidence, a great sensation was caused when he produced the tin box, and related its wonderful history. Juan Flores, the slave captain, and his rascally crew were found guilty and went to prison, while the *Artemoza* was confiscated to the Crown.

The only explanation as to how the papers were recovered that I can give is this: — When Flores threw them overboard, they must have been almost immediately swallowed by one of the sharks which infest those seas, but what strange fate ultimately landed the monster on the deck of the *Somerset* I do not pretend to explain. It was an act of Providence.

Captain Crosse and I remained firm friends up to the time of his death, sixteen years later. Shortly after the recovery of the papers, my command was confirmed; and by-and-by, probably through the Admiral's interest in me, I became captain of the brig *Hawk*. The tin box and the remains of the shark were sent to England, where they may be seen to this day as witnesses to the truth of my yarn.

And now that my fighting days are over, and I sit outside my cottage on the downs, watching the ships go by, I love to tell you boys of how, years ago, I was *Saved by a Shark*. Here is another yarn I often tell — a true one to prove that nothing need be as bad as it first appears.

The brig *Nerina,* of Dunkerque, sailed from that place on Saturday, 31st October, 1840, under the command of Captain Pierre Everact, with a cargo of oil and canvas for Marseilles. Her burthen was about 114 tons. The crew consisted of seven persons, including the captain and his nephew — a boy fourteen years old. At three o'clock in the afternoon of Monday, 16th November, they were forced to heave to in a gale of wind, at about ten or twelve leagues S.W. of the Scilly Isles. At seven o'clock of the same evening a heavy sea struck the vessel, and she suddenly capsized, turning bottom upward. The only man on the deck at the time was thrown into the sea and drowned.

In the forecastle were three seamen — Vincent, Vantaure, and Jean Marie. The two former succeeded in getting up close to the keelson, and so kept their heads above water. Jean Marie was not so fortunate; he must have been in some measure entangled, for after convulsively grasping the heel of Vantaure for a few seconds, he let go his hold and was drowned. The other two, finding that the shock of the upset had started the bulkhead between the forecastle and the hold, and that the cargo itself had fallen down on the deck, contrived to draw themselves alongside the keelson towards the stern of the ship, whence they thought they heard some voices.

At the time of the accident, the captain, the mate, Jean Gallo, and the boy, Nicolas Nissen, were in the cabin. The captain caught the boy in his arms, under the impression that their last moments had arrived. The mate succeeded in wrenching open the trap hatch in the cabin deck, and in clearing out some casks that were jammed in the lazerette, a sort of small triangular space between the cabin floor and the keelson, where stores are generally stowed away. Having done this, he scrambled up into the vacant space and took the boy from the hands of the captain.

In about an hour they were joined by Vincent and Vantaure from the forecastle. There were then five persons closely cooped together. As they sat they were obliged to bend their bodies, for want of height above them, whilst the water reached as high as their waists, from which irksome position one at a time obtained some relief by stretching at full length on the barrels in the hold, and squeezing himself up close to the keelson.

They were able to distinguish between day and night by the light striking from above into the sea, and being reflected up through the cabin skylight, and then into the lazerette through the trap hatch in the cabin floor. The day and night of Tuesday, 17th November, and the day following, were passed without food, without relief, almost without hope; but still each encouraged the others, endeavouring to assuage the pangs of hunger by chewing the bark stripped from the hoops of the casks.

Want of fresh air threatening them with death by suffocation, the mate worked almost incessantly for two days and one night in endeavouring with his knife to cut a hole through the hull. Happily the knife broke before he had succeeded in accomplishing his object, the result of which must have proved fatal, as the confined air alone preserved the ship's buoyancy.

In the dead of the night of Wednesday, the 18th, the vessel suddenly struck heavily; on the third blow the stern dropped so much that all hands were forced to make the best of their way forward towards the bows; in attempting which poor Vincent was drowned. After the lapse of an hour or two, finding the water ebbing, Gallo got down into the cabin, and, whilst seeking for the hatchet which was usually kept there, was forced to rush up again for shelter to avoid being drowned, the sea rising on him rapidly.

Another hour or two of suffering succeeded, and then they were rejoiced to see by the dawning of the day of Thursday, the 19th, that the vessel was fast on the rocks, one of which protruded up through the skylight. The captain then went down into the cabin, and found that the quarter of the ship was stove in, and, looking through the opening, he called out to his companions, "Thank God, we are saved; I see a man on the beach."

Immediately after this the man approached and put in his hand, which the captain seized, almost as much to the terror of the poor man as to the delight of the captain. The people of the neighbourhood were soon assembled. The side of the ship was cut open, and the four poor fellows were liberated, after an entombment of three days and three nights. The spot where the vessel struck is called Porthellick, in the island of St. Mary's, Scilly. She must have been driven on the rocks soon after midnight, at about the period of high water, and was discovered at about seven o'clock on Thursday morning by a man accidentally passing along the cliffs.

In another half hour the returning tide would have sealed their fate. The body of Vincent was thrown on the rocks a short distance from the wreck, and was interred in the burial ground of St. Mary's. Not the least remarkable part of the story is, in the afternoon of Wednesday, the 18th, the wreck, floating bottom upwards, was fallen in with about a league and a half distant from the islands by two pilot boats, which took her in tow for about an hour; but their tow ropes breaking and night approching, with a heavy sea running and every appearance of bad weather, they abandoned her, having no suspicion, of course, that there were human beings alive in the hold of the vessel, which was floating with little more than her keel out of water. Had the vessel not been so taken in tow, the set of the current would have drifted her clear of the isles into the vast Atlantic.

ALONE ON THE DEEP

By R. M. BALLANTYNE

In many stories the albatross is a sign of ill-fortune and disaster, but in this episode from "Coral Island" the albatross heralds the return to the island after fifteen days alone at sea.

During the greater part of that day I had been subjected to severe mental and much physical excitement, which had almost crushed me down by the time I was relieved from duty in the course of the evening. But when the expedition whose failure has just been narrated was planned, my anxieties and energies had been so powerfully aroused that I went through the protracted scenes of that terrible night without a feeling of the slightest fatigue. My mind and body were alike active and full of energy. No sooner was the last trilling fear of danger past than my faculties were utterly relaxed; and when I felt the cool breezes of the Pacific playing around my fevered brow, and heard the free waves rippling at the schooner's prow, as we left the hated island behind us, my senses forsook me, and I fell in a swoon upon the deck.

From this state I was quickly aroused by Bill, who shook me by the arm, saying,—

"Hallo, Ralph boy! Rouse up, lad; we we're safe now. Poor thing! I believe he's fainted." And raising me in his arms he laid me on the folds of the gaff-top-sail, which lay upon the deck near the tiller. "Here, take a drop o' this; it'll do you good, my boy," he added, in a voice of tenderness which I had never heard him use before, while he held a brandy-flask to my lips.

I raised my eyes gratefully as I swallowed a mouthful; next moment my head sank heavily upon my arm, and I fell fast asleep. I slept long, for when I awoke the sun was a good way above the horizon. I did not move on first opening my eyes, as I felt a delightful sensation of rest pervading me, and my eyes were riveted on and charmed with the gorgeous splendour of the mighty ocean, that burst upon my sight. It was a dead calm; the sea seemed a sheet of undulating crystal, tipped and streaked with the saffron hues of sunrise, which had not yet merged into the glowing heat of noon; and there was a deep calm in the blue dome above that was not broken even by the usual flutter of the sea-fowl. How long I would have lain in contemplation of this peaceful scene I know not, but my mind was recalled suddenly and painfully to the past and the present by the sight of Bill, who was seated on the deck at my feet with his head reclining, as if in sleep, on his right arm, which rested on the tiller. As he seemed to rest peacefully, I did not mean to disturb him, but the slight noise I made in raising myself on my elbow caused him to start and look round.

"Well, Ralph, awake at last, my boy; you have slept long and soundly," he said, turning towards me.

On beholding his countenance I sprang up in anxiety. He was deadly pale, and his hair, which hung in dishevelled locks over his face, was clotted with blood. Blood also stained his hollow cheeks and covered the front of his shirt, which, with the greater part of his dress, was torn and soiled with mud.

"O Bill!" said I, with deep anxiety, "what is the matter with you? You are ill. You must have been wounded."

"Even so, lad," said Bill, in a deep soft voice, while he extended his huge frame on the couch from which I had just risen. "I've got an ugly wound, I fear; and I've been waiting for you to waken, to ask you to get me a drop o' brandy and a mouthful o' bread from the cabin lockers. You seemed to sleep so sweetly, Ralph, that I didn't like to disturb you. But I don't feel up to much just now."

I did not wait till he had done talking, but ran below immediately and returned in a few seconds with a bottle of brandy and some broken biscuit. He seemed much refreshed after eating a few morsels and drinking a long draught of water mingled with a little of the spirits. Immediately afterwards he fell asleep, and I watched him anxiously until he awoke, being desirous of knowing the nature and extent of his wound.

"Ha!" he exclaimed, on awaking suddenly, after a slumber of an hour, "I'm the better of that nap, Ralph; I feel twice the man I was;"

and he attempted to rise, but sank back again immediately with a deep groan.

"Nay, Bill, you must not move, but lie still while I look at your wound. I'll make a comfortable bed for you here on deck, and get you some breakfast. After that you shall tell me how you got it. Cheer up, Bill," I added, seeing that he turned his head away; "you'll be all right in a little, and I'll be a capital nurse to you though I'm no doctor."

I then left him, and lighted a fire in the caboose. While it was kindling, I went to the steward's pantry and procured the materials for a good breakfast, with which, in little more than half-an-hour, I returned to my companion. He seemed much better, and smiled kindly on me as I set before him a cup of coffee and a tray with several eggs and some bread on it.

"Now then, Bill," said I cheerfully, sitting down beside him on the deck, "let's fall to. I'm very hungry myself, I can tell you; but—I forgot—your wound," I added, rising; "let me look at it."

I found that the wound was caused by a pistol-shot in the chest. It did not bleed much, and as it was on the right side, I was in hopes that it might not be very serious. But Bill shook his head. "However," said he, "sit down, Ralph, and I'll tell you all about it.

"You see, after we left the boat an' began to push through the bushes, we went straight for the line of my musket, as I had expected; but by some unlucky chance it didn't explode, for I saw the line torn away by the men's legs, and heard the click o' the lock; so I fancy the priming had got damp and didn't catch. I was in a great quandary now what to do, for I couldn't concoct in my mind, in the hurry, any good reason for firin' off my piece. But they say necessity's the mother of invention; so just as I was givin' it up and clinchin' my teeth to bide the worst o't and take what should come, a sudden thought came into my head. I stepped out before the rest, seemin' to be awful anxious to be at the savages, tripped my foot on a fallen tree, plunged head foremost into a bush, an', ov coorse, my carbine exploded! Then came such a screechin' from the camp as I never heard in all my life. I rose at once, and was rushing on with the rest, when the captain called a halt.

" 'You did that a-purpose, you villain!' he said, with a tremendous oath, and drawin' a pistol from his belt, let fly right into my breast. I fell at once, and remembered no more till I was startled and brought round by the most awful yell I ever heard in my life—except, maybe, the shrieks o' them poor critters that were crushed to death under yon big canoe. Jumpin' up, I looked round, and through the trees saw a fire gleamin' not far off, the light o' which showed me the captain and men tied hand and foot, each to a post, and the savages dancin' round them like demons. I had scarce looked for a second, when I saw one o' them go up to the captain flourishing a knife, and before I could wink he plunged it into his breast, while another yell, like the one that roused me, rang upon my ear. I didn't wait for more, but bounding up, went crashing through the bushes into the woods. The black fellows caught sight of me, however, but not in time to prevent me jumpin' into the boat, as you know."

Bill seemed to be much exhausted after this recital, and shuddered frequently during the narrative, so I refrained from continuing the subject at that time, and endeavoured to draw his mind to other things.

"But now, Bill," said I, "it behoves us to think about the future, and what course of action we shall pursue. Here we are, on the wide Pacific, in a well-appointed schooner, which is our own—at least no one has a better claim to it than we have—and the world lies before us. Moreover, here comes a breeze, so we must make up our minds which way to steer."

"Ralph boy," said my companion, "it matters not to me which way we go. I fear that my time is short now. Go where you will; I'm content."

"Well then, Bill, I think we had better steer to the Coral Island, and see what has become of my dear old comrades, Jack and Peterkin. I believe the island has no name, but the captain once pointed it out to me on the chart, and I marked it afterwards; so, as we know pretty

well our position just now, I think I can steer to it. Then, as to working the vessel, it is true I cannot hoist the sails single-handed, but
luckily we have enough of sail set already; and if it should come on
to blow a squall, I could at least drop the peaks of the main and fore
sails, and clew them up partially without help, and throw her head
close into the wind, so as to keep her all shaking till the violence of
the squall is past. And if we have continued light breezes, I'll rig up
a complication of blocks and fix them to the top-sail halyards, so that
I shall be able to hoist the sails without help. 'Tis true I'll require
half-a-day to hoist them, but we don't need to mind that. Then I'll
make a sort of erection on deck to screen you from the sun, Bill; and
if you can only manage to sit beside the tiller and steer for two
hours every day, so as to let me get a nap, I'll engage to let you off
duty all the rest of the twenty-four hours. And if you don't feel able
for steering, I'll lash the helm and heave to, while I get you your
breakfasts and dinners; and so we'll manage famously, and soon reach
the Coral Island."

Bill smiled faintly as I ran on in this strain.

"And what will you do," said he, "if it comes on to blow a storm?"

This question silenced me, while I considered what I should do in
such a case. At length I laid my hand on his arm, and said, "Bill,
when a man has done all that he *can* do, he ought to leave the rest
to God."

"O Ralph," said my companion, in a faint voice, looking anxiously
into my face, "I wish that I had the feelin's about God that you seem
to have, at this hour. I'm dyin', Ralph; yet I, who have braved death
a hundred times, am afraid to die. I'm afraid to enter the next world.
Something within tells me there will be a reckoning when I go there.
But it's all over with me, Ralph."

"Don't say that, Bill," said I, in deep compassion; "don't say that.
I'm quite sure there's hope even for you, but I can't remember the
words of the Bible that make me think so. Is there not a Bible on
board, Bill?"

"No; the last that was in the ship belonged to a poor boy that was taken aboard against his will. He died, poor lad—I think through ill-treatment and fear. After he was gone the captain found his Bible and flung it overboard."

After a short pause, Bill raised his eyes to mine and said, "Ralph, I've led a terrible life. I've been a sailor since I was a boy, and I've gone from bad to worse even since I left my father's roof. I've been a pirate three years now. It is true I did not choose the trade, but I was inveigled aboard this schooner and kept here by force till I became reckless and at last joined them. Since that time my hand has been steeped in human blood again and again. Your young heart would grow cold if I—— But why should I go on? 'Tis of no use, Ralph."

"Bill," said I, " 'Though your sins be red like crimson, they shall be white as snow.' 'Only believe.' "

"Only believe!" cried Bill, starting up on his elbow. "I've heard men talk o' believing as if it was easy. Ha! 'tis easy enough for a man to point to a rope and say, 'I believe that would bear my weight,' but 'tis another thing for a man to catch hold o' that rope and swing himself by it over the edge of a precipice!"

The energy with which he said this, and the action with which it was accompanied, were too much for Bill. He sank back with a deep groan. As if the very elements sympathised with this man's sufferings, a low moan came sweeping over the sea.

"Hist, Ralph!" said Bill, opening his eyes; "there's a squall coming, lad. Look alive, boy! Clew up the foresail. Drop the main-sail peak. Them squalls come quick sometimes."

I had already started to my feet, and saw that a heavy squall was indeed bearing down on us. It had hitherto escaped my notice, owing to my being so much engrossed by our conversation. I instantly did as Bill desired, for the schooner was still lying motionless on the glassy sea. I observed with some satisfaction that the squall was bearing down on the larboard bow, so that it would strike the vessel in the position in which she would be best able to stand the shock. Having done my best to shorten sail, I took my stand at the helm.

"Now, boy," said Bill, in a faint voice, "keep her close to the wind."

A few seconds afterwards he said, "Ralph, let me hear those two texts again."

I repeated them.

"Are you sure, lad, ye saw them in the Bible?"

"Quite sure," I replied.

Almost before the words had left my lips the wind burst upon us, and the spray dashed over our decks. For a time the schooner stood it bravely, and sprang forward against the rising sea like a war-horse. Meanwhile clouds darkened the sky, and the sea began to rise in huge billows. There was still too much sail on the schooner, and as the gale increased, I feared that the masts would be torn out of her or carried away, while the wind whistled and shrieked through the strained rigging. Suddenly the wind shifted a point, a heavy sea struck us on the bow, and the schooner was almost laid on her beam-ends, so that I could scarcely keep my legs. At the same moment Bill lost his hold of the belaying-pin which had served to steady him, and he slid with stunning violence against the sky-light. As he lay on the deck close beside me, I could see that the shock had rendered him insensible, but I did not dare to quit the tiller for an instant, as it required all my faculties, bodily and mental, to manage the schooner. For an hour the blast drove us along, while, owing to the sharpness of the vessel's bow and the press of canvas, she dashed through the waves instead of breasting over them, thereby drenching the decks with water fore and aft. At the end of that time the squall passed away, and left us rocking on the bosom of the agitated sea.

My first care, the instant I could quit the helm, was to raise Bill from the deck and place him on the couch. I then ran below for the brandy-bottle and rubbed his face and hands with it, and endeavoured to pour a little down his throat. But my efforts, although I continued them long and assiduously, were of no avail; as I let go the hand which I had been chafing, it fell heavily on the deck.

I laid my hand over his heart, and sat for some time quite

motionless; but there was no flutter there—the pirate was dead!

It was with feelings of awe, not unmingled with fear, that I now seated myself on the cabin skylight and gazed upon the rigid features of my late comrade, while my mind wandered over his past history and contemplated with anxiety my present position. Alone, in the midst of the wide Pacific, having a most imperfect knowledge of navigation, and in a schooner requiring at least eight men as her proper crew! But I will not tax the reader's patience with a minute detail of my feelings and doings during the first few days that followed the death of my companion. I will merely mention that I tied a cannonball to his feet, and with feelings of the deepest sorrow consigned him to the deep.

For fully a week after that a steady breeze blew from the east, and as my course lay west and by north, I made rapid progress towards my destination. I could not take an observation, which I very much regretted, as the captain's quadrant was in the cabin; but from the day of setting sail from the island of the savages I had kept a dead reckoning, and as I knew pretty well now how much leeway the schooner made, I hoped to hit the Coral Island without much difficulty. In this I was the more confident that I knew its position on the chart (which I understood was a very good one), and so had its correct bearings by compass.

As the weather seemed now quite settled and fine, and as I had got into the trade winds, I set about preparations for hoisting the topsails. This was a most arduous task, and my first attempts were complete failures, owing, in a great degree, to my reprehensible ignorance of mechanical forces. The first error I made was in applying my apparatus of blocks and pulleys to a rope which was too weak, so that the very first heave I made broke it in two, and sent me staggering against the after-hatch, over which I tripped, and striking against the main-boom, tumbled down the companion-ladder into the cabin. I was much bruised and somewhat stunned by this untoward accident. However, I considered it fortunate that I was not killed. In my next attempt I made sure of not coming by a similar accident, so I unreeved the tackling and fitted up larger blocks and ropes. But although the principle on which I acted was correct, the machinery was now so massive and heavy that the mere friction and stiffness of the thick cordage prevented me from moving it at all. Afterwards, however, I came to proportion things more correctly; but I could not avoid reflecting at the time how much better it would have been had I learned all this from observation and study, instead of waiting till I was forced to acquire it through the painful and tedious lessons of experience.

After the tackling was prepared and in good working order, it took me the greater part of the day to hoist the main top-sail. As I could not steer and work at this at the same time, I lashed the helm in such a position that, with a little watching now and then, it kept the schooner in her proper course. By this means I was enabled also to go about the deck and down below for things that I wanted, as occasion required; also to cook and eat my victuals. But I did not dare to trust to this plan during the three hours of rest that I allowed myself at night, as the wind might have shifted, in which case I should have been blown far out of my course ere I awoke. I was, therefore, in the habit of *heaving to* during those three hours — that is, fixing the rudder and the sails in such a position that by acting against each other they would keep the ship stationary. After my night's rest, therefore, I had only to make allowance for the leeway she had made, and so resume my course.

Of course I was to some extent anxious lest another squall should come, but I made the best provision I could in the circumstances, and concluded that by letting go the weather-braces of the top-sails and the top-sail halyards at the same time, I should thereby render these sails almost powerless. Besides this, I proposed to myself to keep a sharp look-out on the barometer in the cabin, and if I observed at any time a sudden fall in it, I resolved that I would instantly set about my multiform appliances for reducing sail, so as to avoid being taken at unawares. Thus I sailed prosperously for two weeks, with a fair wind, so that I calculated I must be drawing near to the Coral

Island; at the thought of which my heart bounded with joyful expectation.

The only book I found on board, after a careful search, was a volume of Captain Cook's voyages. This, I suppose, the pirate captain had brought with him in order to guide him, and to furnish him with information regarding the islands of these seas. I found this a most delightful book indeed, and I not only obtained much interesting knowledge about the sea in which I was sailing, but I had many of my own opinions, derived from experience, corroborated, and not a few of them corrected. Besides the reading of this charming book, and the daily routine of occupations, nothing of particular note happened to me during this voyage, except once, when on rising one night, after my three hours' nap, while it was yet dark, I was amazed and a little alarmed to find myself floating in what appeared to be a sea of blue fire! I had often noticed the beautiful appearance of phosphorescent light, but this far exceeded anything of the sort I ever saw before. The whole sea appeared somewhat like milk, and was remarkably luminous.

I rose in haste, and letting down a bucket into the sea, brought some of the water on board and took it down to the cabin to examine it; but no sooner did I approach the light than the strange appearance disappeared, and when I removed the cabin lamp the luminous light appeared again. I was much puzzled with this, and took up a little of the water in the hollow of my hand and then let it run off, when I found that the luminous substance was left behind on my palm. I ran with it to the lamp, but when I got there it was gone. I found, however, that when I went into the dark my hand shone again; so I took the large glass of the ship's telescope and examined my hand minutely, when I found that there were on it one or two small patches of a clear, transparent substance like jelly, which were so thin as to be almost invisible to the naked eye. Thus I came to know that the beautiful phosphoric light, which I had often admired before, was caused by animals, for I had no doubt that these were of the same kind as the medusæ or jelly-fish which are seen in all parts of the world.

On the evening of my fourteenth day I was awakened out of a nap into which I had fallen by a loud cry, and starting up I gazed around me. I was surprised and delighted to see a large albatross soaring majestically over the ship. I immediately took it into my head that this was the albatross I had seen at Penguin Island. I had, of course, no good reason for supposing this, but the idea occurred to me, I know not why, and I cherished it, and regarded the bird with as much affection as if he had been an old friend. He kept me company all that day, and left me as night fell.

Next morning, as I stood motionless and with heavy eyes at the helm — for I had not slept well — I began to weary anxiously for daylight, and peered towards the horizon, where I thought I observed something like a black cloud against the dark sky. Being always on the alert for squalls, I ran to the bow. There could be no doubt it was a squall, and as I listened I thought I heard the murmur of the coming gale. Instantly I began to work might and main at my cumbrous tackle for shortening sail, and in the course of an hour and a half had the most of it reduced — the top-sail yards down on the caps, the top-sails clewed up, the sheets hauled in, the main and fore peaks lowered, and the flying-jib down. While thus engaged the dawn advanced, and I cast an occasional furtive glance ahead. I now heard the roar of the waves distinctly, and as a single ray of the rising sun gleamed over the ocean I saw — what! Could it be that I was dreaming? — That magnificent breaker with its ceaseless roar! — That mountain-top! — Yes, once more I beheld the Coral Island!

SMASHED BY A WHALE

By FRANK T. BULLEN

Compared with the streamlined methods of modern whaling, the hunting of the largest animals ever to have lived (including the prehistoric monsters!) by men in open boats, was one of the most dangerous tasks ever undertaken.

I gaily flung myself into my place in the mate's boat one morning, as we were departing in chase of a magnificent cachalot that had been raised just after breakfast. There were no other vessels in sight — much to our satisfaction — the wind was light, with a cloudless sky, and the whale was dead to leeward of us. We sped along at a good rate towards our prospective victim, who was, in his leisurely enjoyment of life, calmly lolling on the surface, occasionally lifting his enormous tail out of the water and letting it fall flat upon the surface with a boom audible for miles.

We were, as usual, first boat; but, much to the mate's annoyance, it became immediately necessary to roll the sail up, lest its flapping should alarm the watchful monster, and this delayed us sufficiently to allow the other boats to shoot ahead of us. Thus the second mate got fast some seconds before we arrived on the scene, seeing which we furled sail, unshipped the mast, and went in on him with the oars only. At first the proceedings were quite of the usual character, our chief wielding his lance in most brilliant fashion, while not being fast to the animal allowed us much greater freedom in our evolutions; but that fatal habit of the mate's — of allowing his boat to take care of herself so long as he was getting in some good home-thrusts — once more asserted itself. Although the whale was exceedingly vigorous, churning the sea into yeasty foam over an enormous area, there we wallowed close to him, right in the middle of the turmoil, actually courting disaster.

He had just settled down for a moment, when, glancing over the gunwale, I saw his tail, like a vast shadow, sweeping away from us

167

towards the second mate, who was laying off the other side of him. Before I had time to think, the mighty mass of gristle leapt into the sunshine, curved back from us like a huge bow. Then with a roar it came at us, released from its tension of Heaven knows how many tons. Full on the broadside it struck us, sending every soul but me flying out of the wreckage as if fired from catapults. I did not go because my foot was jammed somehow in the well of the boat, but the wrench nearly pulled my thigh-bone out of its socket. I had hardly released my foot, when, towering above me, came the colossal head of the great creature, as he ploughed through the bundle of *débris* that had just been a boat. There was an appalling roar of water in my ears, and darkness that might be felt all around. Yet, in the midst of it all, one thought predominated as clearly as if I had been turning it over in my mind in the quiet of my bunk aboard — "What if he should swallow me?" Nor to this day can I understand how I escaped the portals of his gullet, which of course gaped wide as a church door. But the agony of holding my breath soon overpowered every other feeling and thought, till just as something was going to snap inside my head, I rose to the surface. I was surrounded by a welter of bloody froth, which made it impossible for me to see; but oh, the air was sweet!

I struck out blindly, instinctively, although I could feel so strong an eddy that voluntary progress was out of the question. My hand touched and clung to a rope, which immediately towed me in some direction — I neither knew nor cared whither. Soon the motion ceased, and, with a seaman's instinct, I began to haul myself along by the rope I grasped, although no definite idea was in my mind as to where it was attached. Presently I came butt-up against something solid, the feel of which gathered all my scattered wits into a compact knob of dread. It was the whale! "Any port in a storm," I murmured, beginning to haul away again on my friendly line. By dint of hard work I pulled myself right up the sloping, slippery bank of blubber, until I reached the iron, which, as luck would have it, was planted in that side of the carcass now uppermost. Carcass I said — well, certainly I had no idea of there being any life remaining within the vast mass beneath me; yet I had hardly time to take a couple of turns round myself with the rope (or whale-line, as I had proved it to be), when I felt the great animal quiver all over, and begin to forge ahead. I was now composed enough to remember that help could not be far away, and that my rescue, providing that I could keep above water, was but a question of a few minutes. But I was hardly prepared for the whale's next move. Being very near his end, the boat, or boats, had drawn off a bit, I supposed, for I could see nothing of them. Then I remembered the flurry. Almost at the same moment it began; and there was I, who with fearful admiration had so often watched the titanic convulsions of a dying cachalot, actually involved in them. The turns were off my body, but I was able to twist a couple of turns round my arms, which, in case of his sounding, I could readily let go.

Then all was lost in roar and rush, as of the heart of some mighty cataract, during which I was sometimes above, sometimes beneath, the water, but always clinging, with every ounce of energy still left, to the line. Now, one thought was uppermost—"What if he should broach?" I had seen them do so when in flurry, leaping full twenty feet in the air. Then I prayed.

Quickly as all the preceding changes had passed came perfect peace. There I lay, still alive, but so weak that, although I could feel the turns slipping off my arms, and knew that I should slide off the slope of the whale's side into the sea if they did, I could make no effort to secure myself. Everything then passed away from me, just as if I had gone to sleep.

I do not at all understand how I kept my position, nor how long, but I awoke to the blessed sound of voices, and saw the second mate's boat alongside. Very gently and tenderly they lifted me into the boat, although I could hardly help screaming with agony when they touched me, so bruised and broken up did I feel. My arms must have been nearly torn from their sockets, for the strands of the whale-line had cut deep into their flesh with the strain upon it, while my thigh was swollen enormously from the blow I received at the onset. Mr. Cruce was the most surprised man I think I ever saw. For full ten minutes he stared at me with wide-open eyes. When at last he spoke, it was with difficulty, as if wanting words to express his astonishment. At last he blurted out, "Whar you bin all de time, ennehaow? 'Cawse ef you bin hangin' on to dat ar wale ev' sence you boat smash, w'y de debbil you hain't all ter bits, hey?" I smiled feebly, but was too weak to talk, and presently went off again into a dead faint.

When I recovered, I was snug in my bunk aboard, but aching in every joint, and as sore as if I had been pounded with a club until I was bruised all over. During the day Mr. Count was kind enough to pay me a visit. With his usual luck, he had escaped without the slightest injury; neither was any other member of the boat's crew the worse for the ducking but myself. He told me that the whale was one of the largest he had ever seen, and as fat as butter. The boat was an entire loss, so completely smashed to pieces that nothing of her or her gear had been recovered. After spending about a quarter of an hour with me, he left me considerably cheered up, promising to look after me in the way of food, and also to send me some books. He told me that I need not worry myself about my inability to be at work, because the old man was not unfavourably disposed towards me, which piece of news gave me a great deal of comfort.

When my poor, weary shipmates came below they were almost envious of my comfort — though I would gladly have taken my place among them again, could I have got rid of my hurts. But I was condemned to lie there for nearly three weeks before I was able to get about once more. In my sleep I would undergo the horrible anticipation of sliding down that awful, cavernous mouth over again, often waking with a shriek and drenched with sweat.

While I lay there, three whales were caught, all small cows, and I was informed that the skipper was getting quite disgusted with the luck. At last I managed to get on deck, quite a different-looking man to when I went below, and feeling about ten years older. I found the same sullen quiet reigning that I had noticed several times before when we were unfortunate. I fancied that the skipper looked more morose and savage than ever, though of me, to my great relief, he took not the slightest notice.

The third day after my return to duty we sighted whales again. We lowered three boats as promptly as usual; but when within about half a mile of the "pod" some slight noise in one of the boats gallied them, and away they went in the wind's eye, it blowing a stiffish breeze at the time. It was from the first evidently a hopeless task to chase them, but we persevered until recalled to the ship, dead beat with fatigue. I was not sorry, for my recent adventure seemed to have made quite a coward of me, so much so that an unpleasant gnawing at the pit of my stomach as we neared them almost made me sick. I earnestly hoped that so inconvenient a feeling would speedily leave me, or I should be but a poor creature in a boat.

In passing, I would like to refer to the wonderful way in which these whales realize at a great distance, if the slightest sound be made, the presence of danger. I do not use the word "hear" because so abnormally small are their organs of hearing, the external opening being quite difficult to find, that I do not believe they *can* hear at all well. But I firmly believe they possess another sense by means of which they are able to detect any unusual vibration of the waves of either air or sea at a far greater distance than it would be possible for them to hear. Whatever this power may be which they possess, all whalemen are well acquainted with their exercise of it, and always take most elaborate precautions to render their approach to a whale noiseless.

BRUSH WITH GREEK PIRATES

By W. H. LONG

In 1825, seafaring and life along the shores of Greece and the whole of the eastern Mediterranean was very hazardous. The Royal Navy was employed to keep what order was possible in these waters, where Greek nationalism was fighting to free itself from the Turks.

His Majesty's ships, *Seringapatam* and *Cambrian*, were lying at anchor in Orcos Bay in the island of Negropont. About three o'clock in the afternoon of the 31st January, 1825 a vessel hove in sight, about 8 or 9 miles distant. Our telescopes were immediately turned to that quarter. The strange sail appeared to be an Ionian brig, with every stitch of canvas set, and coming down the channel between Negropont and the main.

Nothing occurred to excite any particular attention, until the man at the mast-head called out that the brig was followed by two smaller vessels. In a few minutes we descried, emerging from a tongue of land, two Greek misticoes, with every sail set, and plying their oars in chase of the brig. These craft were instantly recognised as pirates, the very gentry we were on the look out for in that station.

Although aware of this, they had the audacity to near our anchorage, and in sight of our ships still continued the chase, evidently gaining on the brig, which they, no doubt, calculated on taking under our very guns.

However, they seemed to think they had carried the joke quite far enough; and knowing that our men-of-war had pretty long arms, they as last hauled their wind, and stood back with all speed for their lurking places. The Ionian then slackened sail.

Our men, little anticipating that any work was to be carved out for them that day, were sprawling about the main deck, listless and longing for something to do, when "Out Boats!" sounded through the ship. "Out Boats!" — the sound was electric. The boats' crews were on their feet in a moment; and the looks of the others showed

172

how they envied them their share in the job. The men were now seen bustling up to the quarterdeck for their cutlasses, which they busily buckled on, while the gunner distributed a pistol and ammunition to each man. They were in great glee; it was quite a treat for Jack.

The boats were soon lowered, and additional ammunition, provisions, and a small cask of water, stowed away in each; the surgeon and his traps were not forgotten, and a party of marines completed the crew.

About four o'clock p.m. the boats, 8 in number, and carrying about 120 men, pushed off from the ships, under the command of Lieutenant Marsham of the *Cambrian*.

The afternoon was beautiful; the weather warm, with a moderate breeze. We proceeded at a rapid rate. The pirates were a long way ahead, and looked like specks on the horizon. We neared the Ionian brig in a few hours; but I do not recollect if any of our boats boarded her to make any inquiries. There was no time for palavering. As evening approached we had evidently gained fast on the misticoes. Soon after the moon shone out with all her usual brilliancy in southern climes, and lit us on our chase. There was a little talk; a whisper now and then; the dip of the oar and the regular monotonous sound of the simultaneous pull in the thwarts alone broke the silence, unless when the rowers were relieved. Six hours and a half had elapsed since we quitted the ships. The Greeks were apparently making for the land, distant about a mile, all sails set and pulling as hard as they could. We were coming up with them hand over hand; our boats were all close together, when a discharge of musketry was poured into us by the large mistico. One poor fellow, who had been relieved from the oars a short time before, was shot through the head. He dropped in the boat like a stone. Several others were wounded; two or three in the arms, which caused one almost to drop his oar in the water, if the man beside him had not caught it. His place was supplied in an instant. Another and another discharge followed, with many single shots. Two more fell — one hit in the shoulder, the shot passing into his body. The men were roused to fury. Our marines returned the fire. The

Greeks swarmed round the sides of their vessels, taking deliberate aim at our boats. Every sinew was strained; the boats were impelled forward with redoubled velocity. The cutlasses were drawn; the men hastily binding them round their wrists by means of a leather thong, technically called the "becket".

Our boats swept round the misticoes on every side, the Greeks blazing away at us, whilst the men could hardly restrain themselves on their seats, muttering curses at the loss they had already sustained from the impudent rascals. One man, at the head of the boat, stretching forward to pull quicker alongside the large mistico, was struck unawares by a Greek from the deck, and severely cut by a *yataghan,* a crooked sabre cutting like a sickle.

The men were already on their feet, the oars pulled in, and a rush was made up the sides of the Greek, the cutlasses dangling loose from their wrists by the becket. In a moment half-a-dozen men were on the enemy's deck, hacking right and left; the rest were scrambling up like wolves, eager for revenge, each helping and pushing up the man that chanced to precede him, to clear the way for himself. I was hoisted up myself in the same rough and ready way. The men were cheering, not loudly, but deeply, as if choked with fury; most of them were young hands, and had not been in a skirmish of the sort before; but they were willing workmen.

A small party ran forward along with me; no one ever dreamed of looking behind to see if he was followed by the rest. No man, to my knowledge, fired his pistol — all seemed to rely on their trusty cutlass. The Greeks were driven to the extremity of their deck, contending boldly enough with our men, who, however, to use a pugilistic phrase, "would not be denied".

The simple, checked shirts and white trousers of our sailors, formed a striking contrast to the rich-coloured garments of the Greeks, many of whom were Albanians, all armed with muskets, pistols, and yataghans. The latter stood no chance with the cutlass, and its blow could be easily parried. The sudden report of the muskets, the short, rapid crack of pistols, the slash of the steel, and dull, heavy fall of the blows, were the chief sounds heard in the scuffle, along with the sturdy stamping of the combatants and occasional cheers of the men coming from the boats and joining their comrades.

Many Greeks sprung on the ship's sides, and then, plunging into the sea, made for the shore, distant about a quarter of a mile; others, attempting the same feat, were cut down by our fellows in the very act of springing overboard, whilst many were pulled back and despatched. The fury of the men knew no bounds, and it was no time to attempt to restrain them. They were mad for the moment, as men usually are in such hand-to-hand sort of work. A tall, fine-looking pirate presented a pistol at my head and fired; ere another moment elapsed, he was cloven down to the left eye by one of our men, a stout, muscular seaman, who always passed for an Englishman, though believed to be an Irishman. This man was very conspicuous for the power of his arm, and his dexterity in the use of his weapon. The pirates attemped to guard their heads by means of their yataghans: this man broke through guard and skull at once with a single blow. Several others displayed similar strength of arm. All the men cut at the heads and shoulders of the pirates; they seldom or never stabbed. The latter manœuvre was too Frenchified and scholar-like for Jack, who hit hatchet-fashion, felling the Greeks like cattle.

Many of the latter, on being wounded, attempted to scramble out of the fray, and seek shelter apart from the combatants. *"Christiano! Christiano!"* they shouted; but their cry for quarter came, I fear, too late, and with a bad grace. The blood of the sailors was on fire — the fate of their messmates stimulated them to ample revenge; and pirates, of all others, are the least entitled to share the mercy they scarcely ever grant. The cries of *"Christiano,"* fell upon deaf ears at that moment.

"Too late, ye ——!" shouted some of the men, following up their words by the *coup-de-grâce*. In general they went silently to work — the silence of a thorough-bred bull-dog.

The struggle was soon decided. All the pirates who survived were wounded, except a young lad, who had been spared.

H.M. BRIG "DOMINICA"
FIGHTS A PRIVATEER

During the long years between 1793 and 1815, when Britain fought the whole might of Napoleon and Europe, there were many single-ship actions. This is the story of one of the best of them.

We had only quitted English harbour a few hours, on our first cruise, when, ere we were properly in fighting or sea-going trim, while working up to our station to windward, off the Island of Dominica, on the night of the 3rd of February, 1808 we fell in with a strange sail. About 1 a.m. I was aroused from my cot, having only left the deck at the end of the first watch, half an hour before, by the hollow and unwelcome mutter of the drum beating to quarters.

On getting on deck, I found everyone busy at their guns, or in making sail in chase of a stranger to the northward, scarcely perceptible at intervals through the dim obscure. Our relative position allowed us to keep a point or two off the wind on the starboard tack, and such was the rapidity with which we gained on her, evidently making no effort to elude us, that with her paying no attention to our night signals, and some other circumstances, soon brought us to the conclusion that she was some dull sailing American trader, or other neutral, with which these seas swarmed, and from whom we had many similar false alarms. This conjecture, already unanimous, was confirmed as we approached still nearer by her subsequent manœuvres.

After a few shot from our bow-chaser, we were quickly within hail, and we now made her out to be a fore-and-aft rigged vessel standing under easy sail to the northward. The pertinacity with which she still kept on her way under easy sail close hauled, unmindful of our bow-gun and musketry, for a few minutes clashed with our preconceived notions. But even this circumstance had little weight; a similar disregard, from obstinacy or inattention, on the part of trading vessels being often experienced.

With some of these it was by no means unusual to lash the helm and leave the vessel to the mercy of winds and waves to steer herself, while the watch went to sleep. Every man, however, continued at his station until within hail on his lee quarter, when the usual peremptory mandate of "shorten sail and heave to" with a threat, and in a tone unusually imperious and vehement, was given through the speaking-trumpet.

One solitary voice replied in good English to this summons; at the same instant the requisition was promptly complied with by hauling down their jib and backing their head-sails.

Not a whisper was heard on board, or the slightest indication of bustle or stir of preparation calculated to excite the smallest suspicion, and which, on board foreign vessels of war, particularly privateers, it is so difficult altogether to repress. The extreme darkness of the night effectually prevented our examining her build, rig, cut of sails, or any of the minute details by which the practised eye of a sailor so readily discriminates between, not only classes, but the flags of the various wanderers of the deep. Altogether, so complete was the deception, that any remaining doubt was fully removed.

In this state of security we ranged up to leeward, within half pistol shot distance. The sail trimmers having hauled up the courses, taken in the topgallantsails and jib, and laid the main-topsail to the mast, were coiling down the ropes and making all snug. Part of the crew were employed securing the guns; the small-arm men were returning their pikes and muskets, while some were listlessly leaning over the gangway and hammock nettings, impatiently waiting the drum's call to retreat to their hammocks, gazing out, and wishing honest Jonathan at old Davy for his untimely disturbance of their slumbers, when, just as we were fairly abreast, and near enough to toss a biscuit aboard, we were suddenly astonished by a deafening shout from some two hundred hoarse throats, accompanied by a salute of round and grape, and a tremendous volley of small-arms. At this instant our commander, stooping down to recover his night-glass, which had fallen, thrust his hand into the reeking skull of a man who had been completely decapitated by a round shot. For an instant all was amazement and confusion, and which, at this critical moment, was further increased by the accidental explosion on the after part of the quarter-deck of the greater part of the returned cartridges, which had been temporarily deposited there on securing the guns.

Had our wily opponent followed up this blow by a few similar doses, or as fairly succeeded, as he promptly attempted, to lay us on board during the first moments of surprise, the result might have been doubtful.

This manœuvre was, however, but imperfectly executed. Instead of laying us fairly alongside, which, as she was to windward, she might have done, paying round off while our vessel was still fast forging ahead, her bows grazing our starboard quarter, her jibboom became entangled with our rigging, and retained her in a position by no means favourable to the attempt. As usual on board most of the vessels of our description in His Majesty's service, we had on the after part of the quarter-deck a sort of poop or platform, sufficiently elevated to command the decks of the enemy. From this our small-arm men, by this time sufficiently rallied, poured in their discharges of musketry, and checked every effort to advance by the bowsprit. In vain were the men urged forward by their officers: repulsed, they wavered, and the golden opportunity was gone by.

After a few ineffectual attempts, during which they must have suffered greatly from our fire, becoming disengaged, she dropped astern, and ranging up to leeward, on the larboard beam, the action was once more renewed. She was now between us and the land, the dark shadows of which effectually concealed her.

After exchanging a few broadsides, suddenly extinguishing all her lights, she bore up under a press of sail, and in a few minutes nothing more of her was to be seen. Having several ports not far distant under her lee, it was easy to elude our pursuit by taking refuge in one of these, and we accordingly learned a day or two after that they had returned to St. Pierre's, the anchorage they had quitted the evening of our encounter.

In this affair we had three men killed and six wounded out of our

little crew. Our opponent, who suffered considerably, turned out to be the *Victor*, a French privateer, commanded by an officer of the Marine Royale, well known on the station for his professional skill and ability; with a force in number and weight of metal — eighteen-pounders — much the same as our own, they added a crew greatly superior, and which was further reinforced by a large body of regular troops which they were transporting to Guadaloupe.

PRISONER OF THE PIRATES

By R. M. BALLANTYNE

After they were rescued from Coral Island (the story comes from Ballantyne's famous book of that name) the castaways were horrified to find that it was a pirate vessel which had taken them aboard.

"So you're blubbering, are you, you obstinate whelp?" said the deep voice of the captain, as he came up and gave me a box on the ear that nearly felled me to the deck. "I don't allow any such weakness aboard o' this ship. So clap a stopper on your eyes, or I'll give you something to cry for."

I flushed with indignation at this rough and cruel treatment, but felt that giving way to anger would only make matters worse, so I made no reply, but took out my handkerchief and dried my eyes.

"I thought you were made of better stuff," continued the captain, angrily. "I'd rather have a mad bull-dog aboard than a water-eyed puppy. But I'll cure you, lad, or introduce you to the sharks before long. Now go below and stay there till I call you."

As I walked forward to obey, my eye fell on a small keg standing by the side of the main-mast, on which the word *gunpowder* was written in pencil. It immediately flashed across me that, as we were beating up against the wind, anything floating in the sea would be driven on the reef encircling the Coral Island. I also recollected — for thought is more rapid than the lightning — that my old companions had a pistol. Without a moment's hesitation, therefore, I lifted the keg from the deck and tossed it into the sea! An exclamation of surprise burst from the captain and some of the men who witnessed this act of mine.

Striding up to me, and uttering fearful imprecations, the captain raised his hand to strike me, while he shouted, "Boy! Whelp! What mean you by that?"

"If you lower your hand," said I, in a loud voice, while I felt the blood rush to my temples, "I'll tell you. Until you do so, I'm dumb."

The captain stepped back and regarded me with a look of amazement.

"Now," continued I, "I threw that keg into the sea because the wind and waves will carry it to my friends on the Coral Island, who happen to have a pistol but no powder. I hope that it will reach them soon; and my only regret is that the keg was not a bigger one. Moreover, pirate, you said just now that you thought I was made of better stuff. I don't know what stuff I am made of — I never thought much about that subject — but I'm quite certain of this, that I am made of such stuff as the like of you shall never tame, though you should do your worst."

To my surprise the captain, instead of flying into a rage, smiled, and thrusting his hand into the voluminous shawl that encircled his waist, turned on his heel and walked aft, while I went below.

Here, instead of being rudely handled, as I had expected, the men received me with a shout of laughter, and one of them, patting me on the back, said, "Well done, lad! You're a brick, and I have no doubt will turn out a rare cove. Bloody Bill there was just such a fellow as you are, and he's now the biggest cut-throat of us all."

"Take a can of beer, lad," cried another, "and wet your whistle after that speech o' your'n to the captain. If any one o' us had made it, youngster, he would have had no whistle to wet by this time."

"Stop your clapper, Jack," vociferated a third. "Give the boy a junk o' meat. Don't you see he's a'most goin' to kick the bucket?"

"And no wonder," said the first speaker, with an oath, "after the tumble you gave him into the boat. I guess it would have broke *your* neck if you had got it.'

I did indeed feel somewhat faint, which was owing, doubtless, to the combined effects of ill-usage and hunger; for it will be recollected that I had dived out of the cave that morning before breakfast, and it was now near midday. I therefore gladly accepted a plate of boiled pork and a yam, which were handed to me by one of the men from the locker on which some of the crew were seated eating their dinner. But I must add that the zest with which I ate my meal was much abated in consequence of the frightful oaths and the terrible language that flowed from the lips of these godless men, even in the midst of their hilarity and good-humour. The man who had been alluded to as Bloody Bill was seated near me, and I could not help wondering at the moody silence he maintained among his comrades. He did indeed reply to their questions in a careless, off-hand tone, but he never volunteered a remark. The only difference between him and the other was his taciturnity and his size, for he was nearly, if not quite, as large a man as the captain.

During the remainder of the afternoon I was left to my own reflections, which were anything but agreeable; for I could not banish from my mind the threat about the thumbscrews, of the nature and use of which I had a vague but terrible conception. I was still meditating on my unhappy fate, when, just after nightfall, one of the watch on deck called down the hatchway,—

"Hallo there! One o' you tumble up and light the cabin lamp, and send that boy aft to the captain — sharp!"

"Now then, do you hear, youngster? The captain wants you. Look alive," said Bloody Bill, raising his huge frame from the locker on which he had been asleep for the last two hours. He sprang up the ladder, and I instantly followed him, and going aft was shown into the cabin by one of the men, who closed the door after me.

A small silver lamp which hung from a beam threw a dim soft light over the cabin, which was a small apartment, and comfortably but plainly furnished. Seated on a camp-stool at the table, and busily engaged in examining a chart of the Pacific, was the captain, who looked up as I entered, and in a quiet voice bade me be seated, while he threw down his pencil, and rising from the table, stretched himself on a sofa, at the upper end of the cabin.

"Boy," said he, looking me full in the face, "what is your name?"

"Ralph Rover," I replied.

"Where did you come from, and how came you to be on that island? How many companions had you on it? Answer me, now, and mind you tell no lies."

"I never tell lies," said I firmly.

The captain received this reply with a cold, sarcastic smile, and bade me answer his questions.

I then told him the history of myself and my companions from the time we sailed till the day of his visit to the island, taking care, however, to make no mention of the Diamond Cave. After I had concluded, he was silent for a few minutes; then looking up, he said, "Boy, I believe you."

I was surprised at this remark, for I could not imagine why he should not believe me. However, I made no reply.

"And what," continued the captain, "makes you think that this schooner is a pirate?"

"The black flag," said I, "showed me what you are; and if any further proof were wanting, I have had it in the brutal treatment I have received at your hands."

The captain frowned as I spoke, but subduing his anger he continued, "Boy, you are too bold. I admit that we treated you roughly, but that was because you made us lose time and gave us a good deal of trouble. As to the black flag, that is merely a joke that my fellows play off upon people sometimes in order to frighten them. It is their humour, and does no harm. I am no pirate, boy, but a lawful trader — a rough one, I grant you, but one can't help that in these seas, where there are so many pirates on the water and such murderous blackguards on the land. I carry on a trade in sandal-wood with the Feejee Islands; and if you choose, Ralph, to behave yourself and be a good boy, I'll take you along with me and give you a good share of the profits. You see I'm in want of an honest boy like you to look after the cabin and keep the log and superintend the traffic on shore sometimes. What say you, Ralph: would you like to become a sandal-wood trader?"

I was much surprised by this explanation, and a good deal relieved to find that the vessel, after all, was not a pirate; but instead of replying I said, "If it be as you state, then why did you take me from my island, and why do you not now take me back?"

The captain smiled as he replied, "I took you off in anger, boy, and I'm sorry for it. I would even now take you back, but we are too far away from it. See, there it is," he added, laying his finger on the chart, "and we are now here — fifty miles at least. It would not be fair to my men to put about now, for they have all an interest in the trade."

I could make no reply to this; so, after a little more conversation, I agreed to become one of the crew, at least until we could reach some civilised island where I might be put ashore. The captain assented to this proposition, and after thanking him for the promise, I left the cabin and went on deck with feelings that ought to have been lighter, but which were, I could not tell why, marvellously heavy and uncomfortable still.

Three weeks after the conversation narrated in the last chapter, I was standing on the quarter-deck of the schooner watching the gambols of a shoal of porpoises that swam round us. It was a dead calm — one of those still, hot, sweltering days so common in the Pacific, when nature seems to have gone to sleep, and the only thing in water or in air that proves her still alive is her long, deep breathing in the swell of the mighty sea. No cloud floated in the deep blue above, no ripple broke the reflected blue below. The sun shone fiercely in the sky, and a ball of fire blazed with almost equal power from out the bosom of the water. So intensely still was it, and so perfectly transparent was the surface of the deep, that had it not been for the long swell already alluded to, we might have believed the surrounding universe to be a huge blue liquid ball, and our little ship the one solitary material speck in all creation, floating in the midst of it.

No sound broke on our ears save the soft puff now and then of a porpoise, the slow creak of the masts as we swayed gently on the swell, the patter of the reef-points, and the occasional flap of the hanging sails. An awning covered the fore and after parts of the schooner, under which the men composing the watch on deck lolled in sleepy indolence, overcome with excessive heat. Bloody Bill, as the men invariably called him, was standing at the tiller; but his post for the present was a sinecure, and he whiled away the time by alternately gazing in dreamy abstraction at the compass in the binnacle, and by walking to the taffrail in order to spit into the sea. In one of these turns he came near to where I was standing, and leaning over the side, looked long and earnestly down into the blue wave.

This man, although he was always taciturn and often surly, was the only human being on board with whom I had the slightest desire to become better acquainted. The other men, seeing that I did not relish their company, and knowing that I was a *protégé* of the captain, treated me with total indifference. Bloody Bill, it is true, did the same; but as this was his conduct towards everyone else, it was not peculiar in reference to me. Once or twice I tried to draw him into conversation, but he always turned away after a few cold monosyllables. As he now leaned over the taffrail close beside me, I said to him,—

"Bill, why is it that you are so gloomy? Why do you never speak to any one?"

Bill smiled slightly as he replied, "Why, I s'pose it's because I hain't got nothin' to say!"

"That's strange," said I musingly; "you look like a man that could think, and such men can usually speak."

"So they can, youngster," rejoined Bill, somewhat sternly; "and I could speak too if I had a mind to, but what's the use o' speakin' here? The men only open their mouths to curse and swear, an' they seem to find it entertainin'; but I don't, so I hold my tongue."

"Well, Bill, that's true, and I would rather not hear you speak at all than hear you speak like the other men; but *I* don't swear, Bill, so you might talk to me sometimes, I think. Besides, I'm weary of spending day after day in this way, without a single soul to say a pleasant word to. I've been used to friendly conversation, Bill, and I really would take it kind if you would talk with me a little now and then."

Bill looked at me in surprise, and I thought I observed a sad expression pass across his sun-burned face.

"An' where have you been used to friendly conversation?" said

186

Bill, looking down again into the sea; "not on that Coral Island, I take it?"

"Yes, indeed," said I energetically. "I have spent many of the happiest months in my life on that Coral Island;" and without waiting to be further questioned, I launched out into a glowing account of the happy life that Jack and Peterkin and I had spent together, and related minutely every circumstance that befell us while on the island.

"Boy, boy," said Bill, in a voice so deep that it startled me, "this is no place for you."

"That's true," said I. "I am of little use on board, and I don't like my comrades; but I can't help it, and at any rate I hope to be free again soon."

"Free?" said Bill, looking at me in surprise.

"Yes, free," returned I, "the captain said he would put me ashore after this trip was over."

"*This trip!* Hark'ee, boy," said Bill, lowering his voice, "what said the captain to you the day you came aboard?"

"He said that he was a trader in sandal-wood, and no pirate, and told me that if I would join him for this trip he would give me a good share of the profits or put me on shore in some civilised island if I chose."

Bill's brows lowered savagely as he muttered, "Ay, he said truth when he told you he was a sandal-wood trader, but he lied when—"

"Sail ho!" shouted the look-out at the masthead.

"Where away?" cried Bill, springing to the tiller; while the men, startled by the sudden cry, jumped up and gazed round the horizon.

"On the starboard quarter, hull down, sir," answered the look-out.

At this moment the captain came on deck, and mounting into the rigging, surveyed the sail through the glass. Then sweeping his eye round the horizon, he gazed steadily at a particular point.

"Take in top-sails," shouted the captain, swinging himself down on the deck by the main back-stay.

"Take in top-sails," roared the first mate.

"Ay, ay, sir-r-r," answered the men. They sprang into the rigging

187

to carry out the order and went aloft like cats.

Instantly all was bustle on board the hitherto quiet schooner. The top-sails were taken in and stowed, the men stood by the sheets and halyards, and the captain gazed anxiously at the breeze which was now rushing towards us like a sheet of dark blue. In a few seconds it struck us. The schooner trembled as if in surprise at the sudden onset, while she fell away, then bending gracefully to the wind, as though in acknowledgment of her subjection, she cut through the waves with her sharp prow like a dolphin, while Bill directed her course towards the strange sail.

In half-an-hour we neared her sufficiently to make out that she was a schooner, and from the clumsy appearance of her masts and sails we judged her to be a trader. She evidently did not like our appearance, for the instant the breeze reached her she crowded all sail and showed us her stern. As the breeze had moderated a little, our top-sails were again shaken out, and it soon became evident — despite the proverb, "A stern chase is a long one" — that we doubled her speed and would overhaul her speedily. When within a mile we hoisted British colours, but receiving no acknowledgment, the captain ordered a shot to be fired across her bows. In a moment, to my surprise, a large portion of the bottom of the boat amidships was removed, and in the hole thus exposed appeared an immense brass gun. It worked on a swivel, and was elevated by means of machinery. It was quickly loaded and fired. The heavy ball struck the water a few yards ahead of the chase, and ricochetting into the air, plunged into the sea a mile beyond it.

This produced the desired effect. The strange vessel backed her top-sails and hove-to, while we ranged up and lay to about a hundred yards off.

"Lower the boat," cried the captain.

In a second the boat was lowered and manned by a part of the crew, who were all armed with cutlasses and pistols. As the captain passed me to get into it, he said, "Jump into the stern-sheets, Ralph; I may want you." I obeyed, and in ten minutes more we were standing on the stranger's deck. We were all much surprised at the sight that met our eyes. Instead of a crew of such sailors as we were accustomed to see, there were only fifteen blacks standing on the quarter-deck and regarding us with looks of undisguised alarm. They were totally unarmed, and most of them unclothed; one or two, however, wore portions of European attire. One had on a pair of duck trousers which were much too large for him, and stuck out in a most ungainly manner. Another wore nothing but the common scanty native garment round the loins and a black beaver hat. But the most ludicrous personage of all, and one who seemed to be chief, was a tall middle-aged man, of a mild, simple expression of countenance, who wore a white cotton shirt, a swallow-tailed coat, and a straw hat, while his black brawny legs were totally uncovered below the knees.

"Where's the commander of this ship?" inquired our captain, stepping up to this individual.

"I is capin," he answered, taking off his straw hat and making a low bow.

"You!" said our captain, in surprise. "Where do you come from, and where are you bound? What cargo have you aboard?"

"We is come," answered the man with the swallow tail, "from Aitutaki; we was go for Rarotonga. We is native miss'nary ship, our name is de *Olive Branch;* an' our cargo is two tons cocoa-nuts, seventy pigs, twenty cats, and de Gosp'l."

This annoucement was received by the crew of our vessel with a shout of laughter, which, however, was peremptorily checked by the captain, whose expression instantly changed from one of severity to that of frank urbanity as he advanced towards the missionary and shook him warmly by the hand.

"I am very glad to have fallen in with you," said he, "and I wish you much success in your missionary labours. Pray take me to your cabin, as I wish to converse with you privately."

The missionary immediately took him by the hand, and as he led him away I heard him saying, "Me most glad to find you trader; we t'ought you be pirate. You very like one 'bout the masts."

What conversation the captain had with this man I never heard, but he came on deck again in a quarter of an hour, and shaking hands cordially with the missionary, ordered us into our boat and returned to the schooner, which was immediately put before the wind. In a few minutes the *Olive Branch* was left far behind us.

THE ESCAPE OF H.M.S. "TALBOT"

By W. H. LONG

*This story gives an unusual but very vivid picture of what seafaring
meant during the Napoleonic Wars.*

At midday, on Saturday, the 30th of November, 1811, with a fair
wind and smooth sea, we weighed from our station here, in company
with the *Saldanha* frigate, of thirty-eight guns, Captain Pakenham,
with a crew of 300 men, on a cruise, as was intended, of twenty days;
the *Saldanha* taking a westerly course, while we stood in the opposite
direction. We had scarcely got out of the loch and cleared the heads,
however, when we plunged at once into all the miseries of a gale of
wind blowing from the west. During the three following days it continued to increase in violence, when the islands of Coll and Tiree became visible to us. As the wind had now chopped round more to the
north, and continued unabated in violence, the danger of getting involved among the numerous small islands and rugged headlands on
the north-west coast of Inverness-shire became evident. It was therefore deemed expedient to wear the ship round, and make a port with
all possible expedition. With this view, and favoured by the wind, a
course was shaped for Loch Swilly, and away we scudded under close-
reefed foresail and main-topsail, followed by a tremendous sea, which
threatened every moment to overwhelm us, and accompanied by
piercing showers of hail, and a gale which blew with incredible fury.
The same course was steered until next day at noon, when land was
seen on the lee-bow. The weather being thick, some time elapsed before it could be distinctly made out, and it was then ascertained to be
the island of North Arran, on the coast of Donegal, westward of
Loch Swilly. The ship was therefore hauled up some points, and we
yet entertained hopes of reaching an anchorage before nightfall
when the weather gradually thickened, and the sea, now that we were
upon a wind, broke over us in all directions. Its violence was such,
that in a few minutes several of our ports were stove in, at which the

water poured in in great abundance, until it was actually breast high on the lee side of the main-deck. Fortunately, but little got below, and the ship was relieved by taking in the foresail. But a dreadful addition was now made to the precariousness of our situation by the cry of "Land a-head!" which was seen from the forecastle, and must have been very near.

Not a moment was now lost in wearing the ship round on the other tack, and making what little sail could be carried, to weather the land we had already passed. This soon proved, however, to be a forlorn prospect, for it was found we should run our distance by ten o'clock.

All the horrors of shipwreck now stared us in the face, aggravated tenfold by the extreme darkness of the night, and the tremendous force of the wind, which now blew a hurricane. Mountains are insignificant when speaking of the sea that kept pace with it; its violence was awful beyond description, and it frequently broke all over the poor little ship, that shivered and groaned, but behaved admirably.

The force of the sea may be guessed from the fact of the sheet-anchor, nearly a ton and a half in weight, being actually lifted on board, to say nothing of the fore-chain-plates broken, both gangways torn away, quarter-galleries stove in, etc., etc. In short, on getting into port, the vessel was found to be loosened through all her frame, and leaky at every seam.

As far as depended on her good qualities, however, I felt assured that we were safe; for I had seen enough of the *Talbot* to be convinced we were in one of the finest sea-boats that ever swam. But what could all the skill of the ship-builder avail in a situation like ours? With a terrible night full fifteen hours long before us, and knowing that we were fast driving on the land, anxiety and dread were on every face, and every mind felt the terrors of uncertainty and suspense.

At length, about twelve o'clock, the dreadful truth was disclosed to us. Judge of my sensations when I saw the surf and the frowning rocks of Arran, scarcely half a mile distant on our lee-bow. To our inexpressible relief, and not less to our surprise, we fairly weathered

193

all, and were congratulating each other on our escape, when on looking forward I imagined I saw breakers at no great distance on our lee; and this suspicion was soon confirmed, when the moon, which shone at intervals, suddenly broke out from behind a cloud, and presented to us a most terrific spectacle.

At not more than a quarter of a mile distance, on our lee-beam, appeared a range of tremendous breakers, amongst which it seemed as if every sea would throw us. Their height, it may be supposed, was prodigious, when they could be clearly distinguished from the foaming waters of the surrounding ocean. It was a scene seldom to be witnessed, and never forgotten.

"Lord have mercy on us!" was now on the lips of every one — destruction seemed inevitable. Captain Swaine, whose coolness I have never seen surpassed, issued his orders clearly and collectedly, when it was proposed, as a last resource, to drop the anchors, cut away the masts, and trust to the chance of riding out the gale. This scheme was actually determined on, and everything was in readiness, but happily was deferred until an experiment was tried aloft. In addition to the close-reefed main-topsail and foresail, the fore-topsail and try-sail were now set, and the result was almost magical. With a few plunges we cleared not only the reef, but a huge rock upon which I could with ease have tossed a biscuit; and in a few minutes we were inexpressibly rejoiced to observe both far astern.

We had now miraculously escaped all but certain destruction a second time, but much was yet to be feared. We had yet still to pass Cape Jeller, and the moments dragged on in gloomy apprehension and anxious suspense. The ship carried sail most wonderfully, and we continued to go along at the rate of seven knots, shipping very heavy seas, and labouring much — all, with much solicitude, looking out for daylight. The dawn at length appeared, and to our great joy we saw the land several miles astern, having passed the cape and many other hidden dangers during the darkness. Matters on the morning of the 5th assumed a very different aspect from the last two days' experience: the wind gradually subsided, and with it the sea, and a favourable breeze now springing up, we were enabled to make a good offing. Fortunately no accident of consequence occurred, although several of our people were severely bruised by falls. Poor fellows! They certainly suffered enough; not a dry stitch, not a dry hammock, had they since we sailed.

The most melancholy part of my narrative is still to be told. On coming up to our anchorage here this morning, we observed an unusual degree of curiosity and bustle in the fort; crowds of people were congregated on both sides, running to and fro, examining us through spy-glasses; in short, an extraordinary commotion was apparent. The meaning of all this was but too soon made known to us by a boat coming alongside, from which we learned that the unfortunate *Saldanha* had gone to pieces, and every man perished.

Our own destruction had likewise been reckoned inevitable, from the time of the discovery of the unhappy fate of our consort five days beforehand; and hence the astonishment excited at our unexpected return. From all that could be learned concerning the dreadful catastrophe, I am inclined to believe that the *Saldanha* had been driven on the rocks about the time our doom appeared so certain in another quarter. Her lights were seen by the signal-tower at nine o'clock of that fearful Wednesday night, December the 4th, after which it is supposed she went ashore on the rocks at a small bay called Ballymastaker, almost at the entrance of Loch Swilly harbour. Next morning the beach was strewed with fragments of the wreck, and upwards of two hundred of the bodies of the unfortunate sufferers were found washed ashore. One man — and one only — out of the three hundred, was ascertained to have come ashore alive, but almost in a state of insensibility. Unhappily there was no person present to administer to his wants judiciously, and upon craving something to drink, about half a pint of whisky was given him by the country people, which almost instantly killed him. Poor Pakenham's body was also recognised this morning amidst the others, and, like these, stripped quite naked by the inhuman wretches who flocked to the wreck. It is even suspected that he came on shore alive, but was stripped and left to perish.

A GALE OFF MARMORICE

This is a story of how fine seamanship saved the fleet when it was surprised by a storm off the coast of Asia Minor.

In the latter end of the month of January, 1801, the day dawned with every indication of bad weather — the mass of dense and heavy clouds, piled upon each other, occupied all space to the south-west; the sun in his course looked with a fiery aspect, and the sea-fowl, with the wonderful instinct that puzzles the wise, from their fore-knowledge of the storm, came screaming in upon the land; the wind blew fiercely and in fearful gusts; the labouring clouds seemed preparing to discharge their overloaded breasts, and distant thunder rolled along the horizon. The masses of clouds, as they sailed along the ocean, nearly shut out the light of day, and rose at opposite extremities into huge mountains of vapour: they were illuminated by fitful flashes of lightning, and looked like giant batteries erected in the heavens. As they moved onwards from the south-west, they shot down vivid streams, which, at times, pierced the water like quivering blades of fire; again the electric fluid took an horizontal direction through the skies, and its dazzling streak fluttered like a radiant streamer, until it lost itself among the clouds. Comparative darkness came on with a suddenness that I never before had observed, and the gusts were terrific.

During this elemental war, the British fleet under Vice-Admiral Lord Keith, and the army under Sir Ralph Abercrombie, closely crammed in men-of-war and transports, to the number of two hundred sails, were carrying a heavy press of canvas to claw off a lee-shore: that shore was Caramania, in Asia Minor, a most mountainous and well-wooded, black-looking coast. We were in search of Marmorice harbour, the appointed rendez-vous of the Egyptian expedition; and the Asiatic pilots, frightened at the dangerous position of the fleet in this tremendous weather, lost the little knowledge they had formerly possessed of this unfrequented and frowning coast, whose mountains towered high above the clouds, on which no vestige of human life could be seen. Every glass, in the clearance between the squalls, was eagerly turned upon the precipitous shore, upon which the heavy waves beat with the most horrific grandeur. It was self-evident to the meanest capacity, that unless the harbour could be entered before night, the transports filled with British warriors would be wrecked on the lee-shore, with no chance of assistance. The men-of-war, by dint of carrying sail, might claw off; but the great majority of this fine army would, in a few hours, become food for the monsters of the deep, or the ferocious and ravenous tenants of the vast forests that seemed interminable to our straining sight. As each withdrew his glass, with a disappointed look, the longitude of their countenances increased, and the round-faced, laughing midshipman lost his disposition for fun or frolic, and all at once became a reflecting, sedate personage.

The admiral, on whom all the responsibility rested, endeavoured to assume a calmness of tone and manner, that the honesty of his open nature would not brook: his agitation was visible in the contortions of his venerable countenance, and the sudden starts of his nervous system.

"Fire a gun, and hoist a signal of attention to the fleet," said his lordship.

"They have all answered, my lord," said the officer of the signal department.

"Now, Mr. Stains, be particular; ask if any one is qualified to lead into Marmorice."

As the negative flag flew at the mast-head of the men-of-war, every countenance proportionally fell. At length, with heartfelt joy, I proclaimed, that one of our sloops had hoisted her affirmative.

"Who is she, youngster? D—n it, boy, do not keep me in suspense."

"The *Petrel,* my lord."

I saw an ejaculation of thankfulness rise warm from the heart on the lips of Lord Keith, as he piously raised his eyes and pressed his hand on his heart.

"Signal for the fleet to bear up, make more sail, and follow the

197

Petrel," said Lord Keith; "Captain Inglis may be depended on."

And we shook out a reef, and set the main-top-gallant-sail, which soon closed our leader in the *Petrel*. As we approached this mountainous and novel land, the idea (and it must be an astounding one) seemed to dwell on and occupy the most unreflecting mind, that should Captain Inglis be wrong, every ship with twenty-five thousand men, would be the sacrifice of such error.

Lord Keith ordered the signal of attention with the Petrel's pendants.

"Captain Inglis, your responsibility is awful," said the telegraph. "Are you perfectly certain of the entrance of Marmorice?"

"Perfectly sure," was the answer, "and right ahead."

"Signal officers on the fore-yard, with their glasses," said the admiral; and slinging our telescopes we ascended: indeed it was time, for now the roar of the waves, as they broke on the coast, throwing their spray on high, conveyed a dismal idea of our impending fate.

"A narrow entrance ahead," called the signal-lieutenant, Stains. "Do the midshipmen make out the same?"

"We all of us discern it, my lord," shouted the whole at the very extent of their voices.

"God be praised for this great mercy!" ejaculated his lordship, uncovering and bowing his head with great devotion; and I do aver and believe that the grateful sentiment pervaded every heart in the *Foudroyant*.

The entrance of Marmorice now became distinctly visible to all on deck, from the contrast of the deep still water to the creamy froth on the shore; and the signal of the fleet to crowd all sail for the port in view, and the men-of-war to haul their wind, until the merchantmen had entered the channel, was flying at the *Foudroyant*'s mast-head, as she shot into the gut of Marmorice. The tremendous mountains overshadowed us, and seemed inclined, from their great height, to come thundering down upon us like the destructive avalanches in the mountains of Switzerland.

We now entered the spacious and splendid harbour, circular in its form, and more than twenty miles in circumference. It created great astonishment from its vast magnitude, being capable of containing all the ships in the world, and from its vast mountainous shore with immense forests. In so small a nook as to be nearly invisible, stands on a rock a fort, and a few wretched houses, surrounded by a high wall, I conjecture for the purpose of keeping out wild beasts, which seemed here lord of the ascendant. This fortification displayed the crescent and was saluted with eleven guns, as we took up anchorage, closely followed by our numerous fleet. Scarcely had we moored, when the heavy masses of clouds that had rested on and capped the high land, now opened upon us in earnest, and the forked lightnings darted among the fleet with fatal effect. The gale increased to a perfect hurricane, and blew from all points of the compass; the flakes of ice, for they were too large to be called hail, came down with such prodigious force as to destroy man and beast; and whoever witnessed that storm, could entertain no doubt of a special Providence in the affairs of men. We were all safe moored, and the heart expanded in thankfulness to the Eternal Power that had watched over our safety.

The following night was beautifully serene, and the suns of other worlds threw their softened and pensive light on this minute speck in the boundless creation — the watch, some of whom paced the deck, castle-building, and imagining scenes of bliss that never were to be realized, while others admired the starry vault of heaven, wondering with what sort of beings yon myriads of worlds were peopled while the talkers who could get listeners, were spinning many a yarn of by-gone days and other scenes. Crombie, a grey-headed young gentleman, (for all midshipmen are called young gentlemen, and with whom the youthful lieutenant of his watch commonly created some mirth by desiring him as youngster to sheer up to the masthead and count the convoy), now seized me by the button, by which he compelled me to listen to his yarn as follows: "I say, youngster, that was an ugly coast we ran down upon yesterday, and reminds me of an occurrence that was particularly mournful:" here he hemmed, and seemed to smother a sigh. "You see, when I belonged to his majesty's sloop — but it will be as well not to mention her name, as I cut and run one day without asking permission; well, we were cruising in the latitude, and, by old Sounding's longitude (but that, by dead reckoning, could not always be depended upon) near where brother Jonathan said he had discovered a dangerous cluster of rocks, to which he had affixed the appropriate name of the 'Devil's Grip': well, I dined in the gun-room that day, and many a hearty laugh at the Yankee notion circulated with the bottle; for the master proved, to the satisfaction of all but one at the table, that rocks could not be in the open sea, so many hundred miles from any known land, and where the deep sea lead could not find bottom, and for which he had often tried in vain: so when the caterer bowed round to signify that the mess allowance of wine, viz., a pint each person, was drunk, the first luff proposed an extra bottle, while we listened to the most extraordinary youth I ever met with, as he, with fluency of speech and elegance of manner, demolished the master's premises and inferences. This young gentleman was called the captain's nephew, and might, I think, have claimed nearer relationship; he was named Paulo, after his mother, Pauline, a Neapolitan Countess, who fled from a nunnery, where she had been immured without asking her consent. She must have been a beauty, for her son, though of a very fragile and delicate make, was remarkably tall and handsome, with a most expressive countenance, generally clouded with a shade of melancholy: he was fond of gazing at the moon, and wrote a deal of poetry, comparing ladies' eyes to the bright stars that shone above him, all about love, and such other nonsense; but our doctor, who was a learned man, pronounced it beautiful, and said he was a genius of the first order, full of susceptibility, and with nerves too finely strung for this coarse and bustling world; at all events, he was universally beloved for his gentleness and kindness of heart: at punishment you would see him with his hands clasped, and his eyes suffused with tears, looking up in his uncle's face with such an imploring look to spare the culprit, while the muscles round his well-formed mouth used to work as the sharp lash fell on the tender skin of the sufferer.

"The captain was a stern unbending man, but his iron countenance softened at the visible agony of this glorious youth, who frequently gained his point, and the last dozen was remitted. He said, as far as I could understand, that the shell of the earth was trifling compared to its interior, which was supposed to be in a state of fusion, and hence arose volcanos and earthquakes, the heaving up of lands that had been the bed of the ocean, and the submersion of others; that the vast Atlantic itself was supposed by some philosophers to have once been habitable and a great continent. All this was too learned, and made no impression on any one but the doctor; so we drank the captain's toast, of good afternoon, and went to our usual duty; mine was to keep the first watch. The gale blew hard, right aft, and we were dashing through a heavy sea in merry style.

" 'I think, sir,' said I, addressing the officer without touching my hat, the night being too dark to notice the omission, (a point on which he was very particular), 'I think, sir, that the sea seems inclined to kick up a bobbery to night, and is rising fast.'

" 'I am of the same opinion, youngster: but what is that ahead?'

"At this moment the look-out man on the bowsprit sung out 'Breakers ahead!' and was reiterated by the cut-headman, "Breakers on both bows!' in that indescribable tone of alarm that carries instant conviction of great danger, and causes a revulsion of the blood.

"This terrific announcement woke even the sleepers, for in less time than I take to tell you, every man and boy was on deck, most of them in their shirts; poor dear Paulo, looking more like an ærial sprite than of mortal mould, ran after the captain, who went out on the end of the bowsprit, and looked steadily around, which required nerves of iron; for right ahead seemed a vast barrier of rocks, on which the sea was wildly breaking, throwing its white spray to the clouds; and on each side, as the mad waves receded, were seen their black tops, peeping through the creamy froth that surrounded us, the gallant ship bounding like a greyhound, at the rate of ten knots, full upon them, that would dash her to atoms; for she seemed to me

201

to increase her speed, probably from an indraught in the reef. Then arose the wild shriek of despair from the timid, and stood still the brave; their manly brows blanched, it is true, for it was a sight of such horror, youngster, that my hair turned perfectly white, and I shut my eyes with the sinner's last ejaculation, of 'God be merciful to me!' but not before I had seen Paulo, the beautiful and good Paulo, with the scream of a maniac, jump into the boiling surf. The manly tone of the captain's voice was heard high above the roar of the breakers, 'Port the helm, port, and silence all of you — your lives depend on your steadiness and prompt obedience. Master, take the weather-wheel, and steer for an opening, two point before the starboard beam: we may find water through the reef where it does not break so heavily. Brace forward the yards;' and the lee-gunnel buried itself in the agitated water, as she sprung to the wind.

"'Let fly the main-topgallant-sheets!' The sail flew to ribands, and saved the topmast. 'Now, master, hard up with the helm, and square away the yards; send her between those high rocks where the sea does not break.' The noble ship leaped between them, while the spray from them washed some of the unnerved over the bulwarks, and their last despairing cry was drowned in the roar of the surf. She steered beautifully in the master's able hands, who had frequently declared he could turn her through the eye of a needle; and this channel between the breakers was like one, and very little wider than her main-yard. Nothing was heard from old Soundings but 'Port it is, starboard withal,' not forgetting 'sir', at the end of each response. As I went to assist him at the wheel, after drawing in a long breath, I heard him mutter, 'Who would have thought the Yankee notion true, but it is the Devil's Grip, and a devilish ugly one it is for sartin.'

"'We are through the reef, thank Almighty God,' said the captain: and it came warm from the heart. 'Master, we will heave-to till daylight.' 'Better take a large offing,' said Soundings: 'the devil may have a young grip forming in the wake of his mother.' 'Keep a good look out for breakers,' called the captain; 'and, Mr. Handsail, shorten sail, laying her to.' And we hove-to, a league to leeward of the most frightful cluster of rocks that ever reared their ugly heads above the wide and open sea. 'But where is my boy, Paulo!' said the captain. I advanced, and gave my doleful story. His strong and pent-up feelings broke down in a torrent of grief; the big tears coursed each other down his weather-beaten cheeks as he exclaimed, 'Oh! Paulo, my good and gentle son, Paulo, would to God that I had died for thee!'

"There is something so affecting in the grief of a strong mind like the captain's — so firm, that he retained his selfpossession in the midst of scenes that paralysed the heart and blanched the boldest front — that all shed tears that heard him exclaim, in the bitter accents of heart-broken misery, that he was bereaved and desolate, and would welcome death as a cessation from intolerable anguish. I alone stood firm, not being of the melting mood, though I dearly loved the boy, who haunts me in my sleep. I saw him last night, plain as I see you, and heard his maniac scream, as he jumped into the agitated waters." Saying this, Crombie pulled off my button and burst into tears; I respected his feelings too much to recall to his mind his previous declaration of stoicism. "The master," said he, "called for a norwester to comfort him, saying, 'grief always made him dry.' The captain did his duty mechanically, but the elasticity of his step, and his manly deportment had, like his son, left him for ever. He was never after seen to smile, retired on half-pay, and soon went to that 'bourne from whence no traveller returns'."

MUTINY IN THE "VITTORIA"

Though the mutiny described in this story happened more than 130 years ago, in 1830, it is still one of the best stories of crime at sea.

A most atrocious act of the basest mutiny and murder took place at the above-mentioned period; a time when the world was at peace, and the ocean only ploughed by the keels of friends vying with each other in commerce, and being only honourable rivals in fair trade.

Our merchant vessels do not carry many men, in peace, as they hire labourers when in harbour to do the drudgery, and carry no more to sea than are sufficient to manage the sails and keep a look-out: in truth, they carry much too few, and many losses occur for want of hands, as the splitting of a topsail for want of hands to furl it, costs more than the wages of three men in a six months' voyage. The *Vittoria* appears to have been very weakly manned, and at Manilla they took on board six Spaniards, we presume, because they were to be had cheap, and Britons were left upon a lee-shore; for it is an undoubted fact, that there are always numbers of English sailors to be had at Manilla, where they congregate on account of the high wages given by the Spaniards to navigate their Acapulco ships, as they well know that Britons are the best and most steady seamen.

Captain Smith cleared out from Manilla to London, and he had not been long at sea ere the Spaniards began to be obstreperous, and refused to perform their duty; they were, however, brought to reason, and by threats of punishment, conducted themselves with assumed forbearance. They had contemplated their murderous intentions from the hour they first went on board, and had secretly provided themselves with stilettos and short pistols. As to the captain of the vessel and the officers, they had no arms whatever, and only one gun on the quarterdeck for the purpose of making signals; and for that there was no shot, only a few cartridges. They rested in perfect safety when this dreadful conspiracy was going on, and Mr. Andrews, alone, had some suspicion of the Spaniards and their pretended propriety; which was all under the mask of deceit, and they were harbouring the most villanous designs which they then attemped to carry out.

In the dead of the night, when all the crew were asleep, except the man at the helm, the Spaniards stole upon deck quietly, and secured the crew as they were asleep, murdering three of them with their long Spanish knives, and wounding several others. They then burst open the captain's cabin-door, and stabbed him in his bed in about thirty places; and to secure their act, they also shot him with their pistols, and threw him on the cabin-floor.

The second mate and the carpenter were killed in their sleep, and thrown overboard in their beds. The chief mate, Mr. Andrews, they put in irons, and a consultation was held what was to be done with him; some were for instantly murdering him; but others knew that they could not navigate the ship without his assistance, and they therefore, from necessity, released him, and compelled him to enter into all their plan. The steward was also spared: but it was agreed among them, that when they made the coast of California, they should murder Mr. Andrews and the rest of the crew, and then dispose of the vessel as well as they could; for there are Spanish merchants who will purchase any vessel and encourage piracy on all sides.

They are under no control by the old Spanish government, and are as careless as the Arabs of the desert. This the Spaniards well knew, and thought to make a good bargain; but Mr. Andrews, who had got an inkling of the intentions of the pirates, consulted with the steward, and this they had many opportunities of doing, for the Spaniards got drunk almost every day.

On the eighth day after the murder of Captain Smith, the mate and steward put their plan into execution. They were well aware of their disparity in point of numbers; but it was life against life, and they knew that by remaining quiet, death would be their portion the moment that they came so near to the land that the pirates could carry the ship into a harbour, without the aid of navigation. Mr. Andrews got possession of a hatchet, and the steward of a knife; and the two principal leaders were struck dead by Mr. Andrews, and one of the others by the steward, who had a short struggle with him on deck, but succeeded in stabbing him to the heart, though he was himself desperately wounded: the remainder of the Spaniards were all secured by the crew, who had joined their officers, and the vessel was once more in the possession of her original crew. The mate, Mr. Andrews, made immediately for the French coast, where the mutineers were brought to trial before a French tribunal; and after a patient hearing they were all condemned to die. The sentence was soon put in execution, and they were put in chains and hung on gibbets as a warning to others.

Mr. Andrews made his voyage to London, and arrived in security; but the security was a painful one, when the loss of Captain Smith and the others of the crew was considered.

The *Vittoria* was insured at the Royal Exchange Office for £ 6,000, and they made a handsome present to Mr. Andrews, and also to the steward, and all the crew. Mr. Andrews has since been made a captain, and is a very young, but an experienced seaman, who must be a valuable servant to those who employ him. A great part of the ship's cargo belonged to the firm of Thornton and West, and was uninsured, so that they were indebted to the intrepid conduct of Mr. Andrews for the safety of their goods, and rewarded him accordingly.

Captain Smith left a wife and five children, and most of them left families. They had a good round sum of money collected for them, and the sailors who were on board all got respectable employment on board of ships out of the port of London, and were much respected.

This ought to be a lesson to ship-owners not to send their ships to sea with so few hands; and, above all, not to engage foreigners where Englishmen are to be had, as one Englishman is worth three Spaniards or Portuguese, at any time; he is a better sailor, and more willing and able to work. But for the sake of a saving of some few shillings, they run the risk of losing not only their vessels but their lives. No blame could be attached to Captain Smith, who acted up to his given instructions, and contrary to his own opinions; for he complained to his mate, Mr. Andrews, previous to their leaving Manilla, that he was so restricted by the owners to the sum he was to give for wages, that he could not get Englishmen to enter at so low a rate, and must take Spaniards. The event was lamentable, and cost him his life; and for the saving of a few pounds, the owners were near to losing the whole of their valuable property.

THE GHOST

Sailors are still superstitious today, but not anything like as superstitious as were sailors of bygone days. This is an old ghost story, one of the favourites which were spun on the forehatch during the Dogwatches in fine weather.

The carpenter of the ship, old Hawkington, fell sick one day, and, after a short illness died. He was a man very much respected on board, and every one was sorry for him. As the ship was ordered into port, where we expected to arrive in a few days, the captain allowed him to be kept, so that he might be buried on shore; and a sentry was placed, as usual, over the cabin-door in the cockpit. The old gentleman had been dead three or four days, I do not rightly remember which; but, as contrary winds had kept us out longer than we expected, it was decided that he should be committed to the deep on the following day. It so happened that I was sentry over the dead body, the night before it was to have been buried.

My lantern was hanging to a beam, through the discoloured horn of which, a purser's dip was throwing a very poor light, and I stopped to endeavour to improve it by snuffing, or lighting a new candle as might be necessary. — While I was thus employed, not having finished my job, the door of the dead man's cabin was thrown back with a loud bang, which could only have been effected by a very powerful hand, and I distinctly heard a gruff, hollow voice, roar out, 'Give us a light, sentry!' The horrid voice and noise so startled me, that I clutched hold of the lantern — when the nail on which it was hung gave way — the lantern fell from my grasp, the light was extinguished, and with two long strides and a spring I reached the upper step of the cockpit ladder.

At length the noises, and some rather heavy footsteps approached the foot of the ladder whereon I had been standing for some considerable time, without moving hand or foot. It now appeared to me only prudent to move on, and I accordingly walked a little forward on the lower deck. I had sufficient courage to look behind me, and I distinctly saw — it's quite true, I assure you — I distinctly saw, as plain as I see you now — the tall, gaunt figure of the carpenter, (he was near seven feet high, I'm sure), rising slowly up out of the cockpit, and then he walked forward after me. So I walked faster, and so did Mr. Hawkington's ghost; I went up the fore ladder, and the ghost followed me: so I walked aft, and it seemed I doubled upon the apparition for I saw it go up the ladder on to the forecastle.

The weather was warm, and the watch on deck were lying about the forecastle, and gangways, some asleep, and some looking at the moon, that was shining as bright as could be. The ghost appeared to take no notice of any of them, but took the walk the old gentleman, Mr. Hawkington, was accustomed to take when alive, and still kept his hands behind him, and his chin upon his breast, like as if he was in deep thought. So presently one of the men makes him out, and he roused his nearest watchmate, and pointed out the ghost to him, saying, 'I say, Tom, I'm blest if there ain't the old carpenter! Here he comes — I shall be off,' and he got up and walked aft. The whisper went the rounds rapidly, and in a few minutes the forecastle was as clear as if it had been raining. 'What do you all want here?' said the officer of the watch to the men, as they crowded aft to the quarterdeck. No one seemed inclined to answer this question at first; but on the question being repeated, accompanied with an order for them to go forward again, the captain of the forecastle, a sturdy old tar, who used to say 'he would sooner face the devil himself at any time than his ghost,' muttered something about the carpenter's ghost. — 'What! What's that you say?' asked the lieutenant. — 'The carpenter's ghost! the carpenter's ghost!' reiterated half-a-dozen voices at once. — 'What about the carpenter's ghost, you blockheads,' replied the lieutenant; 'be off forward, and don't be stopping up the gangway in this manner.' 'He's walking the forecastle!' exclaimed the men, still keeping their station, notwithstanding the order of the officer of the watch. 'Nonsense, men, nonsense!' said the officer; 'Mr. Hawkington's dead; I am astonished at you,' 'He is walking the forecastle *now*, sir,' again urged one of the half-dozen of voices. 'He has got on the very same hat as I covered for him,' rejoined another. 'And the same old monkey-jacket,' added a third. 'With the end of the chalk-line hanging out of his pocket,' continued a fourth. 'Only go forward and see,' exclaimed a fifth. 'Parcel of fools!' said the lieutenant enraged; 'make a lane there, and let me go forward.' A lane was speedily made, and the lieutenant went on very boldly until he got to the bow of the barge, and there, sure enough, as the men had said, he saw the apparition taking his ease, walking backwards and forwards. The lieutenant's courage then began to fail him—And he did not think it prudent to go any nearer. So he stood still at the bow of the boat, and after a great effort, he managed to call out, M-i-s-t-e-r H-a-w-k-i-n-g-t-o-n, i-s i-s i-s i-s tha-that yo-you?' 'Sir,' replied the apparition, raising his head and he touched his hat, and advanced towards the lieutenant. 'Tha-hat will d-do, M-i-s-t-e-r Hawk-Hawk-Hawking-ton,' ejaculated the perfectly satisfied lieutenant, retreating a few steps as the ghost advanced, as though unwilling to lessen the distance between them; and he walked very briskly aft to the quarter-deck, and went into the captain's cabin, to report the remarkable circumstance to the captain. 'The carpenter is on the forecastle, sir,' said the lieutenant to the captain. The captain, just awakened out of a sound sleep, did not appear to hear what was said. 'Well, sir,' responded the captain, rubbing his eyes, and waiting further particulars. 'Mr. Hawkington, sir, is walking the deck, sir,' said the lieutenant again. 'Oh, is that all, sir?' said the captain, turning himself in his cot, and resuming his slumbers, 'then, sir, let him walk, and be d—d.'

It appears that the old carpenter had been all the time in a trance; the doctor only considered him dead.

He came to his senses in time to prevent being drowned. It seems he was quite unmindful of the time which had passed away, and waking and hearing two bells strike, he thought it was the morning watch, and time for him to turn out, and so he roused out, called for a light as usual, fumbled about and found his clothes, and, giving a curse or two to me for putting out the light, *came on deck as was his custom.*

ST. MAUR'S ACCOUNT

By W. H. G. KINGSTON

In the last book of W. H. G. Kingston's famous series about the same set of characters, St. Maur, after being mourned as lost at sea, rejoins his shipmates and gives this account of his adventures.

"By-the-by, I never told you how I came to be playing Robinson Crusoe and his man Friday on yonder barren rock," observed St. Maur, as he and his uncle paced together the deck of the *Empress*.

"You remember the night I was hooked off the yacht by a stranger which ran us down, and, as I thought, sent you to the bottom. I leave you to judge in what a state of fear and anxiety I was left. From the way the fellows talked when I got on board, I discovered that they were Dutchmen. I rushed aft to the skipper and entreated him to heave to and lower his boats to try and pick up any of you who might be floating, but he either did not understand me or would not. When I ran to the helm, intending to put it down, that he might the better comprehend my meaning, he and his mates held me back. I pitched into one fellow and knocked him over, and was about to treat the other in the same way, when the skipper with his big fist hit me a blow on the head which brought me to the deck.

"When I came to my senses it was broad daylight, and I knew that long before that time, if the yacht had gone down, you must all of you have lost your lives. I believe the Dutchman intended to apologize for having treated me in so unceremonious a fashion, but, as I could not understand a word he said, I am not sure. He behaved, however afterwards, far better than I should have expected from the way our acquaintance had commenced. I was never a very good hand at picking up languages, so that it was some time before I could make myself even imperfectly understood by anyone on board. Strange to say, not a man among them spoke a word of English. I wanted the skipper to put into some port, but he replied that, 'Out of his course he would not go for me or any man.' I then begged him, chiefly by

211

signs, that should we fall in with a homeward-bound ship, to put me on board of her. He nodded his head and let me understand that, providing it was during calm weather, he should have no objection, and advised me meanwhile to console myself with his schiedam, of which he had a plentiful supply. Both he and his mates indulged in it pretty largely, I found. I expected that he would touch at the Cape, but to my disgust he ran to the south'ard, in order to fall in with the westerly trades, and I found that he intended to touch nowhere until he reached Batavia.

"This was anything but consolatory, besides which I had no one to talk to, and not a book on board I could read. I tried hard to make out the few Dutch books he had on board, and used to ask him or the mates, or indeed any of the men I found at hand, to pronounce the words, when I tried to discover their meaning. I believe, had the voyage lasted longer, I should have learned to speak and read Dutch fluently; but, as the skipper was drunk half his time, and the mates the other two quarters, I could not get much out of them. The only fellow who really was of use was young Rip Van Winkle. He took a liking to me, as I did to him, from the first, and I often saved him from many a cuff and kick which he was wont to receive from the crew. He was, I confess, a sort of 'dirty Dick' on board, and so he would have continued had I not taught him to clean himself; and now he is as fond of washing as any one, except when the weather is cold, when he rather objects to it, and falls back into his bad habits. My only companion besides Rip was a large dog — no great beauty — whom I called Snarleyow, from being unable to pronounce his Dutch name, and he took to it, as he did to me, immediately, and always came when so called. I treated him as a friend, whereas, from the skipper downwards, he was accustomed to receive more kicks than ha'pence, except from poor Rip, and consequently had no great affection for his masters.

"Besides my anxiety about you, and my disappointment at not being able to take advantage of the new position into which, through Counsellor McMahon, I was placed — not that that weighed very much with me — I could not help feeling anxious about the way in which the ship was navigated. Being unable to understand the Dutch books, I could not myself work out the reckonings, though frequently I took an observation, to keep my hand in.

"I once only had a chance of communicating with England. We sighted a British ship, and as by that time I had picked up enough Dutch to use the signal-book, I hoisted the signal 'British officer on board; heave to for him.' I thought when the skipper saw the other ship heave to that he would do the same, but it was blowing hard, and he obstinately refused to lift tack or sheet or lower a boat, and you can just fancy how I felt when I saw the homeward-bound vessel standing away from us. From the temperature of the weather I now suspected that we had got a very long way to the south, when it came on to blow hard. The Dutchman shortened sail, as he generally did when there was any wind, and continued the course on which he was steering. The old ship, though a tub, was a good sea boat, and I had no reason to fear danger, provided she did not run her stem into an iceberg or strike any rocks or reefs. Blow high, blow low, the skipper walked the deck with his hands in his pockets and a huge meerschaum is his mouth, looking as composed as usual.

"One night I was about turning in, when I felt the ship strike. Of course I sprang on deck, where I was followed by the skipper and the first mate, the second mate having the watch. The crew were singing out that we were lost.

" 'Do not be afraid, boys!' cried the skipper, calling for a light for his pipe, and thrusting his hands into his pockets. 'She'll drive over it. Another hand to the helm. Keep all standing!'

"I knew, by the thickness of his voice, that he was half seas over, for he never exhibited his state in any other way, except when he sank down under the table. Still, I hoped from his composure that he knew where we were, and that we should scrape clear of the sandbank over which the sea was breaking with fearful force. Several seas, indeed, nearly pooped us; but we surged forward, touching occasionally in a way which threatened to split the ship into fragments; but she held together wonderfully. The men, however, had not the same hope that I had; for I saw them gathering on either side, near the boats, taking the falls in their hands, ready to lower them with or without orders.

"Rip came up to me. 'What's going to happen, mynheer?' he asked.

" 'The ship will probably go to the bottom or get knocked to pieces; but we may perhaps escape the danger, and so at last reach Batavia,' I answered. 'Whatever happens, stick by me, Rip, and you can lend me a hand whenever I want it, and I may perhaps save you.'

"Scarcely, however, had I spoken than the ship struck with far greater force than before, the fore and main masts going by the board, but falling clear of the deck. Still she went on; but the carpenter sounded the well, and found that the water was rushing in at a rate which precluded all possibility of keeping the ship afloat. She had gone over the edge of the reef, which rose on the starboard bow, high above the water, and broke the force of the sea. Springing aft, I put down the helm, which the man had deserted, and she rounded to under the lee of the rocks.

"The crew instantly began lowering the boats. The skipper and his first mate tumbled into one, and they with several of the men shoved off; while the second mate took possession of the other, with the rest of the crew, leaving Rip and me still on deck. So overcrowded were they, that I saw they were both likely to go down; and I determined to take my chance in the ship, which I thought, having a light cargo on board, might possibly float long enough to enable us to build a raft. The two boats quickly disappeared in the darkness, without provisions or water, which the men in their hurry forgot to take, while the skipper and his first mate were too drunk to think of it. I bethought me of examining the boat amidships, which I feared might have been crushed by the falling mast; but fortunately it had escaped. I told Rip to cut the lashings clear, reminding him that our lives depended on it — to see that not a rope remained attached to the vessel's deck. I jumped in, followed by Rip and Snarley, who had been left on board with us, and whose instinct showed him that the boat was likely to prove the only ark of safety. The oars, as well as the masts and sails, were stowed in her, with a couple of hen-coops, our last surviving pig, and a variety of other articles. Rip was about to heave the pig overboard, when I stopped him, and told him to hunt about for the plug-hole, which he had just time to stop with a bung, when I saw the water rushing over the deck. The ship did not go down immediately; and I suspect that, had all hands remained on board, we might have kept her afloat until daylight, at all events.

"We got out the oars to shove the boat clear the instant the water rushed over the deck. I do not think I ever experienced a more anxious moment in my life. At last a sea came sweeping along, round the reef, and lifted us clear, right above the bulwarks, and free of the masts and spars still hanging over the side. We pulled away for our lives, and just saw the masts dragged down as the ship went to the bottom. The mizzenmast remained the last above water. We pulled under the lee of the reef; but, having no anchor, we were compelled to hold her in her position by paddling all night. When morning broke, no land was in sight; but as the wind was from the westward, I judged that our safest plan was to steer to the northward, when we might either fall in with some ship, or make Java, or the western coast of Australia, should we not sight any island on the way. We had a small cask of water in the boat, and three empty casks, put there to be out of the way. My hope was that we should be able to fill these with rain water before we got into a more northern latitude, where we were likely to meet with a ship. The reef off which we lay ran half a mile from north to south above the water; how much further below it I could only judge by the line of white foam which extended as far as the eye could reach. As this was a place no ship was likely to approach, the sooner we got out of its latitude the better. The wind having moderated, we accordingly made sail and stood to the eastward.

"We had been three days in the boat, our small cask of water gradually diminishing, while not a drop of rain had fallen to fill our casks, when we sighted this small island. Hoping that it might afford us some shelter, and at all events that we might obtain water, we steered towards it. As we approached we saw the harbour opening out before us. Though I thought that there would be some risk in crossing the bar, yet I determined to make the attempt. Anything was better than dying of thirst. The water appearing to be smoother in the centre, I stood under all sail the boat could carry towards it, for it was still blowing fresh. The bar was reached; and I expected the next instant to be in smooth water, when an abominable roller came tumbling in, swamped our boat, and turned her over, washing Rip away. I clambered up on the bottom, when I saw Snarley, who had just come to the surface. The dog, having looked about him, made towards a point inside the harbour, and, exerting his strength, hauled Rip up. I, meantime, was tossing about on the bar, expecting every moment to be washed off, when I saw Snarley returning. Knowing that I should have his help, I sprang off and swam towards him. I twisted the fingers of my left hand in his long, shaggy hair, and he towed me through the surf safely to the shore, where I found Rip already recovered waiting for me. He threw his arms around my neck and burst into tears, exclaiming in Dutch — 'I thought you had gone, mynheer, and that I was left alone; but now you are come we shall manage to live.' "

THE COMING OF THE ENGLISH

By DOUGLAS V. DUFF

The English come from the flat lands east of the mouth of the River Rhine and gain a first and strong foothold in the land which is to become England.

Painted North Sea grey-green from the truck of her single mast to her keel, to make her as invisible as possible, the long, lightly-built, lean-lined scouting-ship lay stopped and silent in the fog. Her crew, in their coats of sea-green canvas, crouched silently over the twenty long oars; motionless on the thwarts, listening with every nerve astrain to the babel of voices from the sea-robbers hidden in the swirling wraiths of the first greyness of early dawn.

The glass-smooth sea scarcely moved the *Picta,* the advance picket of the Count of the Saxon Shore, as she lay in the midst of the pirate English fleet of open boats, west-bound from the flat lands east of the Rhine-mouth. If they suspected that the Scout was among them, death would swiftly swamp the British seamen manning her. They must remain unobserved if they were to win clear and race home to report the enemy at sea and in strength. Marcus Ambrosius, a Celt for all his Roman name, snarled at the starboard stroke-oarsman whose scabbard-tip clattered alarmingly against the thwart as he turned to listen.

Not a movement, not a sound in the open *Picta,* one of a class named after the Pictish curraghs they resembled. Outboard, all around them, unseen but clear to the ear were the many sounds of a fleet. Brutal laughter, shouted witticisms, clink and clatter of food-vessels and drinking horns being passed as the English rested after a weary night of rowing their heavy, cranky craft. An occasional barked order or a savage curse. Close by, on the port quarter, a man began a swinging song.

Marcus Ambrosius was listening eagerly, trying to estimate the size of the fleet for his report. He must move soon, the fog was growing lighter — sun-up could not be more than half an hour away. With it would come the dawn-wind to blow away the sea-mist that alone was keeping them safe. Before the fog lifted he must work his *Picta* clear of the English fringes.

The long ship quivered, vibrated under the shock of its crew, stiffening convulsively as they heard the one sound they least expected. A woman's voice joined the singer — carrying the burden of the song. Another, then another took it up — in a minute, high, clear female voices rang through the mist from a dozen directions before the deep tones of the men blended with them.

Half-stunned and completely amazed the British crew sat very still. The song ended. Laughter, some cheering followed, then more clinking of pans and dishes. The wail of a child, the crying of a small baby sounded a few yards away to starboard from among the white tendrils already stirring with the first movement of the dawn wind.

"Christ have mercy on Britain," Marcus Ambrosius whispered. Neither he nor his men were religious but every rower along the thwarts murmured *"Amen"*.

With infinite care to make no splashing swirl whose gurgle could betray them, skilfully avoiding trickles from their oarblades, the British paddled gently forward. Marcus Ambrosius at the steering-sweep conning her, straining for sight or sound of any English boat ahead or too near. Like a ghost the green ship stole invisible and unheard through her enemies. She stopped several times when English voices came close, but always resumed her passage to the west when the way cleared.

After ten minutes the shouting, singing and other noises receded and they hoped they were clear. At that moment the white curtains started to shake; in a minute there was twenty feet of clear air between the fog and the surface. Plain in their sight, more than a hundred square, ungainly, flat-bottomed, broad-beamed boats from the shallows of the Frisian shore, covered a square-mile. From each and every one rose shouts of rage as they saw the *Picta*. War-horns blew from the largest vessel; the oars of the two lying just abaft the British scout's beam bit deeply into the water, now ruffled and dark-blue with catspaws of freshening sunrise wind.

With all concealment whipped away the British drove in their oars, making their slender ship leap like a greyhound away from the nearest pirate charging-in broad on the starboard bow. They surged across her bows, a growing white wake spreading V-shape from the slicing stem and bubbling astern.

"Bowmen make sail!" barked Marcus Ambrosius, holding the *Picta* steadily away from the bull-like rush of the English ship. The shorter bow-oars rattled along the thwarts, stowed close to the rowers leaping at their work, fighting for every inch. Fifty to sixty men showed in each of the pirates, all striving to get more speed into their wallowing, ungainly vessels. Among the horned helmets and the rough sea-cloaks of the warriors in the nearer boat, a hundred yards on their quarter, the British saw the long, flaxen plaits of women. Women who were doublebanking their men at the oars in their eagerness to head off the Scout before it could escape to give warning of their approach.

Tiny splashes jetted from the water between. Arrows falling short, the nearest a good twenty feet from the gunwale. The green sail on the tapering yard of the same colour rustled and threshed as it soared aloft with the bowmen's heaving on the halyards. For more than a minute it was touch-and-go whether the *Picta* would dodge that nearer boat. If the wind had not filled the sail as the sheets and braces were hauled aft in the latest possible second, they could not have won clear. When it did the Scout danced ahead, running six yards for every one the English could make under oars alone.

All through the forenoon the north-easterly wind freshened. By noon it was blowing strong. At two o'clock it was close to half a gale and still strengthening. With all oars inboard, her men sitting up to windward to steady her, the *Picta* ran in towards the line of beetling cliffs crowned by wide moorlands, with the north-easter howling broad on her port quarter and white horses piling high astern.

219

On the crest of the tallest cliff was the fortified coastguard station, built fifty years earlier from materials carried from the ruins of a Legionary fortress erected in Rome's first conquest, 500 years before. The men on its seaward wall were studying the *Picta* as she ran past towards the mouth of the estuary three miles south.

"She is Marcus Ambrosius's ship," the grey-bearded veteran in the middle grunted. "Can you make out the signal flag at her port yardarm?"

"Red flag with a white diagonal stripe," a young man called back.

"Signifying she has sighted a fleet of English of more than ten, and less than one hundred and fifty, craft," broke in a weazened little man behind them. "God and His Saints have mercy on us! There will be bloody work along our shores to-morrow. What is that other flag rising to the masthead?"

"The black-and-white swallow-tailed *Urgency* flag which I have seen only once before in all my years of shore-watching," the veteran shouted. "Marcus Ambrosius is not the man to panic. He must have seen something worse than a pirate raiding squadron to fly that flag."

"No sign of the English to seaward," shouted the look-out on the battlements of the turret thirty feet above them. "Looks as if there is going to be plenty more wind."

"Let us pray for a storm," the officer said quietly, before he turned briskly on his coastguardsmen. "Light the three beacons to give the urgent warning," he snapped. "Marcus Ambrosius knows what he is doing."

Men grabbed resin-wood torches, ground them into the guardroom brazier until they spurted flame and smoke. They ran to the eastern tower and fired the three heaps of lard-soaked driftwood piled there, placed as far apart as the fighting-platform permitted. Black with smoking grease, the triple-signal streamed to leeward 'n the rising gale.

"All stations acknowledging," the look-out on the turret reported. Smoke rose on the ridge of the moorland miles away; it swirled from the bold headland jutting into the breakers northwards. The tip of the twin moles shielding the harbour in the estuary threw up its own pillar. They saw the green sail of the *Picta* gliding above the stonework of the nearer jetty, her hull hidden as she ran down the narrow gut into the basin. Four heavy ships, single-masted but with tall, steeply raked bowsprits which were almost a second one, chafed and fretted against the weed-grown, weather-beaten masonry. Between them and the crumbling water-stairs lay three triremes which had been new fifty years before.

The long seas surging through the gate between the moleheads fought the ebbing tide to raise a pother inside the haven. The rising wind piped shrilly through the rigging and spars of the heavy ships and keened along the open oar-decks of the triple-banked triremes. As the *Picta* secured to the stone bollards of the inner wharf the cracked bell on the roof of the Basilica of SS. Peter and Paul, which, once, had been a Temple of Aphrodite, clanged the general alarm.

Into the half-ruined streets men, women and children came running from the remains of palaces, shops, baths and the houses where Roman colonial officials had lived. Inside, their beautiful tessellated pavements, floors of pictured mosaic, lay beneath the ashes of cooking-fires and the grime of generations of slatternly housekeeping. Garbage and the sour reek of human excrement hung heavy in the corners untouched by the fresh winds off the sea. Sculptured capitals, shattered columns and broken statuary cluttered the mud-coated, cobbled and flagstoned streets ringing beneath the running feet of the mob making for the harbour.

The seamen of the warships issued from their frowsy dens; their unkempt wives and filthy, ragged brats carrying their food and sea-gear behind them. A crowd streamed from the six wineshops in the broken Forum. Old Mother Blodwyn, surrounded by her draggle-tailed handmaidens, yelled curses at eight West Countrymen who had dashed from the straw in the Praetors' Hall, glad of the excuse to avoid paying the hire of sleeping companions she had provided for them.

Down the middle of the principal street tramped ten men clad in the *loricas*, the discarded armour of the Legions, helmeted and shielded with the equipment inherited from the auxiliary cohorts in which their grandfathers had served; their swords ready to deal with any outbreak among the 300 oar-slaves they were driving to the triremes from the prison. A gang of older men, carrying the bundled rods and axe of Lictors, sought deserters, laggards, slug-a-beds and drunkards who had not obeyed the order to muster aboard their ships.

Round the long table in the atrium of the semi-derelict Governor's palace, a dozen officers huddled in a council of war. At its head sat a grey-bearded, weather-beaten man swathed in the toga of a Roman senator. Facing him was Marcus Ambrosius, still in his sea-green canvas, his drooping moustaches caked with salt. The officer in the toga, Deputy of the Count of the Saxon Shore, looked straight into the face of the *Picta*'s skipper.

"I believe you were too scared to know just what you did see and hear, Marcus Ambrosius," he sneered. "You and your crew were far too frightened to keep clear minds. Why should the English have their women and children with them? They have never done so in the past. All they desire is a quick and profitable raid before withdrawing to their ships and sailing home, before we can organize sufficient force to bring them to battle. What women are with them, if indeed there were any, may be naught but brazen-faced harlots carried for sport."

"With respect, lord Admiral," the old skipper replied. "No man carries his children and his tiny babies in the same ship with his lights-of-love. Nor do women of that kind encumber themselves with brats."

The Count's Deputy frowned. The skipper had made a point.

"Maybe the barbarians are fleeing from invaders even more barbarous than themselves," the captain of the flagship of the triremes, the *St. Alban,* suggested after the silence persisted many seconds. "They may intend to found new homes in our Britain, holding us to be the weaker of their two foes."

A younger, green-eyed, red-haired giant of a man sprang to his feet, his massive fist pounding the table.

"What nonsense is this?" he demanded, his eyes flashing. "Even if this captain of a little Scout-ship was right, which I much doubt, in saying the English have their families with them, what difference need that make? Let us do as we have so often done before — wait until the raiders have gathered all the loot they have seized ashore and strike at them when they start back for home. Let them be our revenue-collectors as they have been in the past — those dogs who live to the north have paid nothing for the fleet for more than two years. We can collect from their heirs — the men who have slain them — with the advantage that there will be no claims on what we take from the pirates."

"What if they are the coming of a nation meaning to remain in Britain?" the Deputy asked.

"Then that will also be good," the red-headed giant replied. "They will have furniture, stores, equipment with them. They will need to raid the countryside to win a footing. Let them do so and accumulate plunder so that we shall find it ready for us when we appear with the fleet. That way lies profit and the better chance to exterminate them."

"Julius Mercatus speaks sense," said the captain of one of the heavy ships. "In any event we will face mutiny if we try to take our crews to sea in this," and he paused. In the silence they heard the shrill piping of the north-easter through the gaps in the broken walls of the palace. "If our seamen believed they were to get rich plunder they might go, but you will not make them stir with nothing better to offer than a battle against empty-handed English dogs in a heavy sea and a rising gale."

From the summit of a great cube of basaltic rock many miles northwards, its feet washed by the breaking surf on beaches and black reefs white with breakers, a couple of hundred British coast-dwellers watched the English boats drive in. They had mustered when the beacons blazed the evening before. With the dawn they saw the clumsy craft, rising high on the crests of big seas, or swallowed for a moment in the water-valleys, heading for the beaches below.

"No sign of our fleet," a man on the upper rock of the headland called. "The Count of the Saxon Shore is not in sight."

"Nor will there be," growled the chief, in his Roman officer's battered harness. "They will not bother themselves until the pirates have garnered their harvest and slain us. Let us stand and fight so that our families will gain a better start towards the moors. God and the Blessed Virgin aiding us, most of the English dogs will be drowned in the surf and the backwash of the breaking seas. Down to the shore, men, where we can cut down those who stagger in, half-drowned."

In the leading ship, upright in the bows, holding the tall carved-stem post shaped into the figure of a raven, Ethelfrith the Terrible, the dreaded chieftain (whom the Venerable Bede, two centuries later, was to call "The Ravenous Wolf"), stood swaying lithely to the rolling plunge of the vessel. He had been on this coast years before when Ida, King of the Angles, wintered on the crest of this 150-foot-high cube of rock. With one hand he signalled the steersman, conning the ship in.

Seas creamed high over the carved stern. Right aft women and children were huddled in their cloaks, grasping their bundles of treasured possessions, waiting for the moment of touchdown. Amidships, men not wanted to steady her with their oars to keep her running straight in front of the breaking surf, crouched with swords and axes ready, cloaks discarded, feet bare, their helmets horn-sided or tipped with raven-wings dull with sea-rime.

Ethelfrith watched the British running down the steep paths on the cliff-face, forming battle lines on the wet sand above the uppermost mark of the sea-wrack. Astern, the other ships of his fleet, squattering, rolling gunwales-under, sterns lifting, bows dipping, followed where he was leading.

A greater wave than most piled high, lifted the stern as the stem grated on the sand and shingle. For a second it seemed the ship was to be thrown end-over. Then she dropped, swinging broadside on, the rest of the wave spilling over her side, filling her, rolling her on her beam-ends up the beach. Ethelfrith was out, sword bare in his hand, with fifty roaring English fighters behind him. The British met them, breast to breast, spear-point against axe-head and the broad-bladed *saxe*, the dagger-sword, that was the English weapon just as the *kukri is* the modern Gurkha's darling.

Along 200 yards of spouting shore the English craft poured in. Boats overturning, smashing open, breaking their backs in the mighty surf driven by the north-easterly gale.

Soaked, spitting sea-water and fighting-curses, the English poured up the sand, backwash creaming round their knees as they rushed forward to help Ethelfrith and those already at hand-strokes with the British. Women and children staggered on to the sand, helping each other, grasping precious possessions, their long braids limp on their shoulders, clothing saturated with the bitter wind biting through it, the roar of battle a few yards away.

Suddenly, abruptly it was all over. The British broke as the English numbers swelled. The few Celts who got away before they were cut down, raced across the beach or took to the cliff paths like goats. After them raced the fleetest and youngest English, eager to prevent them making any stand on the crest. The women ran forward to plunder the dead, and to secure their fine Roman weapons and armour for their own menfolk.

Ethelfrith left sufficient warriors to protect the women while they gathered all they could save from the flotsam of their fleet. Seamen dragged the few boats left whole above the mark of the ebbing tide. Children and all, they worked to drag smashed planking, beams and scattered goods to safety.

An hour later, led by the Lady Bebba, wife of the Lord Ethelfrith, they were on the crest of the great rock-cube, toiling with axes, mattocks and spades to pile defences around the lip of the cliffs and to strengthen the vulnerable landward approach. By the evening of the second day they had ramparts of stone boulders picked from the cliff-tops, laid in earth-bondings and rivetted with wooden palisades.

8

Five days later the British fleet came confidently cruising towards the shattered wrecks on the strand. When they saw the strength of the new fortifications and the number of the garrison, however, they decided to stay in safety and turned south. Six weeks afterwards the British mustered in their thousands to drive the pirates from their fortress on the rock-top but were smashed during twenty days of siege.

As autumn grew chillier, the barns and the huts the English had made from the timbers of their ships and the stone they forced their British slaves to trim, were stocked with the plunder of the hinterland. The heavy ploughs brought from Germany made ready to break the good soil of the valleys and the seed salved from the ships prepared for sowing later. Flocks and herds of cattle, sheep, pigs and horses thronged in the byres and stables, every beast taken from the British.

Osric, High Priest of Woden, stood at the altar-stone, on which four pale-faced British victims had just been offered to ensure a good winter and a fine ploughing. Long white beard streaming in the gentle breeze of the pleasant late September morning, he led the prayers to Woden, to Thor, to Freya and to all the gods of the North, asking them to inspire the Lord Ethelfrith to name this fortress they had made impregnable.

In his long robes of peace, though Brainbiter his broadbladed sword was belted to his waist, the fierce-faced chieftain rose. Silence fell, deep and complete. No man nor woman dared speak when Ethelfrith the Terrible was on his feet.

He bowed to the lady sitting on the stool beside him, their small son standing wide-eyed, watching what was being done. Ethelfrith took her hand, raising her until she stood slim, golden-haired, fresh-faced, blue-eyed beside him.

"Here we have our home," he cried in his rough, hoarse voice. "Home is where our women and our children may lie safely sheltered to give comfort and ease to men when they return from war and toil in the fields. What better name can I give our home than that of its Lady, Bebba, my wife and the mother of our son, Oswald?

"Let this rock-town for ever be known as *Bebbanburgh*."

"Bebbanburgh," the English yelled, delighted.

Bamborough, with the mighty walls of a later fortress, remains the name of this place where the English first won a toehold in England.

MUTINY AND RETRIBUTION

By JOHN KNOX LAUGHTON

At the end of the eighteenth century and in the first years of the nineteenth century, there were many terrible mutinies in the British fleet. One of the most famous was that in the 32-gun frigate, H.M.S. "Hermione".

Of all the recaptures of lost ships, the one that is most celebrated is that of the 32-gun frigate *Hermione* — celebrated not only for the brilliance of the recapture, but almost equally for the appalling tragedy of her previous loss. It was in September 1797, the year of the great mutinies at Spithead and the Nore, and of numerous smaller mutinies in different parts of the world. It was as if a wave of mutiny swept over the ocean, affecting ships off Cadiz, at the Cape of Good Hope, and in the West Indies. With this infection about, even trifles might cause it to break out in violence; and on board the *Hermione* there were causes which were very far from trifles.

The captain of the *Hermione* — his name was Pigot — was a young man who had been promoted by family interest to the command of a frigate and a ship's company before he had learned to command himself. It may be that his natural disposition prevented his learning, for he was not so young as many who did very well. Swelling with a sense of his importance he conceived that everything must go exactly as he wished it, and his one way of enforcing this idea was brutal punishment for every departure from it.

It was afterwards said that the ship had in her crew a great many Irish — then notoriously disaffected; and a great many foreigners, who would naturally feel even more indignant at the severity with which they were treated. It is impossible to say how far these statements were true. They were never substantiated; and the list of the crew does not show any unusual number of Irish or foreign names. Some, of course, there always were. I believe it was merely a story got up afterwards, to lessen the shame of the terrible business.

228

There had certainly been much dissatisfaction and discontent for some time; but they were brought to a head by a new and disgusting exhibition of brutality. On the evening of the 21st September, when the Hermione was cruising off Puerto Rico, the men were exercising aloft; and the captain, furious at their not being as quick as he thought they might have been, roared out that he would flog the last man down.

No one had any doubt that he would keep his word; and in trying to avoid the promised flogging, two young men, particularly smart sailors, missed their hold, fell to the deck and were killed. "Throw the lubbers overboard," was what the captain said, and he went into his cabin.

The men took twenty-four hours or rather more to consider this, and on the night of the 22nd September they knocked down the officer of the watch and threw him overboard; killed the captain in his cabin and threw him out through the stern port; butchered every officer except the master, the gunner, and one mate, and took the ship to La Guayra, where they handed her over to the Spanish governor.

Morally, it is difficult to condemn the killing of Captain Pigot. His whole conduct for months past had been brutal and tyrannical. He had beyond question caused the death of the two seamen on the evening of the 21st, and if the vengeance of the men had wreaked itself on him alone, morality, at any rate, would have had nothing to object to. But when they took to butchering all the officers, who were equally with themselves the victims of their captain's tyranny, they could only be held to be dangerous madmen, to be hunted down by all honest people.

And this was really done. In one way or another a very large number of the murderers were caught, tried, and hanged. It was said that many more men were hanged than were on board the ship at the time; that in fact, the rage against the criminals was so great that any man or woman having a grudge against any one could bring false witness against him, could swear that he was one of the *Her-*

mione's crew and have him promptly put out of the way for ever.

These stories have long since died out, but even forty years ago they were still told and believed at Portsmouth and Plymouth. I doubt, however, if there was any real truth in them; and though there is no reason to suppose that justice erred on the side of mercy, I do not think that any man was hanged without reasonable evidence that he had been not only on board the *Hermione,* but actually a party to the murders.

The *Hermione* remained a Spanish frigate for a few weeks more than two years. In September 1799, Sir Hyde Parker, the comman-der-in-chief at Jamaica, had news that she was at Puerto Cabello, and was on the point of sailing for Havana. He accordingly sent Cap-tain Edward Hamilton in the 28-gun frigate *Surprise* to look out for her at Point Gallinas, which she would have to pass.

Hamilton waited there for a month, and then, as his provisions were running short, and he was not absolutely certain that the *Her-mione* might not have passed in the night, by keeping well out to sea, or that she had not sailed in some other direction, he resolved to go off Puerto Cabello and see if she was still there.

On the 21ste October the *Surprise* came off Puerto Cabello, and there saw the *Hermione* lying ready for sea, but moored, head and stern, between two batteries which commanded the mouth of the harbour, and were said to mount nearly two hundred guns.

The position appeared impregnable, and for three days Hamilton cruised to and fro before the port, possibly hoping that the *Hermione* might come out and try to capture him; for she was a much larger frigate than the *Surprise,* had been armed by the Spaniards with forty-four guns, and had on board close on four hundred men. So far as the material force went, she was more than double the strength of the *Surprise.* As, however, the Spaniards were not willing to try the wager of battle, Hamilton gradually made up his mind to attempt cutting her out; and after quarters, on the evening of the 24th, he ordered the men to come aft and spoke to them. He reminded them of the way the frigate had been lost, of the disgrace to the British navy as long as she remained in the hands of the Spaniards, of the time he had been waiting for her, and of his hopes to have met her at sea. He concluded in some such words as these:— "It is useless to wait any longer. We shall soon be obliged to leave the station, and that frigate will become the prize of some more fortunate ship. Our only prospect of success is by cutting her out this night."

A tremendous cheering here interrupted him, and showed him that the men were eager to be led in. He continued:— "I will lead you myself. I have here written out the orders for the boats, with the names of the officers and men for each."

During the next few hours all the preparations were made. To each boat was prescribed, in exact detail, where she was to go and what she was to do. There were six boats in all; they were to board on the bow, the gangway, or the quarter, on the starboard side, or on the larboard side, as ordered. Some men were told off to fight, others to cut the cables, others to run aloft and loose the sails, others to remain in the boats, to make fast to the ship and take her in tow. Every man was dressed in blue; no white was to be seen. The password was, "Britannia", the answer, "Ireland". The rendezvous was given, "the *Hermione*'s quarterdeck". It was near midnight before everything was ready and the boats shoved off, Hamilton in the pinnace leading.

He had, of course, hoped to take the enemy by surprise; but about a mile from the mouth of the harbour they were met by two Spanish gunboats, which at once opened fire on them. The men in the pinnace gave three cheers and pushed on for the *Hermione*, but some of the other boats, and especially the launch — the biggest of all — stopped to return the enemy's fire, an act of disobedience which nearly cost the expedition dear.

As it was, the Spaniards on board the *Hermione* were awake and at their quarters, blazing away at some black shadows or imaginary enemy; but they could not or did not see the boats advancing from right ahead; and when Hamilton in the pinnace boarded her on the starboard bow — Hamilton himself being one of the first on board

— most of the crew were at their guns on the main deck. They were actually ignorant that the English were on board; and the boats coming up one after the other, reinforced the leading parties, and drove the Spaniards on deck into the cabin, where they were presently forced to surrender, or down below, where they were comparatively harmless.

The cables were cut; the boats took the ship in tow; the sails were let fall, and as they swelled to the breeze, the batteries, which now realised that something untoward had happened, opened fire on the ship as she was gathering way and leaving the harbour behind. Some of the shots struck her and probably killed several of their own men, but do not seem to have done any harm to the English. And in less than two hours from the time the pinnace boarded her, the *Hermione* was clear of the harbour, out of range of the batteries, and safe in English hands.

It was a very curious fight. One hundred men, exposed in boats or on the open deck, attacked four hundred under cover and prepared, and overcame them, after inflicting tremendous loss on the defenders, whilst they themselves suffered very little.

The total English loss was twelve wounded, including Hamilton, whose injuries were very serious. He had had the butt end of a musket broken over his head; he had a severe sword-cut on one thigh, a wound from a pike-thrust in the other thigh; his shin bruised, though not broken, by a grape shot; his hand badly cut, and, what seems to have been worst of all, his back and loins hurt by a severe fall into the boat as he was boarding. He lived to a ripe old age, but never quite recovered from the injuries to his head and back. The king conferred knighthood on him by letters patent; he received the freedom of the city of London, delivered to him in person at a public dinner on the first anniversary of the fight, 25th October 1800; and many years afterwards he was made a baronet.

Whilst the loss of the English was so small, that of the Spaniards was exceedingly large. It amounted to 119 killed and ninety-seven dangerously wounded — some of whom, it is difficult to say how many, must be attributed to the ill-judged fire of their own batteries. Not to be bothered with the prisoners, who, even after this tremendous slaughter, were still fully equal in number to the crew of the *Surprise,* they were put on board a captured coasting vessel, and sent back to Puerto Cabello. But the ship was taken to Jamaica, where she was restored to the navy under the name of *Retribution.*

CAPSIZE

By W. H. G. KINGSTON

The brig had been a long time at sea and the young heroes of Kingston's series of stories were more than a little anxious when, suddenly, disaster overtook them. This episode is from "Three Admirals".

The brig was at this time under all sail, but the wind was light, and she was making little way. Suddenly her sails gave a loud flap against the mast.

"We are going to have another calm, I fear," said Desmond.

"I'm not quite so sure of that," said Casey. "I've been watching the sky, and it seems to me as if a thick gloom was spreading over it. I've observed a dark bank rising rapidly to the southward and eastward. Look, sir, you cannot see a star in that quarter. If I was the mate, I'd shorten sail at once."

Tom and Desmond took a survey of the horizon in the quarter to which Casey was pointing. The bank was rising rapidly; it looked, indeed, as if a dark curtain was being drawn over the sky.

"I'll point it out to the mate," said Tom.

On going aft, Tom found the mate seated close to the taffrail. Instead of keeping a look-out, he was fast asleep. Tom roused him up, and pointed out the appearance of the sky.

"I don't think it's anything," he observed, rubbing his eyes.

"It is, though," cried Tom. "Listen to that roar."

At that moment a dull rushing sound was heard, and a long streak of white was seen extending from east to south-west across the ocean.

"Turn the hands up! Shorten sail!" cried Tom.

The mate repeated the order. The midshipmen sprang to the main-topsail halyards, Casey and Peter to the fore-topsail; but almost before a rope could be let go, a fierce blast struck the brig. In vain the mate tried to put the helm up. Over she heeled more and more, until the yardarms touched the water. Tom and Desmond seized hold of

Billy, who had just before dropped off to sleep, and scrambled up to the weather bulwarks. Casey and Peter had been doing the same. Another instant and the brig was on her beam ends, with the water rising up to the combings of the hatchway.

Believing that the brig was going over, the midshipmen and their companions got on to the outside of the bulwarks, holding on to the main-chains. As the lee side of the sails was already under water, there was no probability that the brig would rise again. Every moment, indeed, it seemed as if she must go down. Their position was truly a fearful one.

The mate and the man at the helm had apparently slipped off into the water, as they were nowhere visible. Of the two men forward, one only succeeded in gaining the bulwarks, the other had probably shared the fate of the mate. The condition of those below was terrible. Unable to gain the deck, they were probably drowned in their berths. Although the main hatchway was closed, the fore and companion hatches were open.

The wind howled over the doomed brig; the sea was getting up. The midshipmen believed that she must quickly founder and their fate be sealed.

"We have gone through many a danger together," said Tom, to Desmond; "but I believe our time has come at last. I wish my brother Jack could have known our fate. He will be very sorry for us, and so will those at home."

"It cannot be helped," said Desmond. "I should have liked to live longer, and we are better off than the poor fellows drowning in their berths."

"What! Do you think the brig is going down?" cried Billy. "Dear me, how dreadful; can't we get something to float upon?"

"As the water is rushing into her fearfully fast, I don't see what chance there is of her floating," answered Tom. "However, we will not give up all hope while she remains above water. Perhaps, when the squall is passed over, we may manage to scramble out along the masts and cut away the top-gallant yards, and get hold of some of the gratings or spars to fasten together and form a raft which will float."

"We must be quick about it, then," observed Desmond; "for the old craft may go down at any moment."

"While the wind is blowing as it is now, there is no use making the attempt," said Tom. "She does not appear to me to have sunk lower than she did when she first went over. She has a light cargo, and will float longer than a vessel heavily laden."

The midshipmen, however, could not talk much, for it was a difficult matter to make each other hear, what with the sound of the wind and the sea dashing against the hull of the brig, while showers of spray fell over them. They could distinguish the figures of Casey and Peter, with another man holding on to the fore-rigging, but as yet they had been unable to exchange words with them, and were afraid to let go their hold, lest they should be washed off by the sea. The gale continued to blow furiously, and for two hours a perfect hurricane raged. It suddenly ceased, and the sea — though not so rapidly — began to go down. On this their hopes revived. Tom was anxious to ascertain Casey's opinion, and made his way to the fore-rigging.

"I'd stick to the hull, sir," answered Pat. "The brig has floated so long; she may float longer, and we had better wait until daylight before we attempt to make a raft. We may chance to slip off into the sea, or one of those savage sharks may be watching a chance to get hold of us."

Tom followed Casey's advice, and without much difficulty regained his former position. Never had a night appeared so long to any of the party. Notwithstanding their position, however, Billy was constantly dropping off to sleep, and Tom and Desmond had to hold him on, or he would to a certainty have fallen into the water. As the morning approached, the sea became perfectly calm. They would have been thankful for the breeze, which might bring some vessel to their succour. What hope could they have of surviving many hours on the bottom of the brig? The sun rose. Almost exhausted, the midshipmen could with difficulty hold on. As they turned their weary eyes in all directions, not an object was in sight.

"No land to be seen?" asked poor Billy.

"That may be a couple of hundred miles away, I fear," answered Tom.

"Any vessel coming to our help?" again inquired Billy, who, stretched on the rigging, could not lift his head.

"Without a breath of air, there is no chance of that," said Desmond; "but cheer up, Billy, perhaps a steamer will be coming this way."

"There are not many likely to be cruising in this direction," observed Tom. "However, as I have said all along, we will hope for the best."

"Oh! I'm so hungry; so thirsty," moaned the younger midshipman. "Can't you get me something to eat?"

"If we were to go into the cabin, we should find nothing," said Desmond. "The last cask of water was on the starboard side, with the bung out, and must be full of salt water by this time."

The midshipmen again relapsed into silence.

The sun rose higher and higher, its beams striking down with fury on their heads; even Tom, who was the strongest, felt that they could not hold out much longer. Hour after hour went by; still, if they were not to perish, something must be done. He asked Casey and the other men whether they had by chance any fish-hooks in their pockets? They searched, but in vain, and as to going below to look for them, they all declared that it would be impossible. The brig, however, continued to float; that was something, but Tom could not help acknowledging that they would be unable to hold out another night. Even he, as he felt the pangs of hunger and his mouth parched with thirst, began to despair. Desmond and Billy were already far gone. He gazed at the countenances of his two messmates. "They'll never see another sunrise, and shall I?" Tom began seriously to consider how best to prepare himself for his inevitable fate.

Just then Casey sang out, "A breeze! A breeze! I felt it on my cheek, a moment ago!" He endeavoured to wet his finger with his parched tongue, but could hardly do so. He held up his hand. "It's from the southward, and if we can manage to build a raft, we may yet reach the land, or get into the line of vessels running between Sydney and the northern ports."

These exclamations aroused Tom; even Desmond looked up.

"A breeze! Yes, indeed, there is, and a sail too. She is standing towards us!"

He pointed to the southward. A patch of white canvas, on which the sun was shining brightly, appeared on the blue ocean. Casey, at the same time, caught sight of it.

"Hurrah! hurrah! We are saved; she cannot fail to see us."

The cheer was taken up by his companions in misfortune. Even Billy lifted up his head.

"Is it true, Rogers, that you see a sail?" he asked.

"As true as that we are here, but we must not make too sure of being discovered," replied Tom.

"Sure, they would not be after passing us, if they once get sight of the wreck," said Desmond.

"That's just what they may not happen to do," answered Tom, who had become much less sanguine than formerly, and, hungry and worn out, was inclined to look on the dark side of things.

The breeze increased, the stranger drew nearer and nearer. Tom and Desmond were both of opinion that she was a man-of-war. Casey thought the same. The question was, however, whether she would pass them by. She was steering due west, and an object so low in the water as the hull of the brig now was, might not be visible. On she came, until she was about south-east of them, and as yet it was evident that those on board had not seen the wreck, though she herself was easily made out to be a large man-of-war steamer. Proudly she was gliding on, when her yards were braced up and she stood towards the brig.

"Thank Heaven, there is no longer any doubt about it!" cried Tom. "Rouse up, Billy, rouse up, my boy! We are all right! Here comes the steamer to our assistance, and more than that, I'm very sure that she is the *Empress,* or a craft so like her that it would be difficult to distinguish one from the other."

Poor Billy could only raise his head and smile faintly, as he ejaculated, "Thank Heaven, too!"

Tom was undoubtedly right. In a few minutes more the *Empress* was almost within hail, a boat was lowered, and with rapid strokes came pulling towards them. Mr. Norman, from whom they had last parted on the coast of Papua, was in her, but he evidently did not recognize them, supposing them to be part of the brig's crew.

"Slide down, and we will catch you," he cried out, as the boat pulled close to the keel of the brig, the rigging preventing her approaching the deck side.

"Billy shall go first," said Tom, and making a rope fast round their messmate, he and Desmond lowered him down.

"Handsomely, handsomely!" cried the lieutenant, "or that boy's skin will be torn off his back. Why! who have we here?" exclaimed Mr. Norman in astonishment, looking at Billy's haggard countenance and recognizing him rather by his faded and tattered uniform than by his features.

"Don't you know me, sir?" asked Billy, in a faint voice. He could say no more.

"Bless my heart, is it you? And are those Rogers and Desmond?"

"Here we are, to answer for ourselves," said Tom, who, with Desmond, had managed with the aid of the rope to get down close to the boat, into which they were helped by the men, although in their weak state, so overcome were they by the exertion they had made that they could hardly stand. They were handed into the stern sheets, and the boat then moving on took off the other three men in the same fashion. Scarcely were they clear of the brig than she righted, and as she did so began rapidly to settle down.

The midshipmen and their companions were received with hearty congratulations on board the *Empress,* by no one more so than by her captain, who was truly thankful to get back his younger brother, about whose fate he had long been intensely anxious. The *Orion,* which had been astern, now came up, and Adair was informed that his nephew was safe, although apparently in a precarious condition.

RUNNING THE YANKEE BLOCKADE

By WILLIAM WATSON

Among the many stories of Southern blockade-runners during the American Civil War there is none better than the account of how the "Rob Roy" stole out of Galveston.

About the 12th of September a good, steady breeze was blowing from the eastward, which freshened up towards evening. And the chance had come.

We were well to windward, as we intended to run out by the south-west, or Swash Channel, as it was called. At the place where we lay we could see plainly all the blockading fleet and note their position.

Beyond the shoal which separated this channel from the sea, and very near to the outer mouth of the channel, lay a gunboat in what we considered a very bad position for us.

In passing out by this channel the first difficulty was to find it, where it branched off the main channel. On entering it, it led in a south-westerly direction, with from eight to nine feet of water, with the land on the right, and on the left the shoal, which considerably broke the sea and kept the channel tolerably smooth.

At the western extremity of the shoal the channel opened pretty suddenly into deep water, and very close to this mouth lay the gunboat. On the inside, between the gunboat and the shore, there seemed to be very little room to pass without getting dangerously close to the breakers, but on the outside of her there was a good wide space between her and the next vessel, and through which we might pass; but that tempting opening — which was the widest space in the whole fleet — might only be a trap shown during the day, while some of the cruisers which kept steam up and cruised about during the day might take their place there after dark and be ready to pounce upon any craft that might have been lured into an attempt to pass through this wide gate. We, therefore, determined to try to take the narrow path.

Everything was got ready, the large boat was hoisted on board and lodged in a place reserved for it forward of the main-hatchway. Inside of the boat was placed a large coop or arrangement made for the poultry to roost upon, among which was a fine cock, to which some of the men had taken a great fancy, but which was soon afterwards sentenced to death as a traitor. Into the dinghy was stowed some small packages of cotton, made up for the purpose, to shield the steersman in case of shots from boats astern. Double reefs were put in the mainsail and foresail, so that under low canvas we would be shadowed by the dark loom of the land to leeward.

The wind kept increasing, and in the evening there was a fine, steady breeze, and the night was dark.

About eight o'clock we raised anchor and proceeded down the bay. We passed well to the eastward of the wreck of the *Westfield* and the guard-boat, keeping the lead going, and taking care to avoid observation from the Forts. After a little difficulty we found the entrance to the Swash Channel, and got into nine feet of water, with the land on the starboard side. All well so far.

Along this channel we steered cautiously. No lights could be used at the compass; but on entering the channel the course was taken from a star and regulated by the lead.

With my night-glass I looked out for the gunboat, and I soon discovered her on the port bow, close on, and well in shore she was, and there was very little room to pass between her and the breakers. The wind, however, was a little north of east, and there was not a great sea on, and the breakers did not sound loud.

As we got toward the end of the shoal the swell from seaward caused us to keep in the deepest water, and it was evident that we must pass the gunboat very close. The night was dark, and by the dark loom of the land beyond there was not so much danger of us being observed; but the strictest silence was demanded, and orders were passed in an undertone; and I was uneasy at the noise made by the breaking of the water from the bow of the vessel, which had now got past the lee of the reef and into the swell of the open sea, which was causing her to heave considerably.

We were just coming abreast of the gunboat, and every breath was hushed, when "Cock-a-leery-lou!" rang out in a loud and clear note from the hen-coop in the boat amidship.

"Confound that brute," I hissed out, in a rage; "twist its neck."

The order was quickly executed; there was a momentary flutter of wings, and poor chanticleer had given his last crow.

In a few minutes we had brought the gunboat on our weather-quarter, and as there was considerable swell, and the breakers close under our lee, we luffed up and stood off the land a little.

We had not proceeded far when, looking with my night-glass, I discovered another cruiser on the port bow much larger than the one we had passed, evidently with steam up and not at anchor, as she was not riding to the wind like the others.

Hard up and ease off sheets, and we were off before the wind heading towards the shore, expecting every moment to be fired upon; but we soon lost her in the darkness, and had just time to luff up and get sheets hauled in before we reached the breakers, and we now stood a good distance to the westward before we stood off the land again.

This latter vessel had, no doubt, come up after dark to watch the wide gap we had observed before sunset between the first and second vessels on the left wing of the blockading fleet, and had we passed out through that gap she would most likely have picked us up.

Since we had passed the Confederate guard-boat we had seen nothing of the *Mary Elizabeth*, though she raised anchor at the same time, and followed us down the bay; but as we had heard no firing we concluded that she had got out all right.

The object now was to get as far out to sea as possible before day-light, and this was the all-important object of a sailing vessel running the blockade on the outward trip. A steamer could always depend upon making her distance, but if the wind died away a sailing vessel was left helpless in the very jaws of the enemy.

There was no doubt but the sleepy hours of the morning were the best time to pass through the fleet, and were generally taken advantage of on the inward trip when it could be managed; but on the outward trip it was necessary to pass out in the fore-part of the night, so as to get a good offing before daylight.

The danger of capture was not so great from the vessels which actually blocked the harbour as from those which cruised round in the immediate vicinity; and a much greater number of vessels were captured by the cruisers which cruised off the coast and round about the blockaded ports than by the blockading fleet. Therefore, the greater distance which could be run from the port during the night, the greater the expanse of the circle to police and the less chance of capture.

We were now favoured with a fine, strong breeze, and as soon as we were satisfied that we were well clear of the patrols, we luffed up and stood off the coast, took reefs out of the mainsail and foresail, and set staysail and gaff-topsail.

This was the real cream of blockade-running — the first night on the outward trip, with a good cargo of the valuable cotton, a rattling breeze, and every stitch of canvas the vessel could stagger under, neither lights nor look-out, sailing further and further from the cruiser-infested coast and out to the wide range of the open ocean, where the wide expanse made cruisers few and far between.

The breeze kept steady, but I did not leave the deck till 4 p.m., when I calculated that we would be at least seventy miles from the coast. I then turned in for a short nap, telling the mate to scan the horizon well at daybreak, and call me if anything was to be seen.

At daylight the mate called me in something like alarm, saying that a large sailing vessel was on the weather-quarter, bearing down upon us.

I jumped on deck and examined her with the glass, then, laughing at the mate, asked him if he did not know the *Mary Elizabeth*.

He said she had got very small in appearance from the time he first saw her; but when first seen she looked as large as a barque, and

Fred had declared it to be the *John Anderson,* which had chased us so hard on our last voyage.

I said the *John Anderson* was long off the station. The reason she looked so large was the phenomenon of him having seen her at daybreak directly between him and the rising sun. She was about seven miles' distant, and as it got lighter it left no doubt that it was the *Mary Elizabeth,* and I remembered that she was exactly in the same position when we sailed together last voyage.

I now remembered that Captain Shaeffer would know nothing of the understanding made at Havana among blockade-running captains; that if they sighted each other at sea they should stand away from each other, so as to lessen the danger of both being captured should one be sighted by a cruiser; and I had forgotten to tell him of it.

The breeze still continued, but it had gone round a little to the south of east. We had been steering throughout the night about south to get away from the coast, but our course was about south by west. So I changed our course to S.S.W., so as to separate us from the *Mary Elizabeth,* but she followed us on the same course. I then luffed up to south so that the two vessels would meet, and signalled to speak. He either did not see or understand the signal, or perhaps thought that I had seen some danger to the westward and was steering away from it, for he luffed up also. As I saw I could not make him understand I kept away on our course, S. by W.

About this time Father Ryan, who I had not seen or noticed since we left our anchorage, put his head out of the cabin-door.

Father Ryan, who was of Irish birth, proved to be of an exceedingly good-natured and kind-hearted man. Since he came on board he seemed to have ingratiated himself with the crew. While in Galveston Bay he had gone in the boat with them, fishing and gathering oysters —a kind of food of which he was particularly fond. He was also very wishful to make himself useful in assisting the men in any work they might be doing, and was very desirous of learning how to splice or make knots.

"Good morning, Father Ryan," said I, as he looked out. "How

have you passed the night?" I asked him. "Have you been sea-sick?"

"Not a bit of it," said he; "I have been very comfortable, thanks to you."

"When did you turn in?" said I. "I never saw you from the time we raised anchor."

"I daresay not," said he; "you was too much engaged; but I was on deck until you hoisted all the sails, and I heard the vessel making the water fly; but you got out nicely. How far will we be from Galveston now?"

"Well on to a hundred miles, I should say."

"Oh, that is surely good! What vessel is yon?"

"That is the *Mary Elizabeth,* that sailed along with us."

"Oh, indeed!" said he. "You are beating her."

"Not much; the two vessels are much on a par as to sailing."

"Well," said he, looking around, contemplatively, "is not this wonderful! Grand! Beautiful! Captain, when you look around on that great expanse of ocean, with these large, blue waves with their white crests dazzling so beautifully in the morning sun, does it not remind you of the grandeur and purity of God's works?"

"It does, most truly, Father Ryan," said I, sympathetically, for I had got so disgusted with the deceitful actions of mankind that I felt happy at being again on the bosom of the honest ocean.

"Great ocean!" he went on, moralizing, "man can change the face of the land, he can build cities, harbours, railroads, clear away forests, and make the desert blossom as the rose; but the sea he cannot change; it remains the same yesterday, to-day, and for ever."

I had just taken an altitude of the sun, and went below with the sextant and slate, while Father Ryan made his way forward to where the men were at breakfast, crawling over the cotton bales on his hands and knees.

When I came on deck again, Hagan, who was at the wheel, said to me—

"Captain, what do you think old George would have done if he had been on this trip? I swear he would never have left Galveston with us."

"How so?"

"Why! With both a priest and a cat on board."

"Why, what harm is there in either?"

"Oh! None that I know of; but I know George would not have gone with us."

"We could have given the vessel a list to port," said I, "and that would have outbalanced priests and cats and everything else with George; but these are old and foolish superstitions."

"Oh, I know that," said he; "and I am sure I don't believe in them; and I was going to say, what harm could there be in any kind of man or beast being on board; but I am not so sure of that now."

"Why so?"

"Why, what did you think of that cock last night trying to give the alarm just as we were passing close to the Yankee gunboat?"

"What is there supernatural in that?" said I. "It is a very natural thing for a cock to crow when he is wakened out of his sleep. I would have considered it more supernatural if he had held his tongue till we were past the gunboat."

"It would have been better for him, any how; for natural or not, I made short work of him."

"Was it you that killed him?" said I.

"It was; and just as he was flapping his wings to give another crow."

"It is a pity you killed him," said I. "If you could have thrown a bag or something of that kind over him it would have stopped him."

"You cried out to twist his neck, and there was no time to think over it."

Breakfast being ready, the cook had called Father Ryan, and as there were no supercargoes now on board, only Father Ryan, myself, and the mate sat down to breakfast.

"Captain," said Father Ryan, "I hear you have been committing murther last night."

"How is that, Father Ryan?"

"Why, in killing that nice rooster."

"Well, yes; it was a pity; it was done on the spur of the moment;

but they might have heard him on the gunboat, and that would have led to our capture."

"Oh, that it would!" said he. "It was such a loud crow; but is it not a very strange thing that he should have given the alarm just as we were passing the gunboat? Had it been the usual time to crow, it would have been quite natural, but it was not yet nine o'clock, and it is something unnatural for a cock to crow at that hour."

"That is what I find strange about it," said the mate. "I am not superstitious, but it does look strange; and it was a very unusual time for a cock to crow, and just at the moment he could betray us."

"That is what the crew are all saying," said Father Ryan. "You told me, Captain, that your crew were not superstitious, but they are all talking much about it, as ominous of bad luck for the voyage; and they are a little downcast. Hagan maintains that the devil had got on board in the form of a cock, but that he had done for him, anyhow. I told them that they should not indulge in those foolish superstitions, that all such things just happened by chance in the ordinary course of things."

"Well," said I, laughing, "it is astonishing to see how people can manufacture a mysterious affair out of the most commonplace event. There is nothing more easily accounted for than the cock crowing at the time it did. That it was not the usual time for cocks to crow is true enough, but cocks will crow at any time if they are awakened out of their sleep. Now the fowls had all roosted and gone to sleep before we left our anchorage, and you will remember when we got past the reef and got into the open sea the heavy swell coming past the end of the reef caused the vessel to make several heavy lurches?"

"Oh, I remember that," said Father Ryan. "I was standing in the companion, and was nearly thrown down the cabinstair."

"Well," continued I, "I was standing near the fore-rigging, and heard the fluttering of the fowls in the boat as they were thrown from their perches by the rolling of the vessel, and as the rolling subsided a little, and just as we approached the gunboat, the cock having got on to his perch again, naturally began to crow."

"Oh, well, now that explains the whole matter entirely," said Father Ryan; "and I am so glad, and I will soon set the men's minds at rest, for nothing could be more natural."

The mate now laughed, and said that accounted for it exactly; and he seemed greatly relieved in his mind.

"Well now," continued Father Ryan, "does not that show that many things which happen, and are thought mysterious and supernatural and sometimes create superstition in the minds of weak people, might be easily explained if the real causes were known."

Breakfast being over, Father Ryan hastened to explain to the crew the cause of the apparent mysterious affair, which he succeeded in doing, as soon could be seen from their laughing and bantering each other for having entertained serious misgivings in the matter.

Throughout this day the breeze continued, but got gradually lighter, and hauled more round to the southward, which caused us to head more to the westward, but we saw nothing the whole day except the *Mary Elizabeth,* which still kept in sight, though luffing up and standing more to the southwards.

On the following day the wind was light, and nearly due south. The *Mary Elizabeth* was not in sight, which I was glad of, but we could only hold a course about S.W. by W., and as we could do no better, I thought of getting west, near to the coast of Mexico. For although I knew that the current from the south would be stronger against us there, yet I knew that if once south of the Rio Grande we would be more out of the way of cruisers on that coast.

For several days the winds were very light, and from the south, and we made but slow progress, constantly keeping a look-out from the mast-head for cruisers; but we only saw one, which, being observed in time, all sails were taken down, and she passed about ten miles to the northward without observing us.

As last we got south of latitude 25° and longitude 96°, and we considered that we were now out of the most frequented track of the cruisers, but still they might be met anywhere.

PIRATES ABOARD

By W. H. G. KINGSTON

The brig "Susannah", a fine little ship of three hundred tons, was several days out to sea when she met a strange vessel and disaster.

At daybreak on the next morning all hands were roused out to weigh anchor. The second mate's rough voice had scarcely done sounding in my ear before I was on deck, and with the rest was running round between the capstan-bars. "Loose the topsails," next sung out the captain. I sprung aloft to aid in executing the order. Though a young seaman may not have knowledge, he may at all events exhibit activity in obeying orders, and thus gain his superior's approbation. The anchor was quickly run up to the bows, the topsails were sheeted home, and, with a light breeze from the northward, we stood towards the mouth of the Mississippi.

As we passed close to the spot where, on the previous day, the *Foam* lay at anchor, I looked for her. She was nowhere to be seen. She must have got under weigh and put to sea at night. "She's gone, Peter, you observe," remarked Captain Searle, as some piece of duty called me near him. "I'm glad you are not on board her; and I hope neither you nor I may ever fall in with her again."

From New Orleans to Belize, at the mouth of the Mississippi, is about one hundred miles; and this distance, with the aid of the current and a favourable breeze, we accomplished by dusk, when we prepared once more to breast old ocean's waves. These last hundred miles of the father of rivers were very uninteresting, the banks being low, swampy, and dismal in the extreme, pregnant with ague and fevers. Although I rejoiced to be on the free ocean. I yet could scarcely help feeling regret at leaving, probably for ever, the noble stream on whose bosom I had so long floated; on whose swelling and forest-shaded banks I had travelled so far; whom I had seen in its infancy — if an infant it may ever be considered — in its proud manhood, and now at the termination of its mighty course.

These thoughts quickly vanished, however, as I felt the lively vessel lift to the swelling wave, and smelt the salt pure breeze from off the sea. Though the sea breeze was very reviving after the hot pestilential air of New Orleans, yet as it came directly in our teeth, our captain wished it from some other quarter. We were enabled, however, to work off the shore; and as during the night the land-breeze came pretty strong, by daybreak the next morning we were fairly at sea.

Before the sun had got up, the wind had gone down, and it soon became what seamen call a flat calm. The sea, as the hot rays of the sun shone on it, was, as it were, like molten lead; the sails flapped lazily against the mast; the brig's sides, as she every now and then gave an unwilling roll, threw off with a loud splash the bright drops of water which they lapped up from the imperceptibly heaving bosom of the deep. The hot sun struck down on our heads with terrific force, while the pitch bubbled up out of the seams of the deck; and Bill Tasker, the wit of the crew, declared he could hear it squeak into the bargain. An awning was spread over the deck in some way to shelter us, or we should have been roasted alive. Bill, to prove the excess of the heat, fried a slice of salt junk on a piece of tin, and, peppering it well, declared it was delicious. The only person who seemed not only not to suffer from the heat, but to enjoy it, was the black cook; and he, while not employed in his culinary operations, spent the best part of the day basking on the bowsprit-end.

The crew were engaged in their usual occupations of knotting yarns, making sinnet, etc., while the aforesaid Bill Tasker was instructing me — for whom he had taken an especial fancy — in the mysteries of knotting and splicing; but we all of us, in spite of ourselves, went about our work in a listless, careless way, nor had the officers even sufficient energy to make us more lively. Certainly it was hot. There had been no sail in sight that I know of all the day, when as I by chance happened to cast my eyes over the bulwarks, they fell on the topsails of a schooner, just rising above the line of the horizon.

"A sail on the starboard bow!" I sung out to the man who was keeping a look-out forward. He reported the same to the first mate.

"Where away is she?" I heard the captain inquire, as he came directly afterwards on deck.

"To the southward, sir; she seems to be creeping up towards us with a breeze of some sort or other," answered Mr. Dobree. "Here, lad," he continued, beckoning to me, "go aloft, and see what you can make of her. Your eyes are as sharp as any on board, if I mistake not, and a little running will do you no harm."

I was soon at the mast-head, and in two minutes returned, and reported her to be a large topsail schooner, heading north-north-east with the wind about south-east.

"I can't help thinking, sir, from her look, that this is the same craft that was lying off New Orleans two days ago," I added, touching my hat to the captain. I don't remember exactly what made me suppose this, but such I know was my idea at the time.

"What, your friend Captain Hawk's craft, the *Foam,* you mean, I suppose?" he observed. "But how can that be? She was bound to Havanah, and this vessel is standing away from it."

"I can't say positively, sir; but if you would take the glass and have a look at her, I don't think you would say she is very unlike her, at all events," I replied.

"It's very extraordinary if such is the case," said the captain, looking rather more as if he thought I might be right than before.

"Give me the glass, and I'll judge for myself, though it's impossible to say for a certainty what she may be at this distance." Saying this he took the telescope, and in spite of the heat went aloft.

When he came down again, I observed that he looked graver than usual. He instantly gave orders to furl the awning, and to be ready to make sail as soon as the breeze should reach us. "The youngster is right, Mr. Dobree," he said, turning to the mate, and probably not aware that I overheard him.

"It's that piccarooning craft the *Foam*; and Mr. Hawk, as he calls himself, is after some of his old tricks. I had my suspicions of him when I saw him off New Orleans; but I did not think he would venture to attack us."

"He's bold enough to attack any one, sir," said the mate; "but we flatter ourselves that we shall be able to give a very good account of him, if he begins to play off any of his tricks on us."

"We'll do our best, Mr. Dobree," said the captain; "for if we do not, we shall have but a Flemish account to render of our cargo, let alone our lives."

I do not know if I before stated that the *Susannah* carried four guns — two long and two carronades; and as we had a supply of small arms and cutlasses, we were tolerably able to defend ourselves.

The captain walked the deck for some time in silence, during which period the stranger had perceptibly approached to us. He then again went aloft, and scrutinized her attentively. On coming down he stopped at the break of the poop, and, waving his hand, let us know that he wished to address us. "My lads," he began, "I don't altogether like the look of that fellow out yonder, who has been taking so much pains to get up to us. He may be honest, but I tell you I don't think so; and if he attempts to molest us, I'm sure you'll one and all do your duty in defending the brig and the property on board her entrusted to you. I need not tell you that pirates generally trust to the saying, that dead men tell no tales; and that, if that fellow is one, and gets the better of us, our lives won't be worth much to any of us."

"Don't fear for us, sir; we're ready for him whatever he may be," sang out the whole crew with one voice.

The stranger brought along the breeze with him, but as yet our sails had not felt a particle of its influence. At length, when he was little more than a mile off, a few cat's-paws were seen playing on the water; they came, and vanished again as rapidly, and the sea was as smooth as before. In time they came oftener and with more power; and at length our topsails and topgallant-sails were seen slowly to bulge out as the steadier breeze filled them.

The wind came, as I have said, from the south-east, which was directly in our teeth in our proper course to Havanah. The stranger had thus the weathergauge of us; and a glance at the map will show that we were completely embayed, as, had we stood to the eastward, we should have run on the Florida coast, while on the other tack we must have run right down to meet him. We might possibly reach some port, but the probabilities were that he would overtake us before we could do so, and the appearance of fear would encourage him to follow us. We had therefore only the choice of running back to Belize, or fighting our way onward. Captain Searle decided on the latter alternative; and, bracing the yards sharply up on the starboard tack, we stood to the eastward, intending, whatever course the stranger pursued, to go about again at the proper time.

The schooner, on seeing this, also closely hugged the wind and stood after us. There could now be no longer any doubt about his intentions. We, however, showed the stars and stripes of the United States, but he hoisted no ensign in return. It was soon very evident that he sailed faster than we did, and he was then rapidly coming within range of our guns. Our captain ordered us, however, on no account to fire unless we were struck, as he was unwilling to sacrifice the lives of any one unnecessarily, even of our enemies.

Every stitch of canvas the brig could carry was cracked on her: all would not do. The stranger walked up to us hand over hand. Seeing that there was not the slightest chance of escaping by flight, Captain Searle ordered the foresail and topgallant-sails to be clewed up, and, under our topsails and fore-and-aft sails, resolved to wait the coming up of the enemy, if such the stranger might prove.

On came the schooner, without firing or showing any unfriendly disposition. As she drew near, I felt more and more convinced that she must be the *Foam*. She had a peculiarly long cutwater and a very straight sheer, which, as she came up to the windward of us, and presented nearly her broadside, was discernible. As she heeled over to the now freshening breeze, I fancied that I could even discern, through the glass, Captain Hawk walking the quarter-deck. When she got about a quarter of a mile to windward of us, she hove to and lowered a boat, into which several people jumped and pulled towards us. At the same time up went the Spanish ensign at her peak.

Captain Searle looked puzzled. "I cannot make it out, Dobree," he observed. "I still doubt if that fellow is honest, and am half inclined to make sail again; while he bears down to pick up his boat, we may get to windward of him."

"If he isn't honest he'll not trouble himself about his boat, but will try to run alongside us, and let her come up when she can," answered the mate. "There is no trusting to what such craft as that fellow may do."

"Oh, we'll take care he does not play off any tricks upon us," said the captain; and we waited the approach of the boat.

As she drew near, she was seen to contain eight men. Four were pulling, one sat in the bows, and the other three in the stern-sheets. If they were armed, it could not be discovered. When they got within hail, the captain asked them what they wanted.

They pointed to their mouths, and one answered in Spanish, "Aqua, aqua, por amor de Dios."

"They want water, sir, they say," observed the first mate, who prided himself on his knowledge of Spanish.

"That's the reason, then, that they were in such a hurry to speak to us," said the captain. "But still, does it not strike you as odd that a vessel should be in want of water in these seas?"

"Her water-butts might have leaked out; and some of these Spanish gentry, sir, are very careless about taking enough water to sea," replied the mate, who was biassed by the pleasure he anticipated of being able to sport his Spanish.

"Get a water-cask up on deck, and we'll have it ready to give these fellows, whatever they may be," said our humane captain. "Have some pannikins ready to serve it to them. Thirst is a dreadful thing, and one would not keep a fellow-creature in that state a moment longer than one could help."

I do not know what the second mate thought of the strangers, but I remember several of the crew saying that they did not like their looks; and I saw him place a cutlass close to the gun nearest the starboard gangway, while he kept eyeing them in no very affectionate manner. Notwithstanding the heat of the weather, the men in the stern-sheets wore cloaks. On observing this, Bill Tasker said he supposed it was to hide the shabby jackets they wore under them. The other men were dressed in blue shirts, and their sleeves rolled up to the shoulder, with the red sash usually worn by Spaniards round their waist, in which was stuck the deadly *cuchillo*, or cut-and-thrust knife, in a sheath, carried by most Lusitanian and Iberian seamen and their descendants of the New World.

They pulled up at once alongside, and before any one attempted to stop them they hooked on, the man in the bows climbing up on deck, followed by his companions in cloaks, and two of the seamen. The other two remained in the boat, pointing at their mouths, as a sign that they wanted water.

Seamen, from the sufferings and dangers to which they are exposed, are proverbially kind to those in distress. Our men, therefore, seemed to vie with each other who should first hold the pannikins of water to the mouths of the strangers, while a tub, with the fluid, was also lowered into the boat alongside. They eagerly rushed at the water, and drank up all that was offered them; but I could not help remarking that they did not look like men suffering from thirst. However, a most extraordinary effect was produced on two of them, for they fell down on the deck, and rolled about as if in intense agony. This drew the attention of all hands on them; and as we had no surgeon on board the captain began to ransack his medical knowledge to find remedies for them.

While he was turning over the pages of his medical guide to find some similar case of illness and its remedy described, the schooner was edging down towards us. As she approached, I observed only a few men on board; and they, as the people in the boat had done, were pointing at their mouths, as if they were suffering from want of water. The boat was on the lee side.

I think I said that there were some sails, and two or three cloaks apparently thrown by chance at the bottom of the boat. While all hands were engaged in attending to the strangers, and for some minutes no one had looked towards the schooner, on a sudden I heard a loud grating sound — there was the wild triumphant cry of a hundred fierce voices. The seemingly exhausted men leaped to their feet; the helmsman and our captain lay prostrate by blows dealt by our treacherous foes; the second mate and several of the men were knocked down; and before any of us had time to attempt even any defence of the brig, a set of desperadoes, of all colours and nations, were swarming down on her decks from the rigging of the schooner, while others who had been concealed in the boat, sprang on board on the lee side. Never was a surprise more complete, or treachery more vile. In an instant we were helplessly in the power of as lawless a band of pirates as ever infested those seas. The captain and mates were first pinioned; the men were sharing the same treatment. I was at the time forward, when, on looking aft, who should I see but Captain Hawk himself, walking the deck of the brig as if he were her rightful commander! He took off his hat with mock courtesy to poor Captain Searle, as he passed him. "Ah, my dear sir, the fortune of war makes you my prisoner today," he said, in a sneering tone. "Another day, if my people do not insist on your walking the plank, you may hope, perhaps, to have the satisfaction of beholding me dangling at a yardarm. By the bye, I owe you this turn, for you shipped on board your craft a lad who had engaged to sail with me; and I must have him forthwith back again, with a few other articles of your cargo which I happen to require." As he said this, his eye fell on me, and he beckoned me towards him. I saw that there was no use hanging back, so I boldly advanced. "You are a pretty fellow, to desert your colours," he continued, laughing. "You deserve to be treated as a deserter. However, I will have compassion on your youth, if you will swear to be faithful to me in future."

"I never joined your vessel, so I am not a deserter. I cannot swear to serve a man of whose character I know nothing, except that he has taken forcible possession of a peaceable trader." I said this without hesitation or the least sign of fear. The truth is, I felt too desperate to allow myself to consider what I said or did.

"You are a brave young bantam," he answered laughingly. "And though all the rest may hang or walk the plank, we will save you to afford us sport; so set your mind at rest on that point."

"Thank you for my life, for I have no wish to lose it, I can assure you," I replied; "but don't suppose I am going to spend it in your service. I shall do my best to get away from you as soon as possible."

"Then we must tie you by a lanyard on the leg," he answered, without at all appearing angry. "Here, Mark Anthony," — he beckoned to a tall, ill-looking black who had been busy in securing the rest of the crew, — "take charge of this youngster, and render an account of him to me by and by, without a hair of his head injured, mind you."

"Yes, sare," said the Roman general, who I afterwards found was a runaway slave from Kentucky. "I'll not singe his whiskers even. Come here, massa;" and seizing me by the shoulder, he dragged me forward away from the rest of the people. "What's your name?" asked my black keeper, as he made me sit down on the bits of the bowsprit.

"Peter, at your service, Mr. Mark Anthony," said I in as fearless a voice as I could command; for having once taken a line of conduct which seemed to answer well, I determined to persevere in it.

"Den, Massa Peter, you sit dere quiet," he said with a grin. "I no break your skull, because Captain Hawk break mine if I do. I no let anybody else hurt you for same reason."

From his look and voice I certainly did not flatter myself that he refrained from throwing me overboard from any love he bore me; but, on the contrary, that he would have been much more gratefully employed in making me walk the plank, or in tricing me up to the foreyard.

Meantime the pirates were busily employed in ransacking the vessel, and in transferring everything of value to them which they could find from her to their own schooner. The captain and mates were threatened with instant death if they did not deliver up all the money they had on board; and even the crew were compelled to hand over to our captors the small sums they possessed. To make them do this, they were knocked about and beaten unmercifully. And even those who possessed watches and rings were deprived of them.

HURRICANE

By WILLIAM WATSON

One of the finest descriptions of a sailing-ship under attack from a hurricane is given in this account taken from Watson's "Adventures of a Blockade Runner".

One day it fell dead calm, and about noon a large circle was observed round the sun of a purple colour, which some of the men declared indicated the approach of a heavy gale, and that we might in a short time look out for a violent norther. Anything would be a relief to this suspense, and a norther would be welcomed if it did not come too severe.

As it was about dead calm, sails were taken down, and every strop, hook, and cringle examined and made as secure as possible. Flying jib and small sails stowed, and everything about deck firmly lashed and made snug. Double reefs put in mainsail and foresail, and single reef in jib, and sails hoisted again, and we looked for the change in the weather.

We did not have long to wait. About 3 p.m. the sky darkened all round, and by 4 p.m. it was fearfully dark, the sky to the northward being black as ink. There was now no mistake but that we were going to have a heavy gale, but whether it was going to be a West India hurricane or a Texas norther we did not know.

It was not just yet the season for the regular northers, but there were often in those latitudes heavy gales about the equinox which sometimes took the form of northers, and blew with great violence, but they were generally of short duration, and might be said to be something between the Texas norther and the West India hurricane.

There could now be seen under the black cloud to the northward what appeared to be snow hillocks on the horizon, which soon spread out, and was coming towards us. This of course was the sea lashed into a foam by the fury of the wind, but still not a breath of wind had reached us, and the vessel still rolled in a dead calm.

It soon came on, however, direct from the north, and first a few drops of rain struck the vessel, and then the cold wind which indicated, to all appearance at least, it was a norther. It struck the vessel with such violence that I thought it would have torn the masts out of her before she gathered headway.

I was not sure how the *Rob Roy* would lay to under a close-reefed foresail, and I determined, as the wind was fair for us, to make the best of it, and scud before it.

The vessel was now rushing through the water at a great rate, but when the full force of the gale came up it struck her with such violence that it seemed as if it would tumble her stern overhead.

"Get the mainsail off her," I cried.

This was easier said than done. The sheet had been eased off to run before the wind, and the belly of the sail was pressing against the shrouds, and with the awful force of the wind it was impossible to move it. To ease her in the meantime the peak purchase was cast off, and the peak dropped. This did ease her a little, but the gale kept increasing in violence, and the mainsail must come off her.

To handle such a large sail in such a tempest was no easy task, and as the boom was eased off it must be got aboard. No strength could haul it in against the force of such wind; the vessel must be rounded to.

"Hard down your helm!" was the word. The helm was put hard down, but the peak having been dropped she would not come up, but rushed along in the trough of the sea with the full force of the hurricane on her beam. That she did not lose her masts or capsize showed great strength and stability.

"Let go the jib halliards." This was done and the jib hauled down. This had the desired effect, and she came up into the wind. The fore sheet was hauled in, and she was held up till the main sheet could be hauled in, the sail lowered and stowed securely.

The gale had now become terrific, and the wind being directly against the current of the Gulf Stream, the waves rose very fast and to a great height. While we had the vessel thus rounded to, we thought to try if she would lay to in the gale, but the seas having got to a great height, and coming with great force, and the vessel having such a light hold on the water, she was thrown back stern on with every wave, causing her to fall heavily on her rudder, which I feared might be carried away; we thought it best to scud before the wind under a close reefed foresail.

The last reef was then put in the foresail, the jib tack hauled to windward, and part of the jib run up. She payed off quickly, and bounded off before the wind. The jib was then taken down and cleared so as to be run up quickly in case of necessity.

She now scudded along beautifully, but the wind increased far beyond our imagination, and was something appalling, but it did not vary a point in its direction. We steered about due south; everything depended upon the steersman; to have broached to would have been destruction.

The night was very dark, and the terrible roaring of the wind and the hissing of the spray off the tops of the waves seemed at times high over our heads. No one sought to sleep that night; the men were gathered aft, where they stood in silence with their eyes alternately upon the foresail and the man at the helm. Sometimes the silence would be broken by the expression — "Well, that is blowing pretty stiff."

Up till midnight all went well enough, but there was no abatement of the gale; it was rather increasing, and the seas were breaking more. Our only fears were for the foresail splitting.

About 1 a.m. a tremendous sea caused the vessel to yaw a little, and the foreboom jibed from starboard to port like the shot of a cannon, and as she recovered herself it jibed back again with the same force. This was dangerous work, as each time it struck against the fore-shrouds, and might have carried them away. I went with the mate to examine, but found no harm done. The fore-sheet, which worked in a traveller on deck, was taut as a bar, although the boom was pressing hard against the shrouds. Thinking to ease the boom off the shrouds a little, we got all hands to try a pull on the fore-sheet, but such was the pressure of the wind on the sail that we could not gain an inch. To have put a back-tackle on the boom to prevent it jibing would have been madness. So the hauling part of the sheet was made fast to the block at the traveller, and the boom allowed to have its play, and every one warned to keep out from the sweep of the boom, as one blow from it would have sent them beyond hail.

Shortly after this the boom jibed again with a loud report, and as quickly jibed back again, but in jibing back the jaw rope parted, and the boom unshipped from the mast, and lay across ship, with one end pressing against the mast, and the other against the fore-shrouds.

This was a bad state of things, but it was impossible to do anything with it, as such was the force of the wind, and the boom adrift and flying about, that it was dangerous to go near it.

It was evident that we were going to lose the foresail, and as our last resource we must try and get the jib upon her; but just as the men were trying to get forward to loose the jib a tremendous sea came rolling up astern, and a large body of water, detached from the top of it by the fury of the wind, fell on board right amidships, filling the large boat with water, and causing the vessel to reel over almost on her beam end. She quickly recovered herself again, but singularly and fortunately the sudden jerk started the foreboom from where it lay pressing against the mast and shrouds, and shipped it back into its place again. Lucky event!

"Well done, *Rob Roy!*" shouted the mate, as he seized a short piece of rope used as a stopper and darted forward to secure the boom in its place. I was quickly with him with more hands, warning them to keep forward of the mast out of the sweep of the boom. The rope was quickly passed round the neck of the boom, and brought round the mast to hold it in its place till a new jaw rope was got ready, when as many of the purls as could be picked up were strung upon it, and it was rove in its place, and the boom was all right again.

The vessel was now found to be staggering under the weight of the large boat full of water on deck. This must be emptied out; to bail it out would be dangerous work, as the boat was just under the sweep

262

of the fore-boom. The mate remembered that there was a large plug in the boat, but the stopper was in. We tried to get the stopper out, but there were difficulties in the way. It could not be got at from the outside for the deck-load, and the fowls having been all used up, the hen coop had been broken up, and an empty water-cask placed in the boat where it had been. This water-cask was right over the stopper, and the foreboom was just above the water-cask, so that it could not be moved.

The water-cask must be sacrificed. A hammer was got, and the cask knocked to pieces, and the mate, to avoid a stroke of the boom, sprawled along in the water, dived down and withdrew the stopper, and the water rushed out, and very soon the vessel was relieved of that unsteady top weight, and she bounded on all right again.

The gale had now reached its height, but still blew steady from the same point, and we began to imagine that it was abating a little.

As daylight began to appear we observed a small slit in the foresail, which, on being examined from the back or lee side of the sail, was found to be one of the seams which was just beginning to open. A piece of strong canvas was got, which, with a bent needle, was stitched strongly over the back of the place to help it a little.

When daylight broke clear the scene was truly grand. The most experienced man on board had never seen such a sea, but though the waves were tremendously high it could not be called a dangerous cross chop of a sea. It was perfectly regular, and if from our position in it we could not afford to call it sublimely beautiful, we had at least to admit that it was grand and awful.

It seemed like a succession of mountain ridges perfectly straight and parallel to each other, rolling furiously in one direction, and between each a level plain about an eighth of a mile wide covered with white foam. This, I presume, was caused by the violent gale blowing steady from one point directly against the Gulf Stream.

About half-past seven the gale had somewhat abated, and soon after the cook managed to have some breakfast ready. Father Ryan, who had been up most of the night, was gazing on the scene.

"What do you think of that gale, Father Ryan?" said I.

"Awful! Truly awful," said he. "What kind of a gale do you call that? Is that a hurricane?"

"It blows hard enough for one," said I, "although it is too steady from one point for that. I think it is a sort of equinoctial norther. What do you think of that sea?"

"Oh, that is terrible," said he. "I would not think it safe for a small vessel like this."

"Many would think the same, and it is hard enough upon her, but she is buoyant, and rises finely upon it, and has come through it very well so far, and the worst is now past, for the gale has about spent itself."

"Oh, yes," said he, "it is calming down now, but when I looked out upon that awful sea this morning and thought of the calm sea of yesterday, I said, 'Surely awful are the works of the Almighty, and how suddenly He can send on the calmest sea such a storm as will raise it into angry mountains, and yet with the same hand He can guide safely through it a small, helpless vessel like this.'"

I agreed with him, and said we ought to be grateful.

By 9 a.m. the gale had much abated, and the morning, which up till now had been dark and cloudy, began to clear up, and soon after the sun broke through, and I got an observation, and assuming our latitude, found our longitude to be about 97° 20′, which placed us about thirty miles from the coast of Mexico.

We now got more sail upon the vessel, and soon after we observed that the northerly wind of the gale had entirely spent itself, and we were into a light steady breeze from the eastward, although there was still a heavy swell from the northward. This indicated that the gale had not extended much further south, and we were now into the usual weather again.

The danger from the seas being for the time past, the old standing danger again cropped up, which was danger from the enemy, and, as we were now getting near to Tampico, it was exceedingly probable that some of their cruisers would be hovering in the neighbourhood with the view of picking up any blockade runner bound for that port. We, therefore, stood more to the westward, intending to sight the land, and then crawl down along the coast as we had done last trip.

We now began to wonder how it had fared with the *Mary Elizabeth,* which must have caught the gale at the same time with us. I knew that in point of management she would not lack, as she had a master and crew well experienced in these seas and in the management of this class of vessels. She was better provided in that respect than the *Rob Roy,* but she was a smaller vessel, and I knew that her sails were not of the same strength. We looked in all directions from the mast-head, but could see nothing of her.

As we stood to the westward, we saw something that looked like wreckage, but on steering towards it we found it to be large trees floating, which appeared to have been quite recently brought down some river, indicating that there had been heavy rain and floods in the northern parts of Mexico.

I may here anticipate, and say that of the *Mary Elizabeth* nothing was ever heard. Captain Shaeffer's brother afterwards called upon me in Havana to get the last and only information that he could ever obtain, and that was of her being seen by us on the day before the gale, and I have no doubt but that she foundered in that gale; and though she was larger, a better sea-boat, better found, and better managed than a great many of the craft which engaged in that rough and reckless trade, it was, strange to say, the only instance I ever knew of one of them being lost at sea. There was no doubt, however, that the gale, so far as it extended, was the heaviest which had been for some years.

We soon sighted the land, and at noon I got the latitude, and found that we were about fifteen miles to the northward of Tampico River, and we arrived off the mouth of the river about 3 p.m.

We found anchored there two vessels, both schooners. One of them was just such a vessel as the *Sylvia,* which we had met here six months before, and, like her, was from St. John with a cargo of lumber for Tampico. The other was a larger vessel, but she seemed light, as in ballast, and was anchored further out, some little distance away.

The former vessel we sailed up to and spoke with. I cannot remember her name, but will call her the *St. John*, as she was from that port. She had passed to the south of Cuba, and came in from the eastward, and had experienced nothing of the gale, but judged from the swell from the northward that there had been a heavy gale in that direction. They drew about six feet of water, and they wished to cross the bar and go up to Tampico Town.

The pilot's boat had been off in the morning, but it was impossible to take them over the bar at that time owing to the very high sea caused by the heavy swell from the northward, meeting in the channel the strong current of the Tampico River, which was then very high owing to great floods in the interior. The pilots had promised, however, to come out again in the afternoon, when, if the swell had gone down a little, they would be able to take them over.

As this bar at Tampico is of shifting quicksand, the channel through it keeps constantly changing, and it is necessary for the pilots to take soundings regularly—almost every day. It is sometimes very crooked and difficult to pass through, and if a vessel gets on to the shoal it is generally a total loss, and if it should be rough weather it is often attended with the loss of all hands, as no boat can live in the breakers. The entrance to this channel from seaward was supposed at this time to be about half a mile to the southward of where it was when we were here six months before, but it was very difficult to define the exact place.

As the pilots had promised to take over in the afternoon the *St. John*, which drew six feet of water, I conceived they could have no difficulty with the *Rob Roy*, which drew only four feet nine inches. We, therefore, dropped anchor and signalled for a pilot. After waiting about an hour there was no appearance of any pilot-boat coming off, and the sky had suddenly changed, and towards the north-east looked black and threatening. This was alarming.

Any one who knows anything of Tampico Roads knows what a dangerous place it is in a heavy north-easterly wind. A very high sea sets in, and with such violence that no amount of ground-tackling will hold the vessel; and I have known large steamers with both anchors down and working propellers at full speed scarcely able to hold against it and keep off the breakers, while with a sailing vessel it is impossible to claw off.

As soon as I saw this appearance of a change in the weather I set about getting the anchor up to try and get out to sea, and I saw the other vessels doing the same, but it was too late. We had scarcely got sails set when it was down upon us. We set every bit of canvas, and gave full centre-board to see if we could weather the reefs to the southward, but we soon saw that we could not clear them on that stretch, and we tacked and stood to the northward as far as we could reach for the breakers, and then stood back to try again to weather the reefs to the southward; but to our dismay we found that we had not gained an inch, and the sea was now getting up and throwing us more to leeward, and we saw that the other two vessels were not making any more of it than ourselves.

This was something terrible to realize so suddenly and unexpected. To leeward and on each side were the shoals which hemmed us in, and on them the mountainous waves broke with great fury; to windward was the threatening cloud which betokened a heavy gale, and coming it was with certainty, and not the slightest chance of a lull or change in the wind, and night coming on. The gale did not come on with such violence as on the previous day, but it mattered little in the position we were in; it was sufficient to bring on our destruction, and that with certainty and in a very short time, and what would we not have given for the same sea room we had last night, even with the gale in all its fury.

What to do I did not know. The men looked at me, but no one spoke. I pointed to the deck-load of cotton.

"Men," said I, "the charge of every life is mine. Do you think it would help us any to throw over that deckload? If you think so, we will throw it over at once."

"It will do no good," they cried out together; "it eases her aloft and gives her a better hold on the water; and if at last we go on the bar there is a chance of saving our lives by clinging to bales of cotton."

"Then," said I, "we cannot claw off. The gale is increasing, night is upon us, and, do our best, we will be in these breakers before an hour. Now, I propose to make an attempt to run the gauntlet. I have been observing with the glass, and I fancy I see what I take to be the opening to the channel, and I propose to make the attempt to cross the bar. I know it is a desperate and dangerous undertaking, but it is the only chance for our lives. What do you all say?"

"I say try it," said the mate; "it is our only chance."

The men all acquiesced, and said they were ready to obey.

One man then spoke up, and said: "I am ready to leave it to your own judgment, Captain; but if you take my advice when crossing you will steer through where you see the highest seas and the bluest water."

"I believe you are right," I said, "and I intend to do so."

Father Ryan, who stood with an expression something between composure and anxiety on his countenance, looked at me seriously and said, "Try it, Captain, and may the hand of God guide you."

For once at least in my life, I implored the aid of a higher hand. I went to the cabin and took the chronometer and cushioned it in one of the beds, as is usually done in crossing bars, in case of a sudden touch on the ground shaking it, and, going on deck, told the men that everything now depended upon their coolness and prompt action.

The greatest difficulty in crossing a bar through a narrow channel before a heavy sea was to keep the vessel straight in the channel, and prevent her stern being swung round by the heavy seas rolling up astern.

In placing the men, the first point to be determined was who was the best steersman. This was accorded to Hagan. To the cook was assigned the charge of the centre-board, the bar of which being near the door of the galley he had been accustomed to work, and lower or raise as required. The mate would take charge aft, with another man at the peak purchase, and be ready to drop the peak of the main-sail if a heavy sea rolling up astern swung her stern round; while two men would be stationed at the jibsheet to haul to windward and make her pay off, and I would take my station on the top of the cotton amidships, and with my glass look out ahead for the best water, and direct with my hand to the right or left the course to steer. The helmsman would keep his eye on me and steer by the direction of my hand. The mate would also be ready to assist the man at the helm, or to take the helm in case of the steersman being knocked down by a heavy sea coming over the stern. Father Ryan wished to know where he could be of service. I directed him to watch the companion doors, and keep them shut to prevent a sea going down in the cabin.

The most important part was to find the proper entrance to the channel; and we were now approaching the place which I supposed to be the entrance, and as soon as it was under our lee the gaff-topsail was taken in, but everything else was carried full.

Every man now took his place, and I got upon the top of the cotton with my glass and directed with my hand. As we approached the place, it looked awful; the waves toppled up like the walls of a fortress. Sheets were eased off, and under a full pressure of canvas the vessel rushed at it. She plunged violently, every spar and timber seemed to quiver. There was evidently a strong current against her, while the tremendous seas breaking on each side seemed above our heads. Sometimes I thought we were completely locked in, but still some higher and bluer waves gave indication of the deepest water. Sometimes a tremendous sea would come rolling up astern and throw her stern forward and bring her almost broadside on across the channel; but the peak would be quickly dropped and jib hauled to windward, and she payed off again before another sea came, when the same thing was repeated. We were nearly to the midst of it, but we were not making fast progress owing to the strong current of the river against us. This, however, made her steer better, and convinced me that we were in the right channel; but I feared that the shallowest and worst-defined part of it would be the end next the shore, and often the flying spray blinded me and dimmed the glass in my hand so that I had to keep wiping it with my handkerchief. I could only see ahead when lifted on the top of a huge wave, as, when that passed on, the mountain of water shut off for a time the view forward.

I fancied that the water was getting shallower on each side, the breakers worse, and the channel less defined. When looking forward my eye caught the shore in the distance, and I saw a Mexican flag —the pilot's flag—and I saw they were waving directions. First inclined to the north, we altered course to the north, then held up straight—steady; then inclined to the south. We altered course to the south, then up straight again—steady.

I had now some hopes. We continued on, and soon after all in front seemed breakers, and I saw no appearance of a channel or deep water; but the pilot's flag was held up steady to come straight on. It looked fearful, but on we must go. Several heavy broken waves came up, two of which came over our stern. Another heavier one came up, and, nearly burying us, carried us forward some distance, and when it passed she touched the ground, but it was just lightly and for a moment. She payed off again. Another heavy and broken wave followed, and a violent gust of wind at the same time carried us along through a mass of foam into the deep and smooth water inside of the bar.

"Round her to, haul down staysail and jib, and let go anchor," said I.

This was soon done. The men stood round, but said nothing. Father Ryan, whose hat had blown overboard, came up to me bareheaded, drenched with salt-water, and with tears in his eyes. He grasped me warmly by the hand, and said seriously, "Captain, the finger of God was there."

"It was," I said; and I never said two words with more sincerity in all my life. Of the many incidents in my somewhat adventurous life I do not think that any made a greater impression on me than the fortune of the last twenty-four hours, and especially this last hour.

SEA LOVE

An old story which was a favourite on board clipper ships in warm latitudes. It gives some indication of the kind of story which amused the old shellbacks.

I remember once having been told by a young lady who had eloped to be married, that a woman in such a situation never goes off unprovided with a bundle. Whether it be that the woman's love of dress never forsakes her, or that she looks to maintain the conquest her beauty has achieved, by the adventitious aid of the milliner and mantua-maker.

When Captain Brilliant came to the window to Cassandra, at the appointed hour, she had not only dressed in an appropriate manner to elope, but had made up a little bundle of clothes to accompany her.

The admiral was now out, and Brilliant was admitted to her room by Prudence, her faithful servant and confidant, who was ready to partake of the fortunes of her mistress.

"Oh, Brilliant," cried Cassandra, "how I tremble! My hand shakes so that I am utterly incapable of writing a note to my uncle."

"Give me the pen, my dear," said Brilliant; "I will write the admiral a note ship-shape."

Captain Brilliant took the pen, and wrote as follows:—

"Sir, — Your niece being a lass who loves a sailor, declines the marriage settlement of my lord Fiddle-fumble, to be spliced to a man who has no other house but his ship; which will sufficiently explain the motive of her shoving her boat off.

> "I have the honour to be, &c.
> "Bryan Brilliant."

The every-day writers of tales have an invariable custom of making their lovers elope at the conclusion of their histories; but, disdaining such rules, behold the hero and heroine of this page running away in the middle of my eventful story: or, in language more correct, run away with by four blood horses, and pursuing their course to the

New Ferry Passage. Yes, let the reader picture to his imagination Cassandra, Prudence, and the captain, sitting in a comfortable chaise and galloping hurry-skurry to the altar of Hymen.

Captain Brilliant was married to Cassandra at Bristol; and it would require language superior to that of mortals to paint the bliss of Captain Brilliant, when he found himself in the arms of his beloved Cassandra. It has been said by the poet "man never is but always to be blest." Here Pope deceived himself, for Brilliant was supremely blest in the possession of so much loveliness. And had Pope tasted the happiness of the marriage state, he never would have advanced such a position.

It now remains for me to relate that Captain Brilliant proceeded with his lady to Portsmouth, where his orders had fortunately arrived only an hour before.

"Bravo!" cried the captain to his wife. "Everything smiles upon our union. Touch and go is a good pilot."

"I am ready, now," said Cassandra, throwing her arms round his neck.

"Well, then, my love," cried the captain. "I will write a note to my first lieutenant, to get the whip ready for you."

"My dear Brilliant!" said Cassandra, "surely you are not a Russian. What have I done to deserve the whip?"

Here the captain laughed heartily (as I humbly trust my readers will do) when having explained himself to Cassandra, he wrote his first lieutenant a note.

"DEAR HURRICANE,

"Get the whip ready. I am spliced.

"Yours
"BRYAN BRILLIANT."

The coxswain of the barge returned with the following answer:
"DEAR SIR,

"So am I! And a devil of a splice I have made.

"I have the honour to be, &c.
"HENRY HURRICANE."

272

Captain Brilliant having dined with Cassandra, at the hotel on the Point, and introduced his bride to Lord Fearless, Sir Joshua Invincible, and the honourable Captain Cutwater, who commanded ships lying in the harbour, he embarked with Cassandra and Prudence, and a French lap-dog, in the barge, and was conveyed on board the *Desdemona*.

But, on ascending the ship's side, our noble captain could not repress his astonishment at the uproar that prevailed on the quarterdeck of the frigate.

There was a young woman leaning against the capstan, stamping her cap under her foot, and upbraiding the first lieutenant with the most opprobrious epithets that an enraged woman could utter.

"You deceitful man!" cried the lady. "Was it for this I married you before my last husband was laid in his grave, and put you in possession of a bag full of joes? Shame on you, you low fellow. To descend to a strumpet, when you had a wife on board your ship."

"Indeed, Flora, you are wrong."

"What! Have I not the use of my eyes, that you thus exculpate your conduct. Did I not see the woman take you by the arm. Did you not smile on her? Ha! You thought I was snug on board, and ignorant of your villany. But I suspected your conduct. Put me, I say, ashore. I will not stay another moment on board."

"Avast there, Flora! The boats are all hoisted in. We have got our sailing orders on board. The foretopsail is loose. Captain Brilliant is come. I must get the ship under weigh."

Cassandra and Prudence were now hoisted on board, and the former was melted into tenderness on beholding the distraction of a young and beautiful girl.

"What, my dear," said she to her husband, "is the matter?"

"Faith," cried the captain, "here is the devil to pay and no pitch hot. I think I have had the pleasure of seeing that lady before. Mrs Factor, if I mistake not?"

"Yes, sir," sobbed the lady, "my name was Factor. You not long ago had the goodness to take me and my husband into your ship. You remember the morning I left you, Mr. Factor died the same night, of convulsions, in his bed, Not knowing a soul at Portsmouth, I returned on board the ship and wanted to see you, hoping you could recommend me to some lady to lodge with. You was gone to your friends, but your first lieutenant received me, and when I told him my tale, he affected to feel for me; beseeched me not to afflict myself, and immediately accompanied me to Mrs. Read, who accommodated me with a first floor on the Point. At that time, sir, I had no more thoughts of him than I have now of you; and I was not a little surprised to receive from him a letter. I will read it to you."

"Avast there!" cried the lieutenant, "Avast, and spare my blushes."

"This is the letter, sir," said Flora.

"DIVINE FLORA!

"The havoc committed by shells thrown into the sea-port of an enemy is a mere trifle in war time, compared, queen of queens, to the destruction of my heart from the fire of your eyes. Yes! Goddess of goddesses! A shot from either one or both of those heavenly bow-chasers has raked my heart fore and aft, and knocked it into splinters; splinters that no carpenter can repair, but the magic of your smiles. Alack! Alack! Every time I lie down in my hammock, I fairly make the clues strand, conceiting I hold you, beautiful Flora, in my arms: and if this be not a proof of my most ardent love, I know not in which point of the compass it lies. Lowering my top-gallant sails to you,

"I am, your dying lieutenant,
"HENRY HURRICANE."

To be grave on hearing this letter read, exceeded all power of face; "Ha! Ha! Ha!" roared the captain. "Bravo, Hurricane! By the piper that played before Moses in the woods, you went upon the right tack. Ay! Let a sailor alone for laying an anchor to windward of a fair lady?"

"Well, sir," continued Mrs. Factor, "the next morning he came ashore in a full suit of uniform, a gold laced hat, and a swaggering sword by his side; and being admitted to my presence, threw himself at my feet. He swore I was more beautiful in my undress (I was then in my deshabille) than a seventy-four gun ship in full sail; and after heaping a thousand praises on what he called my top-lights, he implored I would suffer him to send for a chaplain to splice us together. At first, I could with difficulty repress my smiles; but when I saw the man take his handkerchief from his pocket and cry like a school-boy—"

"I beg pardon for interrupting you, madame," said the captain, "but I suspect Mr. Hurricane had an onion in his pocket."

"Upon my soul, sir," answered the lieutenant, "when I thought she scorned my passion, I wept like a child."

"Belay there!" cried the captain; "you may tell that to the marines, but I'll be d—d if the sailors will believe it."

"Well, sir," returned Flora, "beholding a man weep for me, who I knew but a few days before was burning with impatience to encounter the enemies of his country, my heart was melted into tenderness, and I will candidly acknowledge that the ardour of a young sea-officer soothed into oblivion the memory of my old merchant."

"Yes, Flora," interrupted the lieutenant, "you found me no Plato-comic lover."

"Well, captain," continued Flora, "I now thought myself happy; and I put into the hands of my new husband a bag full of joes; I also accompanied him on board the frigate, and I loved him so in my heart, that I would have gone with him, cheerfully, on a voyage round the world. But I soon found my happiness vanish like a dream. My husband pretended that he had business at the dock-yard, and desired I would amuse myself with a book till he returned. But, suspecting that in reality, he was tired of my company, I followed in another boat, and popped upon my dying lieutenant at the door of a bad house, toying, in the company of some more lieutenants, with several vulgar wenches, whose bold looks would have disgusted a man of the least sentiment."

"Hurricane," said the captain, "here is a grand charge against you.

Were you to be tried by a court-martial, where there was a jury of husbands, you would certainly be transferred to the bottom of Hymen's list."

"Indeed, sir," said the lieutenant, "I am an innocent fellow."

"Yes," rejoined the captain, "so it appears."

"Why, sir," said the lieutenant, "the fact was this: Having dined at the Blue Posts, with three or four of my old messmates, in walking down together to the boat at the Point, we passed a house where there were half a dozen young women before the door. They all of them hailed us; but all I wanted was to luff up, to bear away, and keep clear of the fleet; for I had now got a wife, and had entirely done with drifting. But I was embarrassed in the clinch. For just as I was endeavouring to shove off my boat from them, a girl laid hold of me, stock and flute, and swears I shall not leave her."

"Yes," cried Flora, "she hanged and lolled upon you; and you smiled, and was ready to accompany her into the house."

"How now?" rejoined the lieutenant, "I was trying to get from the house, and had already cleared myself from the arms of the woman, when, lo! my wife appears, and reads the articles of war to me."

"Well," said the captain, "we will hoist the barge in upon the strength of it."

The yard and stay-tackles of the frigate were now hauled down and hooked to the barge; the falls were manned, and the boatswain, together with his three mates, began to tune—

> "The shrill whistle, which doth order give
> To sounds confus'd."

The sailors were making a run of the tackle-falls, and Mr. Hurricane the lieutenant, was heard to exclaim, "Silence there! Step out, men; step out. Walk away with him, cheerily."

In one minute the barge was suspended in the air, between the main and fore-yards. And now were heard the following orders, which had the magic to place the boat upon the booms.

"High enough with the stays. Avast there! Lower away the yards! Lower away the stays! Let go!"

THE FISHERMAN'S TALE

Another Dog-watch tale, probably first told aboard one of the China clippers on a fine evening when she was becalmed.

There is a village in Scotland called Gourloch, situated on the shore of a fine bay, about three or four miles from the town of Deling-burn, and inhabited mostly by fishermen, who let part of their houses in summer months, to people who resort thither for the purpose of bathing.

Perhaps no other part of Scotland, or of the British Islands, presents so much richness and variety of scenery. From the summit of a hill of very precipitous ascent, a little way to the east of the village, the view is particularly fine, embracing an extent of country unusual in such situations, where the intervention of mountains commonly shuts in the landscape too abruptly.

When descending one day, during my visit to the west country, from this commanding spot, I sat down, wearied with the exertion, on a huge isolated rock, near the narrow path, by which alone the hill is accessible. Presently, an elderly man, of grave aspect, and maritime appearance, winding slowly up the hill, came and sat down near me on the rock. I guessed him to be one of the better class of fishermen from the village, who had purchased with the toil of his youth and his manhood, a little breathing-time to look about him in the evening of his days, ere the coming of the night. After the usual salutations we fell into discourse together, and after a pause in the conversation, he remarked, as I thought, in somewhat a disjointed manner, "Is it not strange, sir, the thoughts that sometimes come into the brain of man, sleeping or waking, — like a breath of wind that blows across his bosom, coming he knows not whence, and going he knows not whither, — and yet, unlike the wind, that ruffles not the skin it touches, they leave behind them an impression and a feeling; are as things real and authentic, and may become the springs of human action, and mingle in the thread of human destiny? I was thinking at this moment of something which has sat, for many days past, like a millstone on my mind; and I will tell it to you with pleasure."

So I edged myself closer to him on the stone, that I might hear the better; and without more preamble the Scottish fisherman began his story, as nearly as I remember, in the following words:—

"About six months ago, a wedding took place in our village; and a more comely and better looked-on couple never came together. Mr. Douglas, though the son of a poor man, had been an officer in the army, an ensign I'm thinking; and when his regiment was disbanded, he came to live here on his half-pay, and whatever little else he might have. Jeanie Stuart at the time was staying with an uncle, one of our folk, her parents having been taken away from her; and made up for her board as far as she could, by going in the summer season to sew in the families that came out then, like clocks, from the holes and corners of the great towns, to wash themselves in the caller sea. So gentle she was, and so calm in her deportment, and so fair to look on withal, that even these nobility of the loom and sugar hogshead thought it no dishonour to have her among them; and unknowingly as it were, they treated her just as if she had been of the same human mould with themselves.

"Well, they soon got acquainted, our Jeanie, and Mr. Douglas, and the end of it was, they were married. They lived in a house there, just beyond the point that you may see forms the opposite angle of the bay, not far from a place called Kempuckstane, and Mr. Douglas just employed himself like any of the rest of us — in fishing, and daundering about, and mending his nets, and such like. Jeanie was now a happy woman, for she had aye a mind above the commonalty; and I am bold to say, thought her stay long enough among those would-be gentry, where she sat many a wearisome day, and would fain have retired from their foolishness into the strength and greenness of her own soul.

"But now she had a companion and an equal, and indeed a superior; for Mr. Douglas had seen the world, and could while away the time in discoursing of the ferlies he had seen and heard tell of in foreign lands, among strange people and unknown tongues. And Jeanie listened and listened, and thought her husband the first of mankind. She clung to him as the honey-suckle clings to the tree; his pleasure was her pleasure — his sorrow was her sorrow — and his bare word was her law. One day, about two weeks ago, she appeared dull and dispirited, and complained of the headache, on which Mr. Douglas advised her to go to bed, and rest herself awhile, which she said she would do; and having some business in the village, he went out. On coming back, however, in the forenoon, he found her just in the same spot, leaning her head on her hand, but she told him she was better, and that it was nothing at all. He then began to get his nets ready, saying he was going out with some lads of the village to the deep-sea fishing, and would be back the next day.

"She looked at him long and strangely, as if wondering at what he was doing, and understanding not anything that was going on. But finally when he came to kiss her, and bid her good-bye, she threw her arms round him, and when he would have gone, she held him fast, and her bosom heaved as if her heart would break — but still she said nothing.

" 'Stay with me to-day!' she said at last, 'Depart not this night — just this one night — it is not much to ask — and to-morrow I will not be your hindrance a moment.'

"But Mr. Douglas was vexed at such folly, and she could answer nothing better to his questions, than that a thought had come into her head, and she could not help it. So he was resolved to go, and he kissed her, and threw his nets on his shoulder and went away. For some minutes after, Jeanie stood just on the spot, looking at the door where he had gone out, and then began to tremble all over like the leaf of a tree; at length, coming to herself with a start, she knelt down on both knees, and throwing back her hair from over her forehead, turned her face up towards Heaven, and prayed with a loud voice to the Almighty, 'that she might still have her husband in her arms that night.' For some moments she remained motionless and silent, in the same attitude, till at length a sort of brightness, resembling a calm smile, passed over her countenance, like a gleam of sunshine on the smooth sea, and bending her head low and reverently, she rose up. She then went as usual about her household affairs, and appeared not anything discomposed, but as tranquil and happy as if nothing had happened.

"Now the weather was fine and calm in the morning, but towards the afternoon, it came on to blow — and indeed, the air had been so sultry all day, that the old sea-farers might easily tell there would be a racket of the elements before long. As the wind, however, had been rather contrary, it was supposed the boats could not have got far enough out, to be in the mischief, but would put back when they saw the signs in the sky. But in the meantime the wind increased, till towards night it blew as hard a gale as we have seen in these parts for a long time; the ships out there at the tail of the bank, were driven from their moorings, and two of them stranded on their beam-ends, on the other side; every stick and stitch on the sea, made for any port they could find; and as the night came on, in darkness and thunder, it was a scene that might cow even the hearts that had been brought up on the water, as if it was their proper element, and been familiar with the voice of the tempest from their young days. There was a sad lamenting and murmuring then among the womenfolk — especially them that were kith or kin to the lads on the sea; and they went to one another's houses in the midst of the storm and rain, and put in their pale faces through the darkness, as if searching for hope and comfort, and drawing near to one another, like a flock of frightened sheep, in their fellowship of grief and fear. But there was one who stirred not from her home, and who felt no terror at the shrieking of the night-storm, and sought for no comfort in the countenance of man — and that was the wife of Mr. Douglas. She sometimes, indeed listened to the howling of the sea, that came by fits on her ear like the voice of the water kelpie, and starting, would lay down her work for a moment; but then, she remembered the prayer she had prayed to Him, who holds the reins of the tempest in his hands, and who says to the roaring water, 'Be still,' and they are still — and of the glorious balm she had felt to sink into her heart, at that moment of high and holy communion, even like the dew of Heaven on a parched land. So her soul was comforted, and she said to herself, 'God is not a man that He can lie,' and she rested on this assurance as on a rock, and laughed to scorn the trembling of her woman's bosom — for why — the anchor of her hope was in Heaven, and what earthly storm was so mighty as to remove it? Then she got up and put the room in order, and placed her husband's shoes to air at the fire-side; and stirred up the fuel, and drew in the arm-chair for her weary and storm-beaten mariner. Then would she listen at the door, and look out into the night for his coming, but could hear no sound, save the voice of the waters, and the foot-step of the tempest as he rushed along the deep. She then went in again, and walked to and fro in the room with a restless step, but an unblanched cheek. At last, the neighbours came to her house, knowing that her husband was one of them that had gone out that day, and told her they were going to walk down to the Clough, even in the mirk hour, to try if they could not hear some news of the boats. So she went with them, and we walked all together along the road, it might be some twenty or thirty of us; but it was remarked that though she came not hurriedly, nor in fear, yet she had not even thrown her cloak on her shoulders to defend her from the night air, but came forth with her head uncovered, and in her usual raiment of white, like a bride to the altar. And as we passed along, it must have been a strange sight to see so many pale faces, by the red glare of the torches they carried, and to hear so many human wailings, filling up the pauses of the storm; but at the head of our melancholy procession, there was a calm heart and a firm step, and they were Jeanie's. Sometimes, indeed, she would look back, as some cry of womanish foreboding from behind would smite on her ear, and strange thoughts would crowd into her mind; and once she was heard to mutter — if her prayer had but saved her husband, to bind some other innocent victim on the mysterious altar of wrath! And she stopped for a moment, as if in anguish at the wild imagination. But now as we drew nearer the rock where the lighthouse is built, sounds were heard distinctly on the shore, and we waved the torches in the air, and gave a great shout, which was answered by known voices — for they were some of our own people, and our journey was at an end. A number of us then went on before, and groped our way among the rocks, as well as we could for the darkness; but a woeful tale met our ears; for one of the boats had been shattered to pieces, while endeavouring to land there, — and when we went down, they were just dragging the body of a comrade, stiff and stark, from the sea. When the women behind heard it, there was a terrible cry of dismay, for no one knew but it might have been her own brother or son: and some who held torches dropped them for fear, trembling to have the terrors of their heart confirmed. There, was one, however, who stood calm, and unmoved by the side of the dead body. She spoke some words of holy comfort to the women, and they were silent at her voice. She then stepped lightly forward, and took a torch from the trembling hand that held it, and bent down with it beside the corpse. As the light fell one moment on her own fair face, it showed no signs of womanish failing at the sight and touch of mortality; a bright and lovely bloom glowed on her cheek, and a Heavenly lustre burned in her eye; and as she knelt there, her long dark hair floating far on the storm, there was that in her look which drew the gaze even of that terrified group from the object of their doubt and dread. The next moment, the light streamed on the face of the dead — the torch dropped from her hand — and she fell on the dead body of her husband.

"*Her prayer was granted*. She held her husband in her arms that night, and although no struggles of parting life were heard or seen, she died on his breast."

A DISGUISED SHIP

By W. H. G. KINGSTON

This is another thrilling tale of pirates and how they were nearly trapped by a disguised man-of-war.

The stranger saw our approach, and from the eager way in which we carried our sail, those on board must have had some suspension of the character of the schooner. She was a fine large ship, and was evidently a fast craft, but still the schooner managed to overhaul her. As we had hitherto stood on under easy sail, the *Dove* was able to keep up with us, but now we left her far astern. Before we parted company, however, the captain signalized her where to meet him. I forgot to say that for some time we did not know the name of the pirate chief, but at last we heard him called Captain Bruno. Though this name had a foreign sound, he was, as I have before said, either an Englishman or an American. The schooner was called the *Hawk,* and she was not ill named.

As we drew near the ship we ran up English colours, while in return, up went at her peak the stars and stripes of the United States. On we stood. The ship, so Jerry and I concluded, did not suspect the character of the schooner, for she made no attempt to escape us, but appeared as if those on board expected a friendly greeting. I observed Captain Bruno very frequently turn his telescope towards the stranger, and examine her narrowly. The officers, too, began to talk to each other, and look suspiciously at her. I asked Mr. M'Ritchie, who was near us, whether he thought the pirates would attack the ship and murder the crew, as we believed they had done that of the brig.

"I dread something terrible, but I have very little apprehension for the fate of the people on board the ship," he answered, in a low tone. "In my opinion, the pirates will find that they have caught a tartar. Mark me — yonder craft is no merchantman, but a ship of war either American or English, or perhaps Chilian. I should not be surprised to find that she is on the watch for our friends here. Scarcely do I know what to wish. If they fight at all, they will fight desperately, and we shall run as great a chance of being killed as they will — though, if they are captured, we may regain our liberty. If, on the other hand, they escape, our captivity will be prolonged."

"But if yonder ship prove to be what you suppose, and the schooner is captured, perhaps we may be hung as pirates," said Jerry. "How can we prove that we are honest people?"

"There will be but little difficulty about that," answered Mr. M'Ritchie. "The pirates themselves will acknowledge that we have been brought on board against our will, and the account we can give of ourselves is too circumstantial not to gain credit. At all events, we must hope for the best. But see, Captain Bruno at last suspects that something is wrong."

We had by this time got almost within the ordinary range of a ship's guns. Suddenly the captain sprang to the helm. "Haul aft the main and fore sheets!" he sang out in a voice of thunder. "Brace up the yards! Down with the helm! Keep her as close as she'll go!" The crew flew to obey these orders. They knew full well that their lives depended on their promptness. Already the schooner had approached too near the stranger. That she was a man-of-war, she no longer left us in doubt. Before the orders issued by Captain Bruno were executed, a line of ports were thrown open, and eight long guns were run out, threatening to send us to the bottom if we showed a disposition to quarrel, and aft at her peak flew the stars and stripes of the United States.

The pirates saw that they were caught through their own folly and greediness, but the captain showed himself to be a man of undaunted courage, and full of resources. "Hold on!" he sang out, before a sheet was hauled in. "We may lose our sticks if we attempt to run. I'll try if I cannot deceive these clever fellows, and put them on a wrong scent." The pirates seemed mightily pleased at the thought of playing their enemy a trick, and highly applauded the proposal of their captain. The schooner, therefore, stood steadily on, till she ran close down to the corvette. Then she hove to, well to windward of the ship, however. A boat was lowered, and Captain Bruno, with four of the most quiet-looking of the crew, got into her, and pulled away for the ship. When we hove to, the corvette did the same, an eighth of a mile to leeward of us. We watched the proceedings of the pirate with no little anxiety.

"If that fellow succeeds in deceiving the captain of that ship, I shall acknowledge that impudence will sometimes carry the day," observed Mr. M'Ritchie.

"Couldn't we contrive to make a signal to let the people of the man-of-war know that we are kept here in durance vile?" observed Jerry.

While he was speaking, I looked round, and saw two of the most ruffianly of the crew standing close to us, with pistols cocked in their hands, held quietly down by their sides. I hoped that our captors had not overheard what Jerry had said. I touched him as if by chance on the shoulder, and after his eye had glanced at the pistols he said nothing more about making signals to the corvette. Our position was every instant growing more and more critical. If the pirate captain was seized on board the man-of-war, it was impossible to say how his followers might wreak their vengeance on our heads. We watched him with no little interest, till he ascended with perfect coolness the side of the ship. Our anxiety still further increased, after he reached the deck and disappeared below. Minute after minute slowly passed by, still he did not return. The pirates with their pistols got up closer to us, and one, a most hideous black fellow, kept looking at us and then at his weapon, and grinning from ear to ear, as if he was mightily eager to put it to our heads and pull the trigger. We tried to look as unconcerned as possible, but I must own that I could not help every now and then turning round, to ascertain in what direction the muzzle of the pistol was pointed. The black and his companion looked so malicious, that I feared, whatever occurred, we should still remain in captivity; or should he be suspected and detained, probably the pirates would revenge themselves on us. I was afraid of speaking, and almost of moving, lest, even should I lift an arm, it might be construed into the act of making a signal, and I might get a bullet sent through my head. The American corvette, with her spread of white canvas, looked very elegant and graceful as she lay hove-to, a short distance from us. I wished very much that I was out of the pirate, and safe on board her, even though the former might get free away without the punishment she deserved. But all such hopes it appeared, were likely to prove vain. After the lapse of another ten minutes Captain Bruno himself appeared on deck. As he stood at the gangway, he shook hands cordially with some of the officers. He seemed to be exchanging some good joke with them, for he and they laughed heartily when he went down the side, and stepped into the boat. As he pulled back to the schooner, he waved his hand, and took off his hat with the most becoming courtesy. "Well," thought I to myself, "certainly impudence will sometimes carry the day."

He was soon again on board. "Make sail," he said with a calm smile; "the corvette and we are going in search of a rascally pirate, which has committed all sorts of atrocities. I wonder whether we shall find her." The joke seemed to tickle the fancies of all on deck, for a quiet chuckle was heard on every side. "Keep the rest of the people, below'" he said to Silva; "it might surprise the crew of the man-of-war to see so many ugly fellows on board a quiet trader." The order was strictly obeyed. A few only of the crew appeared on deck, and they were soon seen employed in the usual occupations of a merchantman. The wind was light, so the schooner began leisurely to set sail after sail, till every stitch of canvas she could carry was spread. The corvette did the same, and both vessels were soon going along under a cloud of canvas. The schooner, we saw, had the advantage. Gradually we were increasing our distance from the man-of-war. Captain Bruno chuckled audibly. Still, at times, he cast an anxious look astern.

Jerry and I were allowed to walk about the deck, and to observe what was going on. We remarked the captain watching the corvette. "Depend on it," said Jerry, "he has been leaving some forged papers with the Americans, or playing them some trick which he is afraid will be found out." I thought at first this must be Jerry's fancy. We had no opportunity of asking Mr. M'Ritchie's opinion without being overheard. Away we glided over the smooth ocean. More and more we increased our distance from the corvette. The further ahead we got, the more Captain Bruno seemed pleased; and as I watched his countenance, I became convinced that Jerry's surmises were correct. As we walked the deck and watched the captain, we agreed that if he dared he would like to wet the sails to make them hold more wind. An hour or so passed away, when suddenly the corvette yawed a little, a puff of white smoke appeared, with a sharp report, and a shot came flying over the water close to us. "Ah! have you found me out, my friends?" exclaimed Captain Bruno, leaping down from the taffrail. "All hands on deck! Swing up the long guns! We must try to wing this fellow before he contrives to clip our feathers." In an instant everybody was alert: tackles were rove, and, in a short time, two long and very heavy guns were quickly mounted and run out, and a brisk fire kept up at the corvette. She also continued to fire, but as to do so with effect she had to yaw each time, the schooner, which could fire her stern guns as fast as she could load them, had a considerable advantage. It was a game at long bowls, for the two vessels were already so far apart that it required very good gunnery to send a shot with anything like a correct aim. Silva seemed to be one of the best marksmen on board. Several times, when he fired, the shot went through the sails of the ship of war. The great object of the pirates was to cripple her, as was that of the Americans to bring down some of the schooner's spars. Had the latter found out the trick sooner which had been played them by the pirate, the probabilities are that some of our rigging would have been cut through and we should have been overtaken; now there appeared every chance that we should effect our escape. Still, several of the shots which came from the corvette struck us, or went through our sails; but the damage was instantly repaired. The crew had got up from below a store of spare ropes, and sails, and spars, so that even should we receive any severe injury, it could, we saw, be speedily put to rights. As I before said, our prospects of getting our throats cut, or our brains blown or knocked out, were pretty well balanced against those of our being made free, should the corvette come up with us; so we scarcely knew what to wish for. Every time a shot came near the vessel, the pirates cast such angry glances at us, as if we had something to do with the matter, that we half expected some of them would let fly their pistols and put an end to our lives.

Hour after hour thus passed away. A stern chase is a long chase as everybody knows, and so the Americans must have thought it. The wind continued much as at first for some time. This was all in favour of the schooner, which sailed in a light wind proportionably better than the corvette. Towards evening, however, clouds began to gather in the eastern horizon. The bank rose higher and higher in the sky. Now one mass darted forward — now another — and light bodies flew rapidly across the blue expanse overhead. First the surface of the ocean was crisped over with a sparkling ripple, and then wavelets appeared, and soon they increased to waves with frothy crests; and the schooner sprang forward, the canvas swelling, the braces tautening, and the masts and spars cracking with the additional strain put on them. For some time, though she still continued to fire, scarcely a shot from the man-of-war had come up to us, as we had still further increased our distance from her. She, however, now felt the advantage of the stronger breeze, and our pace became more equal. Still the breeze increased. The captain stood aft, his eye apparently watching earnestly every spar and rope aloft, to see how they stood the increasing strain. Away we now flew, the water hissing under our bows, and the spray leaping up on either side, and streaming over us in thick showers. The white canvas bulged, and tugged, and tugged, till I thought it would carry the masts away, and fly out of the bolt ropes. Captain Bruno, however, gave no orders to take it in. He looked astern; the corvette was going along as fast as we were — perhaps faster. This was not an occasion for shortening sail. The crew seemed to have the same opinion. They were fighting with halters round their necks, everyone full well knew; and though this consciousness may make men desperate when brought to bay, it will assuredly make them run away like arrant cowards if they have a possibility of escape.

The sea by this time had got up considerably, and the schooner began to pitch into it as she ran before the wind. The corvette at first came on rather more steadily, but she likewise soon began to feel the effects of the troubled water; and away we both went, plunging our bows into the sea as we dashed rapidly onward. I could not help feeling that the movements of both vessels showed that serious work was going on. The corvette, with her wide fields of canvas spread aloft, every sail bulging out to its utmost extent, looked as if intent on the pursuit; while the eager, hurried way in which the schooner struggled on amid the foaming waves, made it appear as if she were inbued with consciousness, and was aware that her existence depended on her escaping her pursuer.

It was now blowing a perfect gale. Every instant, as I kept looking aloft, I expected to hear some dreadful crash, and to see the top-masts come tumbling down over our heads; but though the top-gal-lant-masts bent and writhed like fishing-rods with a heavy fish at the end of the line, they were too well set up by the rigging to yield, even with the enormous pressure put on them.

Captain Bruno called Silva to him again. They held a consultation for some minutes. They looked at the corvette, and then at their own sails. The result was, that some of the people were summoned aft, and once more the long guns were run out, and, watching their op-portunity, as the stern of the vessel lifted, they opened fire on their pursuer. "If we could but knock away their fore-top-mast with all that spread of canvas on it, we should very soon run her out of sight," observed Silva, stooping down to take aim. He fired. The canvas stood as before; but, as far as we could judge, the shot had reached the men-of-war, and hands were seen going aloft to repair some damage which it had caused.

The pirates cheered when they saw that the shot had taken effect.

"Hurrah! hurrah! Fire away again, Silva; fire away!" they shouted. Thus encouraged, he continued firing as fast as the guns could be loaded. Shot after shot was discharged. Still the pursuer came on as proudly and gallantly as before. Now and then a shot was fired from her bow chasers; but the difficulty of taking anything like an aim in such a sea was very great, and they generally flew excessively wide of their mark. Silva, indeed, after the first shot, had but little to boast of as a marksman. His anger seemed to rise. He looked with a fierce glance at our pursuer. Both the guns were loaded. He stooped down to one and fired; then, scarcely looking up to watch the result, he went to the other. The schooner was sinking into a sea; as she rose to the summit of the next, a shot left the muzzle of the gun. Away it winged its flight above the foaming ocean. Now the pirates cheered more lustily than ever. Good cause had they. As if by magic, the wide cloud of canvas which had lately towered above the deck of the corvette seemed dissolved in air. The race is not always to the swift, nor does Fortune always favour the best cause. The pirate's shot had cut the corvette's foretop-mast completely in two, and we could see it with its tangled mass of spars, and sails, and rigging hanging over the bows, and still further stopping the ship's way.

"Now we may shorten sail," sang out Captain Bruno. "Aloft, my lads; quick about it." The men needed not to be told of the importance of haste. They flew aloft, and soon handed the top-gallant-sails, and took two reefs in the top-sails. Relieved of the vast weight which had been pressing on her, and almost driving her over, the schooner now flew much more easily over the seas, and with scarcely diminished speed.

We kept watching the corvette. She, of course, could carry sail on her main-mast, but it took some time to clear away the wreck of the fore-top-mast, and to set up the fore-stay, which had been carried away. This it was necessary to do before sail could be set on the main-top-mast. All this work occupied some time, and enabled the schooner to get far ahead. Night, too, was coming on. The weather promised to be very thick. The pirate's chance of escape was very considerable. Our hearts sank within us as we saw the prospect of our prolonged captivity. Proportionably the pirates were elated as they felt sure of escaping. On we flew; the sails of the corvette grew darker and darker, till a thin small pyramid alone was seen rising against the sky in the far horizon. Mr. M'Ritchie, who had joined us on deck, heaved a deep sigh. To him captivity was even more galling than to us. Darkness came on, and the corvette was lost to sight.

It was a terrific night. The wind increased, and the sea got up more than ever — the thunder roared, and the lightning flashed; and as the schooner went plunging away through the foaming ocean, often I thought that she was about to sink down and never to rise again. The dark, stern features of the pirates were lighted up now and again, as they stood at their posts, by the lightning as it played around us; but, strange to say, they appear to have far more dreaded the anger of their fellow-men than they did the fury of the elements. Now and then, perhaps, conscience whispered in the ears of some-one not totally deaf to its influence, that his last hour was approaching and that he must soon stand in the presence of an offended God, whose laws he had long systematically outraged; but, generally speaking, the consciences of that reckless crew had long since been put to sleep, never to awake till summoned, when hope should have fled, at the sound of the last trump. On every side those countenances — bold, fierce, God-defying — broke forth on me out of the darkness as the bright lightning gleamed across them. Each individual face of the dreadful picture is indelibly impressed on my memory. At length the doctor went to his berth, and Jerry and I followed him to the cabin and crept into ours — wet, hungry, and sorrowful. We slept — we had been so excited all day that we could not help that from very weariness; but my dreams, I know, were strangely troubled.

At last I awoke, and found that it was daylight. I sprang up, calling Jerry, and we went on deck to learn what had become of the corvette. She was nowhere to be seen. The wind had gone down very much, but it was still blowing fresh, and a heavy sea was running.

The sky, however, was blue and clear, and the waters sparkled brightly as the beams of the rising sun glanced over them. The schooner had escaped all damage in the gale. Our spirits rose somewhat with the pure fresh air of morning, and very well pleased were we to devour a good breakfast, when our friend the black cook placed it before us on deck, in a couple of large basins, with heavy silver spoons to feed ourselves.

All day we were looking out in expectation of seeing the corvette again. Hour after hour passed, but she did not appear.

CAPE HORN HONEYMOON

By DOUGLAS V. DUFF

The story of a courageous young woman and a formidable journey round Cape Horn.

Millicent Dow kept her promise to marry Charles Nichols as soon as he had won his first command, but she insisted on him keeping his pledge of a honeymoon voyage around the Horn and back again. Millicent was not one of those shoreside girls who marry sailors without realizing the risks they run; her father was a ship-captain, so were her two brothers.

Charles Nichols' new command was the wooden, three-masted barque *Patmos*, outward-bound from Cardiff to Valparaiso with Welsh coal. She was a good ship, well-found with a comfortable cuddy and a large captain's cabin across the whole width aft. Since Millicent was five, she had sailed with her father until she had to go to school on her twelfth birthday. Without rousing any heart-burnings or annoyances, she occasionally visited the galley, bringing variety to the eternal salt-beef, biscuits and dried peas of sailing-ship fare.

Everything went well at first. They were running between the Falklands and Staten Island on the sixty-first day out from Cardiff, having carried a fair wind all the way. Hopes soared that they might round Cape Horn with none of the weeks of beating back and forth so many ships suffered. Even the oldest shellback in the forecastle grunted that, for once, the old superstitions about the bad luck following any ship carrying corpses, women or parsons did not seem to be working out.

When another couple of days would have seen them safe around the world's corner, while they were well to the westward of Cape St. John, the wind backed and, in three hours, was heading them. *Patmos* had to beat south to gain sufficient offing from the rocky coast as the wind strengthened to a whole gale, and the massive greybearded seas of Cape Horn came tramping down.

Millicent had been aboard her father's full-rigged ship when it spent fifty-three days tacking back and forth between the edge of the Antarctic ice and the toe of South America, beaten time after time in their efforts to get west of the Horn. On one occasion during that voyage they emerged 300 miles west of the Cape only to be driven back to forty miles east of it to do the long run south all over again.

The farther south, the greater became the danger from ice and a really vast berg sometimes draws a mile of water. Far smaller ones can sink a ship crashing into it in darkness or the smother of a gale. She was not in the least worried however for, in her superlative faith in her young husband's skill and seamanship, she dismissed all thought of danger. Concentrating on making life a little pleasanter for everyone aboard, she was a tower of strength to the freezing men, drenched with the grey-beards broaching over the sides as the ship fought for victory over Cape Stiff.

They were well down south, with the gale at its fiercest, the ship washing down fore and aft, under close-reefed storm canvas, when disaster struck her. Captain Nichols was having high-tea in the reeling cuddy, waiting to go on deck and relieve the Mate when they would tack in an hour's time to begin the reach to the north. Millicent, proudly displaying a new dish she had made from the inevitable salt-beef, dried peas and biscuits, was taking no notice of the mad motion of the barque, the tremendous noise of the gale in her rigging and the smash of the ice-cold sea against the hull and along the decks.

Feet clattered down the ladder from the poop above and the streaming, oilskinned figure of the Boatswain almost fell into the warm and brightly lighted cuddy. He gazed at the clean linen beneath the "fiddles" on the table holding the dishes from sliding off on to the deck, and looked very scared.

Captain Nichols, his fork balanced, glared at him. Foremast hands were not often seen in the cuddy, especially at meal-times. Before he could bark an angry question the Boatswain blurted out:

"There's smoke pouring into the forecastle, Cap'n."

The Mate's deep voice boomed behind him, with unaccustomed anxiety.

"Aye, I'm afraid she's on fire, sir," he said ."Looks like the cargo's ablaze."

Captain Nichols grabbed his own oilskins, swinging in an arc on the white-enamelled bulkhead, tied the chinstay of his southwester and turned to his wife as he went.

"Don't worry, my dear," he said. "It won't be anything we can't tackle."

She was quite sure that it could not be. She was content to leave it to him and busied herself helping the steward clear the table.

It was bitterly cold on deck. The spindrift and spray froze as it fell. Aloft they had to chop at tackles and blocks to keep them from icing solid. But the coal in the holds was well alight, and it had been for days. Now that it had begun to find air, the flames were spreading quickly. Working like demons they battened her down afresh, anxious to stop any vents.

They tacked ship and ran north, with spontaneous combustion growing more violent with every hour, a westerly gale hammering them as they scuttled towards the toe of America. The decks were constantly wet with broaching, freezing seas. Two days later, the raging furnace burned through the oakum caulking between the planks of the deck — making the pitch in the seams melt and run. The smoke which curled up from the cracks added to the intensity of the inferno in her holds.

The fumes and soot filled the cuddy and the cabins under the poop; they drove the men out of the forecastle. Millicent, who had taken over all the cook's duties to free one more hand for the fire-fighting, moved her things out of the lovely, white-enamelled stern cabin which her husband had so lovingly fitted for her, to the coach on the poop, a small, dark shelter with wind and sea for ever playing on it.

The seamen took heart from the plucky nineteen-year-old girl who never faltered, and was always cheerful, ever ready with a joke. She told them her husband was the best man in the world to have aboard in such an emergency and, because she believed it herself, the men did so as well. The morale aboard *Patmos* was superb and its cornerstone was Millicent's faith in Captain Nichols.

As they dragged northwards there were new dangers. The wooden hatch-covers, charred and burned through, collapsed and at all costs had to be renewed. They must be kept air-tight if the wooden ship was not to be transformed into a blazing torch. There was no chance of their abandoning her; no boat could have lived in the great seas running. They were not likely to be picked up at that time of year in those deserted seas. Their one chance was to reach the coast, find shelter in some cove or bay and only then see what was best to be done.

Day and night, never relaxing for a moment, all hands fought to keep the air from the flames. The 'tween-deck was aflare; whenever *Patmos* rolled and the water she had just shipped drained into the lee-scuppers, lines of smoke oozed from the burning spaces in the deck planking. The sea-water leaking through added to the risk of explosion.

Millicent kept the coppers boiling so that the men could have hot food and drink to help them in the never-ending labour. The little galley was filled with choking smoke from below, welling up through the deck. When they were still fifty miles from Cape Horn the hatch-covers, pounded by great seas, finally collapsed. Water rose rapidly in her; the well showed deeper soundings every hour. The fresh-water tank spouted steam like a giant kettle.

Captain Nichols drove the stumbling, exhausted crew to the smoke-streaked braces, halyards and sheets, and brought *Patmos* over on to the other tack where she lay in a little more easily. Then, with flames licking from the ever-widening gap of the collapsed hatches, he drove her north again, until, when the towering cliffs of Cape Horn were in sight, the flames burst through the poop and drove everyone from the helm and quarter-deck.

There was nothing more any man could do to save her. They were in sight of the land, but too late to run her into shelter. The men roused out the longboat from its lashings on the booms. One of Millicent's self-imposed duties during the long days while the men were busy elsewhere, had been to make sure no embers or tongues of fire reached the boat. She helped the steward load biscuits and salt-beef from the smouldering stores. Some of the boiling water in the fresh-water tank was drawn off and put into breakers to be stowed in the boat. She rescued a thick Shetland shawl, one of her wedding presents, and, because he was afraid she might be swept away by the seas smashing across the almost submerged waist, her husband carried her to the forward part of the blazing hull. He snatched some oilskins and bade her get into them under the lee of the galley while he saw to the launching of the longboat.

All hands were mustered on the forecastle, the only part clear of the flames as she lay hove-to. The longboat was lashed to the forecastle-rail and Millicent was passed down into it. The hands followed her, while Captain Nichols took a last look around to make sure there was no hope of saving her. He had sent the ship's papers and log-book into the stern-sheets. Night was coming on, the wind making the ever-increasing furnace roar with a hundred tongues, the flames leaping higher as they found fresh oxygen. Sheets of fire streamed down to leeward, showering cascades of white-hot sparks. Her staysails suddenly took light and her bows fell away from the wind as the canvas disappeared. Spars cracked, red ribbons sketched the tracery of her standing and running rigging. The masts were smouldering even though, to delay the flame, they had cut away the coatings earlier.

Patmos swung; the stream of white-hot flame no longer streamed aft as it had done while she lay head-to-wind. Soon it would be raking the forecastle. Seas smashing inboard over her bulwarks, raised mighty clouds of steam as they struck the red fury below. Captain Nichols jumped into the longboat as the ship settled almost awash. Without fuss, they thrust clear of the bows and bowsprit. *Patmos* was settling by the stern. Lit by the glare of the fire, great billows of yellow-black, greasy smoke belched from the hatches. White steam, flying spray, diamond bright in the glare, made a terrific picture of a ship lying down to die in desolation.

There was a chance she might remain afloat if the sea drowned out the fires. If she did, even as a water-logged hulk they might yet be able to save her; other ships have been brought back from the dead. They watched her all through the night. By dawn the fires were out but the ship was still wallowing on the surface. Captain Nichols at the steering-oar, was holding the boat's head up to sea and weather.

They lay watching her all that day, while *Patmos* settled deeper and the men bailed out the icy water from the longboat. After the ship finally plunged, Captain Nichols drove the boat northwards, hoping to find some inlet or bay where they could land. Millicent never flagged. A tiny figure in her big oilskins above her thick shawl, she saw to the issuing of food and water as it was ordered and sang to the exhausted men the songs they had learned when they were boys.

The next night was the most frightening and terrible of all. They bailed and pulled and tried to shelter themselves, struggling to make northward progress but having to round-to and ride the squalls every little while. When dawn broke at last they saw, as they rode the crests, the jagged outlines of the Cordilleras above the coastline of Tierra del Fuego. Close inshore, a large fourmasted barque, sailing close-hauled, was fighting hard to claw-off the spouting reefs, her lower topsails goose-winged as she battled for her life.

She represented less risks than landing on that merciless shore and the captain urged the men to a last effort, fighting to meet the barque as she drifted to leeward. They struggled for several hours, the voice of Millicent, cracked and hoarse, singing in time with the swing of the oars, adding her own tiny strength to double-bank the rowers. It was almost noon before the ship saw them and let them know she had done so by firing a gun. They did not hear the report in the confusion of wind and sea but the puff of grey-white smoke, whipped quickly away from her rusted sides, told them what they wanted to know. As she approached the castaways saw her rails were lined with faces. She was an iron ship, red with rust-streaks, low in the water, rolling wildly as she threshed slowly ahead, with the wind as far forward of her beam as it could go and still move her.

A line snaked down. Millicent, despite her protest, was secured to its bight and hauled smartly inboard when the *Pretricia* rolled towards the boat. *Patmos*'s men scrambled into her chains, the last to go being Captain Nichols, with the ship's papers safely slung around his shoulders in a canvas bag. As he jumped, the longboat filled with a broaching sea and was swept away, capsizing as she went.

Millicent was waiting for her husband at the head of the poop-ladder, the well-deck awash below her as seas broached over the bulwarks. Along the starboard side the grim coast lay threatening and close, the outermost breakers bursting within a mile. The captain of the *Pretricia* was elderly, maybe twenty years the senior of Millicent's husband, grey-faced and haggard, exhaustion in every line.

"Maybe you'll regret leaving your own boat," he said, nodding towards the coast. There were four men at the wheel with the growl of the surf roaring clear above the noises of the gale. As the squalls hit her she listed over, dragging lumpishly down to leeward, drifting closer to the rocks, unable to claw close enough into the wind to maintain headway against the force driving her helplessly on to a dead lee-shore. It was the first time Captain Nichols had noticed the barque's condition — he had been far too busy about his own affairs.

"We've been steadily losing ground for hours," *Pretricia*'s captain told them. "We're only hanging on by the skin of our teeth. We're bound to strike on this wretched, iron-bound coast before we're much older."

As he spoke the wind veered a little, blowing even more directly on-shore, as though Old Dame Sea meant to show them she intended to have their bones on the sea-floor to lie among the rusted ribs of their ship. The gale rose into stronger, gustier squalls. Captain Nichols looked around swiftly, but there was nothing he could say though he thought he saw a fighting-chance. A castaway cannot tell the captain of the rescuing ship what he ought to do. Captain Nichols' face was set hard, fighting to keep his tongue between his teeth.

Millicent knew just what was happening between the two captains. She was bred to the sea and understood its etiquette.

"My husband knows these coasts well, Captain," she said. "Maybe he could tell you something about them if you are not so conversant with them."

"I'm not," the old man replied. "I've not been so near Cape Horn since I was an apprentice and that's nearly forty years ago. Think you can do anything, Captain?" he asked, whirling on Nichols.

"It's your ship, sir," the younger man demurred. "I would think it impertinent to say anything."

"She's doomed. You take her, young man. It won't make any difference. It's impossible to stop her drifting ashore, especially now that the wind's strengthening."

"Do you really wish me to take charge?" Captain Nichols wanted to make sure.

"The captain has asked you to give him your advice, dear," Millicent put in, very quietly, as though she were chiding him for making things needlessly embarrassing for their host. She was still in her oilskins, the soaked shawl visible above the collar. Spray rattled against her sou'-wester; the roar of the surf was perceptibly louder, the line of spouting breakers much closer.

"I'll try, sir," Nichols replied and turned to the rail. "All hands!" he yelled, to the *Pretricia*'s crew and his own rescued men. "All hands. Shake out those goose-wings! Loose the topsails. For your own hides' sake, up with you all! Up, men! Up and don't stand there dawdling." He sprang to the side of the struggling helmsmen to con the ship.

New hope surged along the streaming decks. Men leaped to obey, the ratlines were black with seamen racing aloft as the ship rolled steeply. Captain Nichols glanced approvingly at her new steel standing rigging, her fine metal turn-buckless and her strong iron masts.

301

Here was a ship that could take strain and punishment far better than his old wooden *Patmos*. With his double crew he roused-down the chain-sheets of the wildly threshing lower-topsails, manned the upper-topsail halyards on the fore-, main- and mizzen-masts, pinching her by inches closer up to windward, piling on the heavy canvas in a fashion that thoroughly alarmed the old skipper. The four hands at the wheel fought like madmen to keep control as Captain Nichols ordered the helm eased. *Pretricia* was borne over and down, until her lee-rail lay buried deep, the water lapping her mast-coasts. She was almost on her beam-ends, her iron hull groaning with the punishment, her weather-bilge thundering like a great drum under the pounding of the seas hitting it hard.

But she was moving — moving ahead, no longer stalled and sagging down to leeward. The men worked like demons. As fast as sails were blown out of their bolt ropes they were replaced; staysails were rigged one after another as Captain Nichols piled on the canvas until it seemed sure she must capsize. As she gathered headway, he eased her a little, so that she trembled in the stroke of the breaking seas.

Millicent was still on deck. She had found a rope's-end and taken a turn of it round her body, lashing herself to the mizzen-mast. She was watching every order and movement her husband made, listening for each of his orders, joying to see the hard-driven seamen leaping to obey, taking the craziest of risks in the rigging and along the yards, fighting like demons for the ship's life and their own continued existence. The old captain had gone below, sure that the young man above would turn his ship keel-up to the lowering scud above.

For many minutes victory or defeat hung balanced. Then, as though *Pretricia* recognized her master, she met and bested the sea. Farther and farther astern the deadly coast faded into the distance until it was hidden in the spume and the wrack. As the deep Antarctic night fell, the fine Clyde-built ship ratched clear and found plenty of sea-room. Captain Nichols, when the ship was clawing clear, stepped across to the small figure against the mizzen-mast.

His nineteen-year-old wife had her back to him. She did not even see him as he came closer, for she was kissing the mast. He heard her say:

"Bless you, my dear old lady! I knew you could do it with Charles to help you."

THE LOSS OF THE "BETSEY"

By GEORGE WINSLOW BARRINGTON

One of the classic tales of survival in open boats at sea. The "Betsey" was a small sloop sailing in the Caribbean.

The sloop *Betsey,* commanded by Philip Aubin, and bound for Surinam, sailed from Carlisle Bay, in the island of Barbadoes, on the 1st of August, 1756. The vessel was about eighty tons burthen, built entirely of cedar, and freighted by Messrs. Roscoe and Nyles, merchants of Bridgetown, with a cargo consisting of all kinds of provisions and horses. The latter part of the cargo was in consequence of a law which the Dutch passed, that no English vessel should be permitted to trade with the colony, unless horses constituted a part of her cargo, as they were then greatly in want of a supply of these animals; and this condition was so rigidly enforced by the Dutch, that if the horses chanced to die on the passage, the master of the vessel was obliged to preserve the ears and hoofs of the animals, and to make oath, upon entering the port of Surinam, that they were alive when he embarked and destined for that colony.

The coast of Surinam, Berbice, Demerara, Oronooka, and all the adjacent ports are low lands, and inundated by large rivers which discharge themselves into the sea. All along this coast the bottom is composed of a kind of mud or clay, in which the anchors sink to the depth of three or four fathoms, and upon which the keel sometimes strikes without stopping the vessel. The sloop being at anchor three leagues and a half from the shore, in five fathoms water, the mouth of the river Demerara bearing S. by S.W., and it being the rainy season, the crew drew up water from the sea for their use, which was as sweet and good as river water. The current occasioned by the trade winds, and the numerous rivers which fall into the sea, carried them at the rate of four miles an hour towards the West and North-west.

In the evening of the 4th of August, they were tacking about between the latitudes of ten and twelve degrees north, with a fresh breeze, which obliged them to reef the sails. At midnight the captain found that the wind increased in proportion as the moon, which was then on the wane, rose above the horizon, and that the sloop, which was deeply laden, laboured excessively; he therefore would not retire to rest until the weather became more moderate, but told his mate, whose name was Williams, to bring him a bottle of beer, and both of them sat down. While thus occupied, the vessel suddenly turned with her broadside to windward. The captain called to one of the seamen to put the helm-a-weather, but he replied it had been so for some time; he then directed the mate to see if the cord was not entangled, but he answered that it was not. At this instant the vessel swung round with her head to the sea and plunged, and immediately her head filled in such a manner that she could not rise above the surf, which broke over them to the height of the anchor-stocks; and they were very soon up to their necks in water, and everything in the cabin was washed away, while some of the crew, which consisted of nine men, were drowned in their hammocks without uttering a cry or groan. When the wave had passed, the captain took the hatchet that was hanging up near the fire-place, to cut away the shrouds, so as to prevent the ship from upsetting, but his efforts were in vain. The vessel upset and turned over again, with her masts and sails in the water; the horses rolled one over the other and were drowned, forming altogether a spectacle the most melancholy that can be conceived.

They had but one small boat, about twelve or thirteen feet in length, and she was fixed, with a cable coiled inside of her, between the pump and the side of the ship. Providentially for their preservation, there was no occasion to lash her fast, but at this time they entertained no hope of seeing her again, as the large cable within her, together with the weight of the horses and their stalls, entangled one among another, prevented her from rising to the surface of the water.

In this dreadful situation, holding on by the shrouds, and slipping off his clothes, the captain looked around him for some plank or empty box, by which he might preserve his life as long as it should please the Almighty, when he perceived his mate and two seamen hanging by a rope, and imploring God to receive their souls. He then advised them to undress, as he had done, and to endeavour to seize the first object that could assist them in preserving their lives. Williams, the mate, followed his advice, stripped himself quite naked, and instantly betook himself to swimming, at the same time looking out for anything he could find. He had not been in the water many minutes, before he cried out, "Here is the boat, keel uppermost!" upon which the captain immediately swam to him, and found him, then set to work to turn her, but their exertions were unavailing, till at length Williams, who was the strongest and heaviest man of the two, contrived to set his feet against the gunwale of the boat, while he laid hold of the keel with his hands, and with a violent effort nearly succeeded in turning her. The captain being to windward, pushed and lifted her, and with the assistance of the surf, they turned her over; but she was full of water. The captain then got into her, and endeavoured, by means of a rope belonging to the rigging, to draw her to the mast of the vessel, as, in the intervals between the waves, the mast always rose to the height of fifteen or twenty feet above the water. He passed the end of the rope fastened to the boat once round the head of the mast, keeping hold of the end; and each time that the mast rose out of the water, it lifted up both him and the boat: he then let go the rope, and by this expedient the boat was about three-fourths emptied; but having nothing to enable him to disengage her from the mast and shrouds, they fell down upon him, driving him and the boat again under water.

After repeated attempts to empty her, in which he was cruelly wounded and bruised, he began to haul the boat, thus filled with water, towards the vessel by the shrouds; but, by this time, the sloop had sunk to such a depth, that only a small part of her stern was visible, upon which the mate and two other seamen were holding fast by a rope. He then threw himself into the water, with the rope that was attached to the boat in his mouth, and swam towards them, to give them the end of the rope to lay hold of, in the hope that by their united strength they would be able to haul the boat over the stern of the vessel, to accomplish which they exerted their utmost efforts; and at this instant the captain nearly had his thigh broken by a shock of the boat, as he was between her and the ship. At length they succeeded in hauling her over the stern, but in this manœuvre they had the misfortune to break a hole in her bottom. The captain, as soon as his thigh was a little recovered from the blow, jumped into her with one of the men, and stopped the leak with a piece of his coarse shirt. This man not being enabled to swim, had not stripped like the others, and had thus preserved his coarse shirt, a knife that was in his pocket, and an enormous hat in the Dutch fashion. The boat being fastened to the rigging, was no sooner cleared of the greatest part of the water, than the captain's dog came to them, running along the gunwale; they took him in, and returned thanks to Providence for thus sending provision for a time of necessity. A moment after the dog had entered, the rope broke with a jerk of the vessel, and the boat drifted away, leaving the mate and the other seamen hanging to the wreck. The mate had fortunately found a small spare topmast, which afterwards served them for a rudder, and with this they swam to the boat, where they were assisted in by the others, and soon afterwards they lost sight of their ill-fated barque.

It was then about four o'clock in the morning, as they judged by the dawn of day, which was then beginning to appear, so that about two hours had elapsed since the calamity that had compelled them to abandon their vessel. That which prevented her foundering sooner, was their having on board about a hundred and fifty barrels of biscuit, as many or more sacks of flour, and three hundred firkins of butter, all of which floated upon the water, and were soaked through but slowly. As soon as they were clear of the wreck, they kept the boat before the wind as well as they could; and when it grew light, they perceived several articles that had floated from the vessel. Soon after the captain saw his box of clothes and linen, which had been carried out of the cabin by the violence of the waves. This unexpected circumstance gave great joy, as the box contained some bottles of orange and lime juice, a few pounds of chocolate, sugar, &c. Reaching over the gunwale of the boat they laid hold of the box, and made use of every effort to open it on the water, for they could not think of getting into the boat a box of size and weight sufficient to sink her; but in spite of all their endeavours, they were, to their unutterable disappointment, obliged to leave it behind, with all the good things it contained; and to add to their distress, the efforts they had made to accomplish what they desired, had almost filled their boat with water, and had more than once nearly sunk her.

They however had the good fortune to pick up thirteen onions, but were unable to reach any more, although they saw many. These thirteen onions and the dog, without a single drop of fresh water, or any liquor whatever, were all that they had to subsist upon; and they were at that time, according to the computation of the captain, about fifty leagues from land, having neither masts, sails, nor oars to direct them, nor any description of article, except the knife of a sailor who could not swim, his shirt, a piece of which they had already used to stop the leak in their boat, and his wide trousers. This day they cut the remainder of his shirt into strips, which they twisted for rigging, and then went to work alternately, to loosen the planks with which the boat was lined, by dint of time and patience, cutting round the heads of the nails that fastened them. Of these planks they made a kind of mast, which they fixed, by tying it to the foremost bench; a piece of board was substituted for a yard, to which they fastened the two parts of the trousers which served for sails, and assisted in keeping the boat before the wind, while they steered with the small topmast, which the mate had brought on board.

As the pieces of plank which they had detached from the inside of the boat were too short, and were not sufficient to go quite round the edge, they were obliged, when the sea ran very high, to lie down several times along the gunwale on each side, with their backs to the water, in order to prevent the waves from entering the boat; and thus with their bodies to repel the surf, whilst the other, with the Dutch hat, was constantly employed in baling out the water; besides which the boat continued to make water at the leak, which they were unable to stop entirely.

It was in this melancholy situation, and all of them quite naked, that they kept the boat before the wind as well as they could. The night of the first day after their shipwreck arrived before they had well completed their sail; but although it became quite dark, they contrived to keep the boat running before the wind at the rate of about a league an hour. The second day was more calm; they each ate an onion, at different times, and soon began to feel the effect of thirst. Towards night the wind became violent and variable, sometimes blowing from the north, which caused them great uneasiness, as they were then obliged to steer south, in order to keep the boat before the wind, and their only hope of being saved was on their proceeding from east to west.

On the third day their sufferings were excessive, as they had not only to endure hunger and thirst, in themselves sufficiently painful, but also the heat of the sun, which scorched them in such a manner, that from the neck to the feet their skin was as red and as full of blisters as if they had been burned by a fire. Smarting under this accumulation of bodily pain, the captain seized the dog, and plunged the knife into his throat. They caught his blood in the hat, receiving in their hands and drinking what ran over, and then drinking in turn out of the hat, with which they felt themselves very much refreshed.

The fourth day the wind was extremely violent, and the sea very high, so that they were more than once on the point of perishing; it was on this day, in particular, that they were obliged to make a rampart of their bodies to repel the waves. About noon a ray of hope dawned upon them, but only to experience bitter disappointment. They perceived a sloop, commanded by Captain Southey, a particular friend of Captain Aubin, which like the *Betsey*, belonged to the island of Barbadoes, and was bound for Demerara; and this vessel came so near that they could see the crew walking upon the deck, and shouted to them; but unfortunately they were neither seen nor heard. Being obliged by the violence of the gale to keep the boat before the wind, for fear of foundering, they had passed her a great distance before she crossed them, the sloop steering direct south, and they bearing away to the west. This disappointment so discouraged the two seamen, that they refused to make any more exertions to save their lives; in spite of all that could be said, one of them would do nothing, not even bale out the water, which was every minute gaining upon them. In vain did the captain have recourse to entreaties, and, falling on his knees, implored the assistance of the obdurate seaman, he remained unmoved; till at length the captain and mate prevailed by threatening to kill them instantly with the topmast, which they used to steer by, and to kill themselves afterwards, in order to put a period to their misery. This menace seemed to make some impression on them, and they resumed their occupation of baling as before.

The captain this day set the others the example of eating a piece of the dog with some onions: it was with great difficulty that he swallowed a few mouthfuls, but in the course of an hour afterwards he felt that this small morsel of food had given them new vigour. The mate, who was of a much stronger constitution, ate more. One of the men also tasted it; but the other, whose name was Comings, absolutely refused to swallow a morsel, protesting that he could not.

The fifth day was more calm, and the sea much smoother. At daybreak they perceived an enormous shark, fully as large as the boat, which followed them for several hours as a prey that was evidently destined for him; they also found in the boat a flying-fish, which had dropped there during the night; this they divided into four parts, which they chewed to moisten their mouths, and it proved a very seasonable relief, though so little adequate to their necessities, that on this day, when pressed with hunger and despair, the mate, Williams, had the generosity to exhort his companions to cut off a piece of his thigh, in order to refresh themselves with the blood and support life. The wind freshened during the night, and they had several heavy showers, when they tried to get some rainwater by wringing the trousers which served them for a sail, but when they caught it in their mouths it proved to be as salt as that of the sea, the men's clothes having been so often soaked with sea-water, that they, as well as the hat, were impregnated with salt. They had, therefore, no other resource, but to open their mouths, and catch the drops of rain as they fell upon their tongues to cool them; after the shower was over they again fastened the trousers to the mast.

On the sixth day the seamen, notwithstanding all the remonstrances of the captain and mate, persisted in drinking sea-water, which purged them so excessively that they fell into a kind of delirium, and were no longer of the slightest service in managing their frail bark. As for the others, they each kept a nail in their mouths, and, from time to time, sprinkled their heads with water to cool them; from these ablutions they found their heads were more easy, and themselves generally better. They also tried several times to eat of the dog's flesh with a morsel of onion, and thought themselves fortunate if they could get down three or four mouthfuls.

On the seventh day the weather was fine, with a moderate breeze, and the sea perfectly calm. The two men who had drunk sea-water grew so weak about noon that they began to talk wildly, like those who are light-headed, not knowing any longer whether they were at sea or on shore. The captain and mate were also so weak that they could hardly stand on their legs, or steer the boat in their turns, much less bale the water from the boat, which now made considerably at the leak.

On the morning of the eighth day, John Comings died, and about three hours afterwards the other seaman, George Simpson, also expired. That same evening, just before the sun had withdrawn his light, they had the inexpressible satisfaction of discovering the high lands on the west point of the island of Tobago. Hope inspired them with courage and infused new strength into their limbs. They kept the head of the boat towards the land all night, with a light breeze and a strong current, which was in their favour. The captain and mate were that night in an extraordinary situation; their two comrades lying dead before them, with the land in sight, having very little wind to approach it, and being assisted only by the current, which drove strongly to westward. In the morning, according to their own computation, they were not more than five or six leagues from the land, and that happy day was the last of their sufferings at sea. They kept steering the boat the whole day towards the shore, though they were no longer able to stand. Towards evening the wind lulled, and at night it was a perfect calm; but about two o'clock in the morning the current cast them on the beach of the island of Tobago, at the foot of a high shore, between Little Tobago and Man-of-War Bay, which is the easternmost part of the island. The boat soon bulged with the shock, and her two fortunate occupants crawled to the shore, leaving the bodies of their two deceased comrades in the boat, and the remainder of the dog, which, by this time, had become quite putrid.

They clambered as well as they could on all-fours along the high coast, which rose almost perpendicularly to the height of three or four hundred feet. A great number of leaves had fallen on the place where they were, from the numerous trees which grew over their heads, and these they collected to lay down upon while they began to search for water, and found some in the holes of the rocks, but it was brackish, and not fit to drink. They also found on the rocks several kinds of shell-fish, some of which they broke open with a stone, and chewed them to moisten their mouths.

Between eight and nine o'clock in the morning they were perceived by a young Carib, who was alternately swimming and walking towards the boat. As soon as he had reached it, he called his companions with loud shouts, at the same time making signs of the greatest compassion. His comrades instantly followed him, and swam towards the captain and mate, whom they had perceived almost at the same time. The eldest of the party, a man apparently about sixty years of age, approached them with the two youngest, whom they afterwards learned were his son and son-in-law. At the sight of the poor sufferers, these compassionate men burst into tears, while the captain endeavoured, by words and signs, to make them comprehend that he and his mate had been at sea for nine days, in want of everything. The Caribs understood a few French words, and signified that they would fetch a boat to convey them to their dwelling. The old man then took a handkerchief from his head, and tied it round the captain's head, and one of the young Caribs gave Williams his straw hat; the other swam round a projecting rock and brought them a calabash of fresh water, some cakes of cassava, and a piece of boiled fish; but they had been so long without food that they were unable to eat any. The two others took the corpses out of the boat and laid them upon the rock, after which all three of them hauled the boat out of the water. They then departed to fetch their canoe, leaving the poor shipwrecked mariners with every mark of the utmost compassion.

About noon they returned in their canoe, to the number of six, and brought with them, in an earthen pot, something resembling soup, which they thought to be delicious. Of this they partook, but the captain's stomach was so weak that he immediately cast it up again. In less than two hours they arrived at Man-of-War Bay, where the huts of the Caribs were situate. They had only one hammock, in which the hospitable natives laid the captain, while the women, who were in the hut, made them a very agreeable mess of herbs and broth of quatracas and pigeons. They also bathed his feet with a decoction of tobacco and other plants, and every morning the man lifted him out of the hammock and carried him in his arms beneath a lemon tree, where he covered him with plantain leaves to screen him from the sun. There they anointed the bodies of the poor sufferers with a kind of oil, to cure the blisters raised by the sun. Their compassionate entertainers had even the generosity to give each of them a shirt and a pair of trousers, which they procured from the ships that came from time to time to trade with them for turtles and tortoiseshell.

The method pursued by the natives in healing the numerous

wounds which had broken out on the bodies of these unfortunate mariners, was this: after they had completely cleansed the wounds, they kept the patient with his legs suspended in the air, and anointed them morning and evening, with an oil extracted from the tail of a small crab, something resembling what the English called the soldier-crab, because its shell is red, and which is obtained by bruising a quantity of the ends of their tails, and putting them to digest upon the fire in a large shell. After thus anointing them they were covered with plantain leaves till the wounds were healed.

Thanks to the nourishing food procured them by the Caribs, and the humane attention which was bestowed upon them, the captain was able, in about three weeks' time, to support himself upon crutches, like a person recovering from a very severe illness; but anxious to return to his own friends as early as possible, he cut his name with a knife upon several boards, and gave them to different Caribs to show them to any ships which might chance to approach the coast. Still they almost despaired of seeing any arrive, when a sloop from Oronooko, laden with mules, and bound for St. Pierre, in the island of Martinique, touched at the sandy point on the west side of Tobago. The Indians showed the crew a plank, upon which was carved the name of Captain Aubin, and acquainted them with the dreadful situation of him and his companion, which those on board the vessel related, when they arrived at St. Pierre. Several merchants with whom Captain Aubin was acquainted, and who traded under Dutch colours, happened to be there at the time, and they transmitted the information to the owners of the *Betsey*, Messrs Roscoe and Nyles, who instantly despatched a small vessel in quest of the survivors, who, after living about nine weeks with this benevolent and hospitable tribe of savages, embarked and left them; their regret at doing so being only equal to the joy and surprise which they had experienced at meeting with them.

THE WRECKER'S REVENGE

An old wrecking tale which was once a favourite with seamen in the Dog-watches when fine weather kept a sailing-ship snoring happily along with no call to tend sheets and braces.

At the period when this narrative commences, the unhappy Lord of Dunraven had suffered that dreadful domestic bereavement, the deaths of three children at once, by different accidents (all *drowned*), which the whole country regarded as God's revenge against wrecking, and which is recorded by Grose. One son remained, though long un-heard of, who had embarked long since in merchandise to redeem the fortunes of the family, and it was for him (as the more charitable whispered) that the wretched father persisted in his crime, having for his agent and accomplice a desperate character, a ruined smuggler and pirate, for he had once an armed vessel of his own, who resided in a hovel up a creek of that rocky coast, though believed to hoard treasures still. Ralpho or Ralph, the Diaowl ("the Devil") was his nickname, also "Ralph Ironhand", he having lost a hand in a conflict with officers of justice sent against him by Mr. Vaughan, then a real philanthropist, generous but reckless, exerting his strong genius in planning a lighthouse for the sunken rocks thereabout, in framing an apparatus for saving men on wrecks &c. With this man (though be-come his deadly enemy) did his nature's dire revolution incline him to associate, not for the salvation, but destruction of man's life! So prone is human nature to depravation — so uncertain the duration of moral character! *"Corruptio optimi pessima"* well applies to man's nature. Passion (whose name is Legion) resembles a glorious river banked with galaxies of June flowers, with meadows green as spring's buds and beautified with the whitest flocks, which one day's storm changes into a foul flood, burying them all; and the next shows the ruin it has wrought — sheepfolds, prostrate shepherds drooping in misery, flowers, grasses, all viewless under the black slime and sordes which its sky-blue beauty held concealed. The passionate noble heart — the great gifted mind — unguarded by some humbler

315

but vital quality, is but like a palace on fire, a mountain palace, glorified and exalted only to become a dismal beacon to all men, and as a child playing but with fire, or a peasant with his pipe's embers, may be the cause of turning a tower of centuries' standing into smoke and black ashes, so may unwatched moral influences, of the meanest nature at first, prove the dismal incendiaries in the citadel of men, and fire the very palace of the soul.

"Yes, there are real mourners; I have seen
A fair sad girl, mild, suffering, and serene." — CRABBE.

And such an one, — so fair, so mild, so suffering, — was to be seen for years frequenting that shore of romantic grandeur, on one of whose maritime precipices towered the grey strength of the ancient castle of Dunraven. The fair mourner of Crabbe is depicted as haunting a churchyard, and our gentle Welsh maiden might almost be said to resemble her therein, for that great, grand sea, by which she walked continually, was too truly to her a mighty burial-place. It had buried her first young hopes, in love at least, and sad fond fancy for ever sounded in her sunken heart a knell for that love's object — for ever whispered that it had already buried him also — her first love, playmate, everything! — the fond, the faultless, the bold, the beautiful Septimus Vaughan, the self-banished heir of the manor of Dunraven. Margaret of Llangoed was the daughter of a gentleman residing near the castle, but had lost both parents long since, and had been left under the guardianship of Mr. Vaughan, to whose younger children, after the death of his wife, she had supplied the care of a mother, till their lives were lost as related.

There was at that time a humble little sea-side hostelry, or "tavarn", as the Welsh term it, not far from Dunraven, whose old hostess had been Margaret's nurse. In the back was a small room, whose lattice (of mere slips of wood crosswise) had been exchanged for a glazed casement, on purpose to allow the young lady, in all weathers, thence to let her eye wander over the boundless sea; and there she would sit, feeding her sick fancy with the deadly melancholy that seemed to her ever brooding in the watery distance, let it dazzle gloriously with the sinking sun as it might, ever since the parting hour.

It was in the evening of a golden autumnal day, which was closing in heavy fog, with thunder-clouds in the distance, that she stood alone, recalling that hour — for the hour, the prospect, the very aspect of the evening were the very same, and the many years that had elapsed — that great void chasm in her life seemed as but a dismal dream of a terrible and lonesome night; but the sweet morning — his prayed-for return — when would *that* arrive? Far indeed from vanity was the feeling which prompted this lone faithful girl to so often turn to her mirror, pore over her poor white face, fancy "defeatures" which time had *not* written yet, and sometimes half wish to die, ere he should return, so to avoid blurring the fairer image of her which he carried out, and might still preserve. Suddenly she started out of deepest reverie, at the appearance of a tall figure of foreign aspect, standing in the gorge of a rocky creek, near, but too distant for her to recognise his features. Cut off by vast walls of cliff from the rustic homes above, fog and nightfall combining to give solemnity to the low roar of the waves, and deeper solitude to the scene, she grew terrified, and hid herself behind the huge columnar portals of the cavern. Presently he loitered towards what is called the Goat's Staircase (steps in the rock); but the dense fog prevented her viewing his features, though something urged her to pore upon his seemingly sallow face with an eagerness of the mad. Presently she heard a boat rowed away by men, both invisible in the fog. She caught the clank of a chain and voices, and concluded that it had landed this muffled stranger. She had had a wild dream the previous night (which may be hereafter alluded to); her spirits were violently agitated, she felt as if an apparition (a blest and glorious one!) had glided near her in its mist, so vision-like was the transient spectacle, all objects metamorphosed by the hazy medium into something strange, and his very stature increased by the same. She fancied his hand of strange whiteness — fancied she could discern even the blackness of a mourning ring on a finger — she had put one on the hand of Septimus at their last interview, so despondent was her mood in that very spot. Not dreaming of any one there lurking, the stranger stopped, and seemed to fix his eyes (hollow eyes, she fancied!) on the very cavern she occupied, the very spot of their very last endearments! So strong was her perturbation, that her eyes grew dark, she nearly fainted — reviving, with a strong effort, she looked again, but he was gone.

That same evening, as the good dame of the cottage inn, or "public", sat reading the "Welshman's Candle", or "Vicar's Book" — *Lifre y Fycar* — of Rees Prichard, an old volume with brazen clasps, hardly less reverenced than the Bible itself by the South-Wales peasantry — a stranger, stooping to enter under the eaves of thatch, disturbed her with the unwelcome sound of the Saxon tongue. He took refreshment in the little back room already alluded to, and began to inquire about the families in the neighbourhood. The old dame would hold no converse in "Saxon", cutting all short by the eternal "dim Sassenach" ("No Saxon," i.e. English). But her boy, her grandson, was more communicative.

"I saw, near the sea," the stranger said, "an old man, of wretched appearance, with a beard (as I thought, at least, through the fog), as we rowed along the coast — who is that?" "He of the great house, sir, — the Squire Vaughan." The stranger started. — "What! You do not tell me that old miserable man was Mr. Vaughan himself?" Assured it was he, the stranger's countenance fell, and he was long silent. Desirous to interrogate the old woman, he adressed her, at last, in the Welsh tongue, and loosed her tongue, in so doing, as by a charm, but still preserved a studied concealment. He inquired about the lady of Llangoed, Margaret's paternal seat, and sighed to hear of the death of both her parents. When told that she had been seated, not an hour since, at that very window — had slept one night, it being stormy, in that very bed (which filled up one side of the old room), the colour mounted into the bronzed cheek, and strange light and exquisite softness, into the full eye of the guest. Grasping the withered hand of the hostess, he bade "God bless her," in her own language, forced on her a piece of gold — on her grandson, one of silver —

departed, none knew whither, leaving them all wonder and all joy.

Remorseful for the injury he had done to his son's future interest, Mr. Vaughan, as has been already related, abandoned himself to despair. His only companion, besides the gentle orphan (whose attachment to his long absent son endeared her to him the more), was an aged domestic, named Jenan, who had enlivened his revelries in former days, by his skill on the harp, and whose love for the boy-exile, whom he had many a time carried on his back, when a child, was only second to the father's own. He would sit speechless for hours, then hurry to his high turret window to look out over the sea, murmuring to himself, "A father or no father? Is my blood stopped utterly except in this old foul heart? Three at once! — all at once! And all by water, water! — all watery deaths! It was indeed *like* a judgment! — What say *you*, Jenan? Am I a father yet?"

Margaret, on her return, tried to rouse his spirits, by telling how she dreamed his son was returned, well and happy, — that she held his hand in hers, but concealed (in her bashfulness) that it was before the *altar,* that their hands so met. She withheld also, the darker sequel — that suddenly she lost him in the darkness of a total eclipse; yet somehow the hand was not unlocked from hers, but gleamed to the ghastly light — a dreadful red — ring and all being covered with blood.

That same evening, or rather night, a vessel, which had been long lying to, came aground, and became a wreck, through the act of Ralph "the Diaowl", who had kindled a fire on the beach, and, cut off by the walls of cliff, had the shore as a solitude for himself and his black purpose. Descrying the red gleams below, from his high lattice, Mr. Vaughan hurried down, followed by Jenan, bearing a life-preserving apparatus for reaching the wreck. They caught the sound of a clanking chain and faint clamour of voices, as of persons taking to the boat. A sudden, dreadful silence ensued. It was, no doubt, swamped. Mr. Vaughan urged the hardy wrecker to venture to swim out with the apparatus to the beating vessel, to ascertain if anyone were still on board, and he consented.

The melancholy pair stood listening in the sort of cavern hollow formed in the mixed fog and sea-mists, by the red light of the watch-fire, and heard only the sound of a bell, which, being fixed in the ship for calling the crew together on occasion, now kept time to the rolling of the wreck with almost the regularity of a passing-bell. "Think you he has reached the vessel yet?" Mr. Vaughan continually inquired. There are on that coast singular crannies and passages called wind holes, which pierce far into the rocks and open above, occasioning sounds, sometimes of melancholy grandeur, like those of an enormous Æolian harp, or many such, and which the superstitious hear with awe and forebodings in wild weather. Deceived by these, perhaps, Mr. Vaughan exclaimed — "I could fancy I heard two voices in the pauses of the gust! He's on the hulk by this time — that dismal, dreadful bell! How strange, how solemn it sounds, above all the weltering and breaking of the waves and hissing of this pebbly beach! — Hark! hark! hark!" His last exclamation expressed intense alarm or awe, and in his eagerness to listen, he laid his finger on Jenan's lips, to prevent his speech. "It's only the noise of the wind-holes, sir," he said at last — "I've stood in wild evenings and heard such sounds; they seemed like screams of raving madness, and presently, as the wind sunk, like sweet voices, but melancholy — dirges or 'waking' of corpses — one might fancy anything." "True! — anything; fighting or praying for life and mercy — cursing and blasphemy of murderers — anything!" "Why did you start, sir? — What made your hand tremble so violently as you laid your finger on my lips just now? — What did you fancy you heard?" — "Tell me, first, what did *you* fancy you heard?" — "But no, it was a wild fancy of my own brain, Jenan, that was all. — What does that devil on the wreck so long? — Ralph, you villain! Ralph! come back, I say!" "Alas! dear master, your voice can't reach him — he is but looking about for what he can lay hands on." "Lay hands on! — lay violent hands! No, no — there was no living thing there! — it was but my fancy. Yet *you* might have a wild fancy, a shocking fancy, as well as I — hark; oh God! Again!" and he grasped his companion's arm with a hand that shook so as to shake the old man's whole person, he remaining dumb as death, in intensity of listening the while. *"Now,* did you hear nothing?" he burst forth. "I *did* hear a sound, as of a voice." "Ay, and it must be a long, a strong, a dreadful sound, to be heard above all the sea, and all the sounds of these caves and winds! *A* voice you mutter — *a* voice! — Go on — *Whose* voice did you fancy it was? But I am mad — no matter what *I* fancied — what did *you*? But we might both have a mad conceit. Did you fancy *any*thing particular." "I seemed to hear two voices." "So did I! — Come back, you wretch — you wrecker — murderer! — or may that dark sea or hollow hell at once swallow you quick! — Come back, and put an end to this dream, if it be a dream!" "Pray, sir, do not exhaust yourself thus — the sea's too loud." "Then, end it *you* — you, yourself — now, now! Did you not think it *his* voice, my poor boy's own? I know you did! — Answer me, and speak me dead at once! You know it — who could forget it? Speak — I'm ready!"

But ere the answer came, the sound of the wrecker himself regaining land rivetted his whole mind, while so deep a darkness, from invisible clouds of thunder (which already growled in the distance) joined to the fog, came over the night, that he was made conscious of the wrecker's presence by his standing up, dim, before him, a black and figured shadow, for the embers shot light but a few feet into the mass of fog. "Was aught alive on board? — Speak, for the love of God!" — The sullen and malignant man baulked his frantic eagerness by a long pause, then muttered, carelessly — "There is nothing alive on board." " '*Was* anything alive on board?' was my question, dog!" he said in fury, between his teeth. "Well, then, there was one dog on the wreck;" replied the ruffian, laughing. A mountain's weight seemed heaved from off the breast of the fancy-fraught father. The suddenness of the relief was of itself a shock. "Only a dog — a poor dog," he rejoined, calmly, his suddenly softened nature melting toward even this humbler object. "And you left it to die? It would have been merciful to bring him ashore. The tide is running out — will he be likely to get to land?" "And so bar *our* claim to the ship? Blood!

Something has strangely wrought on you to-night! Why, there's a rich cargo, that will lie dry by morning — I had it from the captain and owner, himself, that it's a rich one." "The rack again! — why, you said there was only a dog!" exclaimed Mr. Vaughan, in agony. "Ay, a dog of my breed! — did you not say I was a dog, just now? Did ye hear him howl when I — but never fear, he'll never witness against us, never howl more, unless in the night of the judgment!" "Wretch! What name? What country? What—" The wrecker had retired into the darkness, but soon reappearing in the narrow circumference of the dying light of the embers, proffered his hand to the impatient questioner — "Be pleased, sir," he said, "to accept the hand of poor Ralph, in token of his forgiveness for your causing the loss of his other!" "What means the mysterious wretch?" Mr. Vaughan exclaimed. "Answer my question, or return to the poor stranger on the wreck, if you be a man! — Horror of death! fellow," he added, shuddering — "what a cold hand thou hast!" A laugh of ferocious and triumphing insult sounded through the dark, while, to his astonishment, Mr. Vaughan perceived his figure moving away, he still holding what he had believed to be his hand. "Wish me joy, sir!" the villain shouted, while he touched Mr. Vaughan with a hand of living warmth! — "wish me joy of possessing *two* hands, once more! Now I'm satisfied — now we are *friends*! There is a ring on that hand; shew it to the fire there, and see if you know it. The poor gentleman, when I got the better of him, entreated me to give that to the young lady, your ward, and his dying love and farewell to you. But when he was dead, it came into my mind to bring you hand and all!" — The unhappy father remained like a statue, speechless, holding a dead hand — the hand of his long-lost son!

The young adventurer was returning, in high hope and fortune, but the ship, bound to a Welsh port, happening to be delayed off the Glamorgan coast, he determined to land, prior to his final return, perhaps to satisfy himself respecting the feelings of his young mistress, after so long an absence — perhaps, also, wishing to surprise his father and her.

On occasion of this tragedy, the wretched wrecker-lord resigned his manor and castle to the family of Butler, and nothing is recorded of his after fate. The ruffian suffered for another crime soon after. The lady is said to have preserved the hand and ring, for the remainder of her wasted life, in a sort of little grave, in an earthen vase, planted with sweet flowers, as the lady in Boccacio's novel preserved all she could retain of her lover in a pot of basil. Such was the fearful catastrophe which the Glamorganshire annals record as "God's Revenge against Wreckers".

CHANNEL CROSSING

So many people have swum the English Channel that the way in which Captain Boyton tried to use his body as a sailing boat is now long forgotten.

Many are the inventions which have been devised for the purpose of assisting swimmers, or for aiding those who cannot swim, to float. One of the most remarkable contrivances of this kind is the American invention known as the Boyton dress.

It is a complete indiarubber suit, which can be filled with air at any point desired, the result being that the wearer can lie down or remain in an upright position in the water, the body being kept as warm — and, if in exertion, warmer — than it would be under ordinary circumstances.

Captain Paul Boyton crossed the English Channel in this dress, floating, paddling and even sailing — for a sail is part of the gear. Meanwhile he was able to take food from the knapsack or receptacle, which is a component part of the dress.

The following account is given of his famous effort to swim across the English Channel:—

There was no time lost after Captain Boyton reached the steps, for the mail steamer was close by, and it was necessary to get out at once to clear her way. Accordingly, at 3.20 a.m. he took the water, a heavy gun, borrowed for the occasion proclaiming the fact, and alarming out of their senses a number of people crowding the wharf within a few feet of its muzzle. Rockets were sent up and blue lights burnt to warn the approaching mail; these were returned, and in a few minutes we were clear of the pier and fairly on our course.

It became at once evident that the task of keeping close to a man in the water upon a dark night was one of extreme difficulty, for although the water was now comparatively smooth, the swimmer could be seen at a distance of fifty yards only and, once lost sight of, it was exceedingly difficult to find him again. It was arranged that he should follow in our wake, but go as slowly as we would we constantly lost him for the N.E. wind drifted him away to leeward much faster than it did the steamer, and it was only after great blowing of fog horns that we succeeded in finding him. This was sufficient to show that in really rough water it would be altogether impossible to keep near him, and that if the next nightfall found us far out at sea in rough water the attempt would have to be abandoned.

At 4.50 day began to break faintly, and we found that the swimmer had in the first hour made nearly as much distance from the land as he had drifted up north by the tide. At this time he paddled up to the steamer and his brother got into a boat, fastened the clog which contains the step for his mast, on his foot, set his sail, and we again got under weigh. The wind was now E.N.E. blowing freshly, and the speed of the swimmer through the water was much increased. It was evident that he would be far enough out to go outside the Goodwins should the tide hold long enough to take him so far, and this will be a useful indication to him should he ever seek to repeat the experiment.

At 5.15 he was again near the steamer, and hailed us merrily. The French pilot who was in charge of him told him not to over-exert himself as he was making capital way and might expect to reach Boulogne in twelve hours after his start. After sunrise the *Rambler* hoisted her colours, the Geneva red cross at the fore, the stars and stripes at the peak, and the Union Jack at the stern. As the American flag went up Captain Boyton gave a cheer. Presently he said he should like a cigar and one was taken to him. At about half-past six the ebb tide met us. At this time the South Foreland and South Sand Head showed that he had made about six miles and a half. The wind was now blowing very freshly, the sea was getting up, and the little sail took the swimmer fast through the water without any exertion on his part; indeed for the rest of the journey, Captain Boyton paddled quietly, using the paddle rather as a means of steering than of propulsion.

At a quarter past seven two carrier pigeons were despatched. For a long time it was questionable whether they would leave the ship, round which they flew for some time; at last, however, they flew off and we afterwards learned reached Folkestone in safety. The day had now set in decidedly squally. A strong wind swept over the water, and a blinding rain began to fall and continued until late in the afternoon. Refreshment was now given to the swimmer, and although the nature of the refreshment was no doubt chemically good, it is a question whether a little more usual food would not have been more relished and eaten. A mixture of beaten up eggs, beef extract, and brandy is scarcely the food a man will devour or rather drink, with an appetite.

At nine o'clock the sea had risen much. Dr. Diver went off and gave him some more eggs, but he refused to eat the bread and butter offered him and seemed drowsy and low. The doctor returned to the ship after twenty minutes, and his report threw the French pilot — an excellent seaman, no doubt but a man given to violent alternations of hope and despondency — into a state of despair. It was of no use continuing the experiment, and Captain Boyton should be taken out of the water at once. This of course was overruled but the pilot's equilibrium was shaken for the day. Soon afterwards Captain Boyton hailed again, and the boat went out, and much time was again thrown away. Captain Boyton removed his clog, stood up in the water and after a time, the sail being hoisted on the other foot, again went on his way.

All these delays told against him, told their tale, and it was now evident, both from the appearance of the water and the tale told by the soundings that the point upon which the pilot had all along been so anxious was lost, and that instead of being on the French side of the Ridge shoal he was upon the Ridge itself. Across this the current sweeps towards the English coast and the pilot at once asserted the impossibility of the voyage being completed. The doctor had, however, reported upon his return that Captain Boyton seemed all right again and in consequence his brother refused to listen to the pilot. It was evident, however, that his assertion as to the direction of the current was correct, for in spite of a very strong wind and using his paddles, he made no way at all, and for four hours the lightship on the Verne shoal, our only landmark, remained exactly, as far as our sight could

tell, at the same distance namely two and a half miles astern. Sometimes, indeed, we appeared to be positively losing ground; certainly
none was gained.

For three hours this struggle continued and it was not until one
o'clock that the change of tide permitted him again any to make
headway. Several times he had taken a little brandy, but was indispos-
ed to eat anything solid. He was evidently weak, but was still determined to make France, and answered inquiries cheerfully whenever
he got alongside. Soon after two o'clock the Folkestone boat, *Napoleon the Third*, came along and sheered out of her course to give her
passengers a close view of the swimmer, who was at the moment smoking a cigar. They gave him a hearty cheer, and things looked brighter, the French pilot being now in a hopeful mood, and assuring us and
Captain Boyton that he would get him to French land in three hours.

The weather, however, became worse, the waves increased in
height; near as we tried to keep to the swimmer, it was only when he
came on the crest of a wave that we caught a sight of him, and even
his sail was at times lost, at others could scarcely be distinguished
from the white crests of the waves all around. The weather got more
and more thick, and it became really a matter of doubt where we were,
or how far from land. The English pilot on board, who had no
share whatever in the management, had all along differed from the
French pilot as to the course steered, and at six o'clock it was determined by all on board that something must be done, for that the case
was becoming really serious. No land was in sight, or indeed had been
in sight for eight hours; the direction of the French coast was known,
but its distance was uncertain; all that we knew was that we could
dimly see a large ship ahead, at about four miles distant, and that the
ship would in all probability be keeping fully two miles from shore.

The French pilot said that he would not take the responsibility if
Captain Boyton remained in the water, for that it would be absolutely
impossible to keep him in sight for five minutes in the dark, and once
separated there was no saying where the swimmer, deprived of all
guidance, would be taken by the currents. The tide, too, would change

in an hour, and would again sweep him away. He thought it improbable in the extreme that the swimmer, even if he could keep by the steamer, would reach Cape Grisnez, or any other French land, before morning. The captain of the steamer was of the same opinion.

Under these circumstances, all on board felt that the experiment should cease. Enough had been done to show what the apparatus was capable of, more than enough to have enabled Captain Boyton to reach France had the circumstances been favourable. So evident was this, that it is now certain that Captain Boyton will, if he repeats the experiment on a fine clear day, with somewhat better steering, perform the feat with ease in twelve hours. This being the case, it would have been little better than madness to continue it, with the certainty that we should lose him in the dark, and that he would then, after being sixteen hours in the water, have a long night at the mercy of the wind and currents, with no certainty of being near land in the morning.

A consultation was held, and, backed by the opinions of the pilot and captain, it was unanimously, although with great regret, resolved that Captain Boyton should be asked to give in. This with great reluctance he did, first paddling round the steamer with great rapidity to show that he had plenty of strength left. This he undoubtedly had, although when he reached Boulogne he found that he was more weak and exhausted than he had supposed; but the question of his giving up was irrespective of his strength. He could, no doubt, have lived throughout the night, but when on the sea without provisions, with a heavy sea occasionally breaking in his face, and after a fast of thirty-six hours, his chance of life would have been but small. He was heartily cheered as he came on board, and at a quarter past six we started at full steam for France.

THE JOLLY ROGER AND
THE PORTUGEE

*A tale of pirates on the high seas. How the "Avenger" captured a
Portuguese merchantman.*

The seabreeze had risen in the offing, and was sweeping along the
surface to where the pirate schooner was at anchor. The captain ordered a man to the cross-trees, directing him to keep a good look-
out, while he walked the deck in company with his first mate.

"She may not have sailed until a day or two later," said the captain. "I have made allowance for that, and, depend upon it, as she
makes the eastern passage we must soon fall in with her; if she does
not heave in sight this evening by daylight, I shall stretch out in the
offing; I know the Portuguese well. The sea-breeze has caught our
craft; let them run up the inner jib, and see that she does not foul
her anchor."

It was now late in the afternoon, and dinner had been sent into the
cabin, when, "Sail, oh!" was shouted from the masthead.

"There she is, by G—!" cried the captain.

"A large ship, sir; we can see down to the second reef of her top-
sails," said Hawkhurst, looking down the sky-light. The captain
hastily swallowed some wine from a flagon, cast a look of scorn and
anger on Francisco, and rushed on deck.

"Be smart, lads!" cried the captain, after a few seconds' survey of
the vessel through his glass: "that's her; furl the awnings, and run the
anchor up to the bows: there's more silver in that vessel, my lads,
than your chests will hold; and the good saints of the churches at Goa
will have to wait a little longer for their gold candlesticks."

The crew were immediately on the alert, the awnings were furled,
and all the men, stretching aft the cabin-cable, walked the anchor
up to the bows. In two minutes more the *Avenger* was standing out
on the starboard tack, shaping her course so as to cut off the ill-
fated vessel. The breeze freshened, and the schooner darted through

the smooth water with the impetuosity of a dolphin after its prey. In an hour the hull of the ship was plainly to be distinguished: but the sun was near to the horizon, and before they could ascertain what her force might be the daylight had disappeared. Whether the schooner had been perceived or not it was impossible to say; at all events, the course of the ship had not been altered, and if she had seen the schooner she evidently treated her with contempt. On board the *Avenger* they were not idle; the long gun in the centre had been cleared from the encumbrances which surrounded it, the other guns had been cast loose, shot handed up, and everything prepared for action, with all the energy and discipline of a man-o'-war. The chase had not been lost sight of, and the eyes of the pirate captain were fixed upon her through a night glass. In about an hour more the schooner was within a mile of the ship, and now altered her course so as to range up within a cable's length of her to leeward. Cain stood upon the gunwale and hailed.

The answer was in Portugese.

"Heave to, or I'll sink you!" replied he in the same language.

A general discharge from a broadside of carronades, and a heavy volley of muskets from the Portuguese, was the decided answer: the broadside, too much elevated to hit the low hull of the schooner, was still not without effect — the foretop-mast fell, the jaws of the main-gaff was severed, and a large portion of the standing, as well as the running, rigging came rattling down on her decks. The volley of musketry was more fatal: thirteen of the pirates were wounded, some of them severely.

"Well done, John Portuguese!" cried Hawkhurst. "By the holy poker! I never gave you credit for so much pluck."

"Which they shall pay dearly for," was the cool reply of Cain, as he still remained in his exposed situation.

"Blood for blood! if I drink it," observed the second mate, as he looked at the crimson rivulet trickling down the fingers of his left hand from a wound in his arm; "just tie my handkerchief round this, Bill."

In the interim, Cain had desired his crew to elevate their guns, and the broadside was returned. "That will do, my lads: starboard; ease off the boom sheet; let her go right round, Hawkhurst; we cannot afford to lose our men."

The schooner wore round, and ran astern of her opponent. The Portuguese on board the ship, imagining that the schooner, finding she had met with unexpected resistance had sheered off, gave a loud cheer.

"The last you will ever give, my fine fellows!" observed Cain with a sneer.

In a few minutes the schooner had run astern of the ship. "Now, then, Hawkhurst, let her come to and about; man the long gun, and see that every shot is pitched into her, while the rest of them get up a new foretop-mast and knot and splice the rigging."

The schooner's head was again turned towards the ship; her position was right astern, about a mile distant, or rather more; the long thirty-two-pounder gun amid-ships was now regularly served, every shot passing through the cabin-windows, or some other part of the ship's stern, raking her fore and aft. In vain did the ship alter her course, and present her broadside to the schooner; the latter was immediately checked in her speed, so as to keep the prescribed distance, at which the carronades of the ship were useless, and the execution from the long gun decisive. The ship was at the mercy of the pirate; and, as may be expected, no mercy was shown. For three hours did this murderous attack continue, when the gun which, as before observed, was of brass, became so heated that the pirate captain desired his men to discontinue. Whether the ship had surrendered or not it was impossible to say, as it was too dark to distinguish: while the long gun was served, the foretop-mast and main-gaff had been shifted, and all the standing and running rigging made good; the schooner keeping her distance, and following in the wake of the ship until daylight.

We must now repair on board of the ship: she was an Indiaman; one of the very few that occasionally are sent out by the Portuguese government to a country which once owned their undivided sway, but in which, at present, they hold but a few miles of territory. She was bound to Goa, and had on board a small detachment of troops, a new governor and his two sons, a bishop and his niece, with her attendant. The sailing of a vessel with such a freight was a circumstance of rare occurrence; and was, of course, generally bruited about long before her departure. Cain had, for some months, received all the necessary intelligence relative to her cargo and destination; but, as usual with the Portuguese of the present day, delay upon delay had followed, and it was not until about three weeks previous that he had been assured of her immediate departure. He then ran down the coast to the bay we have mentioned, that he might intercept her; and, as the event has proved, showed his usual judgment and decision. The fire of the schooner had been most destructive: many of the Indiaman's crew, as well as of the troops, had been mowed down one after another; until, at last, finding that all their efforts to defend themselves were useless, most of those who were still unhurt had consulted their safety, and hastened down to the lowest recesses of the hold to avoid the raking and destructive shot. At the time that the schooner had discontinued her fire to allow the gun to cool, there was no one on deck but the Portuguese captain and an old weather-beaten seaman, who stood at the helm. Below, in the orlop-deck, the remainder of the crew and the passengers were huddled together in a small space: some were attending to the wounded, who were numerous; others were invoking the saints to their assistance; the bishop, a tall, dignified person, apparently nearly sixty years of age, was kneeling in the centre of the group, which was dimly lighted by two or three lanterns, at one time in fervent prayer, at another interrupted, that he might give absolution to those wounded men whose spirits were departing, and who were brought down and laid before him by their comrades. On one side of him knelt his orphan niece, a young girl of about seventeen years of age, watching his countenance as he prayed, or bending down with a look of pity and tearful eyes on her expiring countrymen, whose last moments were gladdened by his holy offices.

On the other side of the bishop stood the governor, Don Philip de Ribiera, and his two sons, youths in their prime, and holding commissions in the king's service. There was melancholy on the brow of Don Ribiera; he was prepared for, and he anticipated, the worst. The eldest son had his eyes fixed upon the sweet countenance of Teresa de Silva — that very evening, as they walked together on the deck, they had exchanged their vows — that very evening had they luxuriated in the present, and had dealt with delightful anticipation of the future. But we must leave them and return on deck.

The captain of the Portuguese ship had walked aft, and now went up to Antonio, the old seaman, who was standing at the wheel. "I still see her with the glass, Antonio, and yet she has not fired for nearly two hours; do you think any accident has happened to her long gun? If so, we may have some chance."

Antonio shook his head. "We have but little chance, I am afraid, my captain; I knew by the ring of the gun, when she first fired it, that it was brass; indeed, no schooner could carry a long iron gun of that calibre. Depend upon it, she only waits for the metal to cool and daylight to return: a long gun or two might have saved us, but now, as she has the advantage of us in heels, we are at her mercy."

"What can she be — a French privateer?"

"I trust it may be so; and I have promised a silver candlestick to Saint Antonio, that it may prove no worse: we then may have some chance of seeing our homes again; but I fear not."

"What, then, do you imagine her to be, Antonio?"

"The pirate which we have heard so much of."

"Jesu protect us! We must then sell our lives as dearly as we can."

"So I intend to do, my captain," replied Antonio, shifting the helm as he spoke.

The day broke, and showed the schooner continuing her pursuit at the same distance astern, without any apparent movement on board. It was not until the sun was some degrees above the horizon, that the smoke was again seen to envelop her bows, and the shot crashed through the timbers of the Portuguese ship. The reason for this delay was that the pirate waited till the sun was up to ascertain if there were any other vessel to be seen, previous to his pouncing upon his quarry. The Portuguese captain went aft, and hoisted his ensign but no flag was shown by the schooner. Again whistled the ball, and again did it tear up the decks of the unfortunate ship: many of those who had re-ascended to ascertain what was going on, now hastily sought their former retreat.

"Mind your helm, Antonio," said the Portuguese captain; "I must go down and consult with the governor."

"Never fear, my captain; as long as these limbs hold together, I will do my duty," replied the old man, exhausted as he was by long watching and fatigue.

The captain descended to the orlop-deck, where he found the major part of the crew and passengers assembled.

"My lord," said he, addressing the governor and bishop, "the schooner has not shown any colours, although our own are hoisted. I am come down to know your pleasure. Defence we can make none; and I fear we are at the mercy of a pirate."

"A pirate!" ejaculated several, beating their breasts, and calling upon their saints.

"Silence, my good people, silence," quietly observed the bishop; "as to what it may be best to do," continued he, turning to the captain, "I cannot advise; I am a man of peace, and unfit to hold a place in the council of war. Don Ribiera, I must refer to you and your sons. Tremble not, my dear Teresa; are we not under the protection of the Almighty?"

"Holy Virgin pity us!" exclaimed Teresa.

"Come my sons," said Don Ribiera, "we will go on deck and consult; let not any of the men follow us; it is useless risking our lives which may yet be valuable." Don Ribiera and his sons followed the captain to the quarter-deck, and with him and Antonio they held a consultation.

"We have but one chance," observed the old man, after a time: "let us haul down our colours as if in submission; they will then range up alongside, and either board us from the schooner, or from their boats; at all events, we shall find out what she is, and if a pirate, we must sell our lives as dearly as we can. If, when we haul down the colours, she ranges up alongside, let all the men be prepared for a struggle."

"You are right, Antonio," replied the governor; "go aft, captain, and haul down the colours; let us see what she does now. Down, my boys, and prepare the men to do their duty."

As Antonio had predicted, as soon as the colours were hauled down, the schooner ceased firing, and made sail. She ranged up on the quarter of the ship, and up to her peak soared the terrific black flag; her broadside was poured into the Indiaman, and before the meeting sides, and the bearded pirates poured upon her decks. The crew of the Portuguese, with the detachment of troops, still formed a considerable body of men. The sight of the black flag had struck ice into every heart, but the feeling was resolved into one of desperation.

"Knives, men! Knives!" roared Antonio, rushing to the attack, followed by the most brave.

"Blood for blood!" cried the second mate, aiming a blow at the old man.

"You have it," replied Antonio, as his knife entered the pirate's heart, while, at the same moment, he fell, and was himself a corpse.

The struggle was deadly, but the numbers and ferocity of the pirates prevailed. Cain rushed forward, followed by Hawkhurst, bearing down all who opposed them. With one blow from the pirate captain the head of Don Ribiera was severed to the shoulder; a second struck down the eldest son, while the sword of Hawkhurst passed through the body of the other. The Portuguese captain had already fallen, and the men no longer stood their ground. A general massacre ensued, and the bodies were thrown overboard as fast as the men were slaughtered. In less than five minutes there was not a living Portuguese on the bloody deck of the ill-fated ship.

A GALLANT CHASE

This old story describes one of the many small ship escapades of the Napoleonic Wars.

We were within a few days of our destination, and were rolling down the trades, when, at six in the morning, a strange sail was discovered on our starboard quarter, apparently in chase of us; we immediately hauled to the wind. This manoeuvre disenchanted the golden visions of the stranger, and finding us likely to prove an awkward customer, he likewise hauled upon a bow-line. The chase now began. The lower yards of the pursued (evidently a man-of-war brig) could only be seen from the main-top; but her manœuvres, and the cut of her sails, at once announced her nation. As the sun rose in the heavens, the wind increased, and we had already gained considerably on the chase, when she was under the necessity of reefing in consequence of the strong squalls and fiery trade wind. This was just the weather in which the old *Pompée* shone to the greatest advantage, and we hailed the increasing gusts with pleasure. All hands were kept upon deck ready to shorten sail at an instant's notice. The brig being to windward was a certain guide to us as to the strength of the squalls, and we were prepared to act accordingly. By noon we had her hull up from the deck; she carried on most nobly; her spars bent like bows before she yielded to the blast. As soon as her topsails were observed coming down, every man was on the alert, and the instant the squall struck us, the topgallant-sails were furled, and the topsails down in a trice. The moment its force was expended, up they flew to the mast heads, and the upper sails were again expanded to the breeze. It was one of the most beautiful and soul-stirring chases it has been my fortune to witness.

The little craft was clearly overpressed; not the vantage ground of a hair's breadth was lost on our side. In one of the heavy squalls her lee main-top-sheet was carried away and the sail fluttered in ribbons. We made sure of our prey — "She is ours to a certainty," — when that certainty vanished by the smartness of the Frenchman, who, in double-quick time, bent another main-topsail. The *Pompée's* men had scarcely taken in another reef, when our skilful foe was observed sheeting home, and hoisting away again. It required no great sagacity to discover that her commander was a practically good seaman, who knew full well how to manage his dashing little barky. In a short time away went both his 'fore-topsail sheets. "She cannot escape now — it is impossible." — "By heavens! He has secured his canvas this time. There, he is hauling home his sheets again." — "Well done — gallantly done, Johnny Crapaud; the devil favours his own offspring." — "Blow, good breezes, blow." (The wind was beginning to lull.) "Shake out a reef of the topsails."

And now the fears of losing the brig began to assume a palpable form, as she was observed to hold her own. No sooner were our men laid out upon the topsail-yards, than the brig's men appeared to be occupied with the like duty. "He is determined to give us a run for it." "Blow breezes, blow," was again heard murmuring around; and, by way of coaxing the airs of heaven, the master and first lieutenant were whistling to the wind, in tune something similar to that adopted by ostlers to their horses. All our whistling and coaxings failed in propitiating the wind deities. The sun declined, the wind dropped, and the Frenchman remained upon the gaining side; there was no moon, and the distance too great between us to admit of the hope of keeping him in sight when night should close in. The ship was kept wrapt full to get on her beam, as affording us the best chance of seeing her with the night-glasses. Not a vestige of the chase could be discovered an hour after sunset. A further pursuit was considered both hopeless and unprofitable by the disappointed officers.

We expected the hammocks to be piped down, and the ship to be kept on her course again; but Captain C— had acquired too much experience of our cunning adversary's shiftings and doublings to resign, prematurely, a quarry in every way worth our attention. The plan he pursued displayed the sound judgment that always guided his conduct in cases of difficulty and uncertainty, at once inspiring hope, security, and confidence, in those around him. He noted the spot where he had first fallen in with the brig, and her precise situation, when last seen; and concluded that the wary Frenchman would stand on under all sail till nine o'clock, then tack, and bear up before the wind to take his original position. Accordingly, at the hour he expected the chase to tack, we went abroad, and shortened sail to the topsails. The wind had previously fallen to a light breeze. In due time we edged away to meet him, on the supposed line of his course. All hands were ready stationed to make sail in an instant; the main-deck guns were cleared away; officers and men were peering in all directions, endeavouring to penetrate the darkness that surrounded the vessel. Meanwhile the captain, who had retired for a few minutes to consult the chart, upon which he had marked the expected point of meeting, returned to the quarter-deck. "Keep a sharp look-out on the weather bow," said he; and turning round to the officers, added, "if my conjectures are correct, we ought to be close on board of her."

"Take the night-glass forward, Mr. B——, and keep sweeping the horizon about four points on the bow."

"Ay, ay, sir." — But before the officer had reached the fore-castle, the welcome cry of a strange sail to windward was heard from the cat-head. In an instant the outlines of her extended canvas were visible, standing forth in strong relief from the dark background of a mass of vapoury clouds. The top-gallant sails and fore-sails were speedily set, and the *Pompée* in a line with the stranger. The enemy was thus brought immediately under the muzzle of our guns. At the first shot he prudently let fly every tack and sheet, and hove to; we were equally expeditious, and both vessels were laying so close, that every attempt on the part of the brig to escape would have subjected her to certain destruction. The first boat brought on board the captain, who was minus an arm by our countrymen on a former occasion. The prize was a fine man-of-war brig *Le Pylade*, carrying sixteen thirty-two-pound carronades, and one hundred and nine men. She had run successfully the whole of the war, had just left Martinique, and was an excellent sailer, of which qualification we had incontestable proof. She had afforded us a chase that might have inspired and interested the most fastidious amateur in these matters. Both vessels were so admirably managed, the possible loss and probable advantages so nicely balanced on both sides, that I do not think either of them could be said to win upon the other in point of skill during the whole of the morning's manœuvres. Strategem eventually favoured us, and the neat finale to the pursuit was sagaciously planned and successfully executed.

The under-writers at Lloyd's had paid dearly for the various depredations of this industrious little brig. The poor Frenchman, it appeared, did not perceive us till we were actually alongside of him, and the whistling of the shot between his masts dispelled his dreams of security. At the very moment they fell into our power, they were congratulating themselves upon their escape. On looking over a log book belonging to one of the officers, in which his hopes and fears during the day had been carefully registered I observed that at five o'clock, when the wind had fallen and the brig appeared to have rather gained upon us, the Frenchman had written down "Dieu merci, nous ne serons pas pris aujourd'hui. Adieu, Jean Boull! — Adieu, rosbif!"

A TALE OF SIX DESERTERS

By GEORGE WINSLOW BARRINGTON

During the Napoleonic Wars, this story of the sufferings of six deserters was posted on regimental notice-boards and read out to the assembled troops to persuade them not to quit their duty.

On Dec. 12, 1799, a court of inquiry was held at St. Helena, before Captain Desfontain, to investigate the case of six deserters from the artillery of the island of St. Helena. A statement was made on oath, by John Brown, one of the survivors:—

"In June, 1799, I belonged to the first company of artillery, in this garrison, and on the 10th of that month, about half an hour before parade time, M'Kinnon, gunner and orderly of the second company, asked me if I was willing to go with him on board of an American ship, called the *Columbia*, Captain Henry Lelar, the only ship then in the roads. After some conversation I agreed, and met him about seven o'clock, at the playhouse, where I found one M'Quin, of Major Seale's company, another man called Brighouse, another named Parr, and the sixth, Matthew Conway.

Parr was a good seaman, and said he would take us to the island of Ascension, or lie off the harbour till the *Columbia* could weigh anchor and come out. We went down about eight o'clock to the West Rock, where the American boat, manned with three seamen, was waiting for us and took us alongside the *Columbia*. We went on board; Parr went down into the cabin, and we changed our clothes, after having been on board half an hour.

Brighouse and Conway proposed to cut a whale-boat out of the harbour, to prevent the *Columbia* from being suspected. This they accomplished, taking in her a coil of rope, five oars, and a large stone by which she was moored.

We observed lanterns passing on the line towards the Sea-gate, and hearing a noise, thought we were missed and sought for. We immediately embarked in the whale-boat, with about twenty-five pounds of bread in a bag, and a small keg of water, supposed to contain three gallons, and one quadrant, given to us by the commanding officer of the *Columbia*.

We then left the ship, pulling with two oars only, to get ahead of her. The boat was half full of water, and we had nothing to bale it out. In this condition we rode out to sea, and lay off the island at a great distance, in hourly expectation of the American ship taking us up.

About twelve o'clock the second day, no ship appearing, by Parr's advice we bore away, steering N. by W., and then N.N.W. for the island of Ascension, using our handkerchiefs as substitutes for sails. We met with a gale of wind, which continued two days; the weather then became very fine, and we supposed we had run about ten miles an hour. M'Kinnon kept a reckoning with pen, ink, and paper, with which, together with maps and charts, we were supplied by the *Columbia*.

We continued our course till about the 18th in the morning, when we saw a number of birds, but no land. About twelve that day, Parr said he was sure we must be past the island, accounting it to be eight hundred miles from St. Helena. Each of us then took off our shirts, and with them we made a small spritsail, lacing our jackets and trousers at the waistband to keep us warm; and then altering our course to W. by N., thinking to make Rio de Janeiro, on the American coast. Provisions running very short, we allowed ourselves only one ounce of bread, and two mouthfuls of water for twenty-four hours.

On the 25th all our provisions were expended. On the 27th M'Quin put a piece of bamboo in his mouth to chew, and we all followed his example. On the night of that day it was my turn to steer the boat, and recollecting to have read of persons in our situation eating their shoes, I cut a piece off one of mine; but being soaked with salt water, I was obliged to spit it out, and take the inside sole, of which I ate a part, and distributed the remainder to the rest; but we found no benefit from it.

On the first of July Parr caught a dolphin, with a gaff that had been left in the boat. We all fell on our knees, and thanked God for his goodness to us. We tore up the fish, and hung it to dry; about four we ate part of it, which agreed with us pretty well. On this fish we subsisted till the 4th; about eleven o'clock, when finding the whole consumed, Parr, Brighouse, Conway, and myself, proposed to scuttle the boat, and let her go down, to put us out of our misery; the other two objected, observing that God, who made man, always found him something to eat.

On the 5th, about eleven, M'Kinnon proposed that it would be better to cast lots for one of us to die, in order to save the rest, to which we consented. William Parr, being seized two days before with the spotted fever, was excluded. He wrote the numbers and put them into a hat. We drew them out blindfolded, and put them in our pockets. Parr then asked whose lot it was to die; none of us knowing what number we had in our pocket, it was agreed that number five should die, and the lots being unfolded, M'Kinnon's was the fatal number.

We had concluded that he on whom the lot fell should bleed himself to death, for which purpose we had provided ourselves with sharpened nails, which we got from the boat. With one of these M'Kinnon cut himself in three places; in his foot, hand, and wrist; and praying to God to forgive his sins, he died in about a quarter of an hour.

His flesh lasted us till the 8th; when it being my watch, and observing the water, about break of day, to change colour, I called the rest, thinking that we were near the shore, but saw no land, it being not quite daylight.

As soon as day appeared, we discovered land right ahead, and steered towards it. About eight in the morning we were close to the shore. There being a heavy surf. we endeavoured to turn the boat's head to it, but, being very weak, we were unable. Soon afterwards the boat upset. Parr, Conway, and myself got on shore, but M'Quin and Brighouse were drowned.

We discovered a small hut on the beach, in which were an Indian and his mother, who spoke Portuguese; and I understanding that language, learned that there was a village, about three miles distant, called Belmont. The Indian went to the village, with the information that the French had landed; and in about two hours the governor of the village, a clergyman, and several armed men, took Conway and Parr, tied them by their hands and feet, and slinging them on a bamboo stick, conveyed them to the village, I being very weak, remained in the hut some time, but was afterwards taken.

On our telling them we were English, we were immediately released, and three hammocks provided, in which we were taken to the governor's house, who resigned to us his own bed, and gave us milk and rice to eat; but as we had taken no food for a considerable time, we were jaw-locked, and continued so till the 23rd. During this time our host wrote to the governor of St. Salvador, who sent a schooner to Porto Seguro, to take us to St. Salvador. We were conducted on horsback to Porto Seguro, passing through Santa Cruz, where we remained about ten days. We afterwards embarked; and on our arrival at St. Salvador Parr, on being questioned by the governor, told him that our ship had foundered at sea, and that we had saved ourselves in the boat; that the ship's name was the *Sally,* of Liverpool, that she belonged to his father, and was last from Cape Corse Castle, on the coast of Africa, to touch at Ascension for turtle, and then bound for Jamaica. Parr likewise said that he was the captain.

We remained at St. Salvador about thirteen days, during which time the inhabitants made up a subscription of £ 200 each man. We then embarked in the *Maria,* a Portuguese ship, for Lisbon; Parr as mate, Conway as boatswain's mate, and myself, being sickly, as a passenger. In thirteen days we arrived at Rio de Janeiro. Parr and Conway sailed for Lisbon, and I was left in the hospital.

In about three months, Captain Elphinstone, of the *Diamond,* pressed me into his Majesty's service, giving me the choice of remaining in that station, or to proceed to the admiral at the Cape. I preferred the latter, and was put, with seven suspected deserters, on board the *Ann,* a Botany Bay ship, in irons, with the convicts. When I arrived at the Cape, I was put on board the *Lancaster,* of sixty-four guns. I never entered, but at length received my discharge; since which I engaged in the *Duke of Clarence,* as a seaman. I was determined to surrender myself the first opportunity, in order to relate my sufferings to the men of this garrison, and to deter others from attempting so mad a scheme."

This is, perhaps, one of the most extraordinary accounts upon record, and shows, in a forcible manner, the folly of attempting such enterprises without any corresponding incentive.

ROBINSON CRUSOE'S FIRST VOYAGE

By DANIEL DEFOE

In telling the story of how Robinson Crusoe made the coasting voyage from Hull to London, Daniel Defoe gives a true picture of what life was like aboard small craft in the North Sea in the late seventeenth century.

Being one day at Hull, where I went casually, and without any purpose of making an elopement that time; but I say, being there, and one of my companions being going by sea to London, in his father's ship, and prompting me to go with them, with the common allurement of seafaring men, viz. that it should cost me nothing for my passage, I consulted neither father or mother any more, nor so much as sent them word of it; but leaving them to hear of it as they might, without asking God's blessing, or my father's, without any consideration of circumstances or consequences, and in an ill hour, God knows, on the 1st of September, 1651, I went on board a ship bound for London: never any young adventurer's misfortunes, I believe, began sooner, or continued longer than mine. The ship was no sooner gotten out of the Humber, but the wind began to blow, and the waves to rise in a most frightful manner; and as I had never been at sea before, I was most inexpressibly sick in body, and terrified in my mind: I began now seriously to reflect upon what I had done, and how justly I was overtaken by the judgment of Heaven for my wicked leaving my father's house, and abandoning my duty; all the good counsel of my parents, my father's tears and my mother's entreaties came now fresh into my mind.

These wise and sober thoughts continued all the while the storm continued, and indeed some time after; but the next day the wind was abated and the sea calmer, and I began to be a little inured to it: however, I was very grave for all that day, being also a little sea-sick still; but towards night the weather cleared up, the wind was quite over, and a charming, fine evening followed; the sun went down perfectly clear and rose so the next morning; and having little or no wind, and a smooth sea, the sun shining upon it, the sight was, as I thought, the most delightful that ever I saw.

I had slept well in the night, and was now no more sea-sick but very cheerful, looking with wonder upon the sea that was so rough and terrible the day before, and could be so calm and so pleasant in so little time after. And now, lest my good resolutions should continue, my companion, who had indeed enticed me away, comes to me,

"Well, Bob," says he, clapping me on the shoulder, "how do you do after it? I warrant you were frighted, wa'n't you, last night, when it blew but a capful of wind?"

"A capful, do you call it?" said I, "'twas a terrible storm."

"A storm, you fool you," replies he, "do you call that a storm? Why it was nothing at all; give us but a good ship and sea room, and we think nothing of such a squall of wind as that; but you're but a fresh-water sailor, Bob; come let us make a bowl of punch and we'll forget all that, d'ye see what charming weather 'tis now."

The sixth day of our being at sea we came into Yarmouth Roads; the wind having been contrary, and the weather calm, we had made but little way since the storm. Here we were obliged to come to an anchor, and here we lay, the wind continuing contrary, viz. at south-west, for seven or eight days, during which time a great many ships from Newcastle came into the same roads, as the common harbour where the ships might wait for a wind for the river.

We had not, however, rid here so long, but should have tided it up the river, but that the wind blew too fresh; and after we had lain four or five days, blew very hard. However, the Roads being reckoned as good as a harbour, the anchorage good, and our ground-tackle very strong, our men were unconcerned, and not in the least apprehensive of danger, but spent the time in rest and mirth, after the manner of the sea: but the eighth day in the morning, the wind increased, and we had all hands at work to strike our topmasts, and make everything snug and close, that the ship might ride as easy as possible. By noon the sea went very high indeed, and our ship rid forecastle in, shipped several seas, and we thought once or twice our anchor had come home; upon which our master ordered out the sheet anchor; so that we rode with two anchors a head, and the cables veered out to the bitter end.

By this time it blew a terrible storm indeed, and now I began to see terror and amazement in the faces even of the seamen themselves. The master, though vigilant to the business of preserving the ship, yet as he went in and out of his cabin by me, I could hear him softly to himself say several times, "Lord be merciful to us, we shall be all lost, we shall be all undone;" and the like. During these first hurries I was stupid, lying still in my cabin, which was in the steerage, and cannot describe my temper: I could ill reassume the first penitence, which I had so apparently trampled upon and hardened myself against: I thought the bitterness of death had been past, and that this would be nothing too like the first. But when the master himself came by me, as I said just now, and said we should be all lost, I was dreadfully frighted: I got up out of my cabin, and looked out; but such a dismal sight I never saw: the sea went mountains high, and broke upon us every three or four minutes: when I could look about, I could see nothing but distress round us: two ships that rid near us we found had cut their masts by the board, being deep laden; and our men cried out, that a ship which rid about a mile ahead of us was foundered. Two more ships being driven from their anchors, were run out of the roads to sea at all adventures, and that with not a mast standing. The light ships fared the best, as not so much labouring in the sea; but two or three of them drove, and came close by us, running away with only their sprit-sail out before the wind.

Towards evening the mate and boatswain begged the master of our ship to let them cut away the foremast, which he was very unwilling to; but the boatswain protesting to him, that if he did not, the ship would founder, he consented; and when they had cut away the foremast, the mainmast stood so loose, and shook the ship so much, they were obliged to cut her away also, and thus to make a clear deck.

Any one may judge what a condition I must be in at all this, who was but a young sailor, and who had been in such a fright before at but a little. But if I can express at this distance the thoughts I had about me at that time, I was in tenfold more horror of mind upon account of my former convictions, and the having returned from them to the resolutions I had wickedly taken at first, than I was at death itself; and these, added to the terror of the storm, put me into such a condition, that I can by no words describe it. But the worst was not come yet; the storm continued with such fury, that the seamen themselves acknowledged they had never known a worse. We had a good ship, but she was deep laden, and wallowed in the sea, that the seamen every now and then cried out she would founder. It was my advantage in one respect, that I did not know what they meant by founder, till I inquired. However, the storm was so violent, that I saw what is not often seen, the master, the boatswain, and some others more sensible than the rest, at their prayers, and expecting every moment that the ship would go to the bottom. In the middle of the night, and under all the rest of our distresses, one of the men that had been down on purpose to see, cried out we had sprung a leak; another said there was four foot of water in the hold. Then all hands were called to the pump. At that very word my heart, as I thought, died within me, and I fell backwards upon the side of my bed where I sat, into the cabin. However, the men roused me, and told me that I that was able to do nothing before, was as well able to pump as another; at which I stirred up, and went to the pump and worked very heartily. While this was doing, the master, seeing some light colliers, who, not able to ride out the storm, were obliged to slip and run away to sea, and would come near us, ordered to fire a gun as a signal of distress. I, who knew nothing what that meant, was so surprised, that I thought the ship had broke, or some dreadful thing had happened. In a word, I was so surprised, that I fell down in a swoon. As this was a time when everybody had his own life to think of, nobody minded me, or what was become of me; but another man stepped up to the pump, and thrusting me aside with his foot, let me lie, thinking I had been dead; and it was a great while before I came to myself.

We worked on, but the water increasing in the hold, it was apparent that the ship would founder, and though the storm began to abate a little, yet as it was not possible she could swim till we might run into a port, so the master continued firing guns for help; and a light ship, who had rid it out just ahead of us, ventured a boat out to help us. It was with the utmost hazard the boat came near us, but it was impossible for us to get on board, or for the boat to lie near the ship side, till at last the men rowing very heartily, and venturing their lives to save ours, our men cast them a rope over the stern with a buoy to it, and then veered it out a great length, which they after great labour and hazard took hold of, and we hauled them close under our stern, and got all into their boat. It was to no purpose for them or us after we were in the boat to think of reaching to their own ship, so all agreed to let her drive and only to pull her in towards shore as much as we could, and our master promised them, that if the boat was staved upon shore he would make it good to their master, so partly rowing and partly driving, our boat went away to the norward, sloping towards the shore almost as far as Winterton Ness.

We were not much more than a quarter of an hour out of our ship but we saw her sink, and then I understood for the first time what was meant by a ship foundering in the sea; I must acknowledge I had hardly eyes to look up when the seamen told me she was sinking; for from that moment they rather put me into the boat than that I might be said to go in, my heart was as it were dead within me, partly with fright, partly with horror of mind and the thoughts of what was yet before me.

While we were in this condition, the men yet labouring at the oar to bring the boat near the shore, sometimes, when our boat mounted the waves, we were able to see the shore, a great many people running along the shore to assist us when we should come near, but we made but slow way towards the shore, nor were we able to reach the shore, till being past the lighthouse at Winterton, the shore falls off to the westward towards Cromer, and so the land broke off a little the violence of the wind; here we got in, and though not without much difficulty got all safe on shore and walked afterwards on foot to Yarmouth, where, as unfortunate men, we were used with great humanity as well by the magistrates of the town, who assigned us good quarters, as by particular merchants and owners of ships, and had money given us sufficient to carry us either to London or back to Hull, as we thought fit.

RESCUE AT SEA

By CAPTAIN BASIL HALL

This is a first-hand account by Captain Basil Hall of a rescue carried out by his ship. The frigate was cruising in the North Atlantic and he was serving as a midshipman at the time.

On the 13th of October, 1811, we were cruising in the *Endymion* off the north of Ireland, in a fine clear day, succeeding one in which it had blown almost a hurricane. The master had just taken his meridian observation, the officer of the watch had reported the latitude, the captain had ordered it to be made twelve o'clock, and the boatswain, catching a word from the lieutenant, was in the full swing of his "Pipe to dinner!" when the captain called out,

"Stop! stop! I meant to go about first."

"Pipe belay! Mr. King," smartly ejaculated the officer of the watch, addressing the boatswain. Which words being heard over the decks, caused a sudden cessation of the sounds peculiar to that hungry season. The cook stood with a huge six-pound piece of pork uplifted, on his tormentors; his mate ceased to bale out the pease-soup; and the whole ship seemed paralysed. The boatswain, having checked himself in the middle of his longwinded dinner-tune, drew a fresh inspiration, and dashed off into the opposite sharp, abrupt, cutting sound of the "Pipe belay!" — the essence of which peculiar note is that its sounds should be understood and acted upon with the utmost degree of promptitude.

There was now a dead pause of perfect silence all over the ship, in expectation of what was to come next. All eyes turned to the chief.

"No! Never mind, we'll wait," said the goodnatured captain, unwilling to interfere with the comforts of the men: "let them go to dinner; we shall tack at one o'clock, it will do just as well."

The boatswain, on a nod from the lieutenant of the watch, at once recommenced his merry "Pipe to dinner" notes; upon which a loud, joyous laugh rang from one end of the ship to the other. This hearty burst was not in the slightest degree disrespectful; on the contrary, it sounded like a grateful expression of glee at the prospect of the approaching good things which, by this time, were finding their speedy course down the hatchways.

Nothing was now heard but the cheerful chuckle of well-fed company, the clatter of plates and knives, and the chit-chat of light hearts, under the influence of temperate excitement.

When one o'clock came, the hands were called, "About ship!" But as the helm was in the very act of going down, the look-out man at the foretopmast-head called out,

"I see something a little on the lee-bow, sir!"

"Something! What do you mean by something?" cried the first lieutenant, making at the same time a motion to the quarter-master at the conn to right the helm again.

"I don't know what it is, sir," cried the man; "it is black, however."

"Black! Is it like a whale?" asked the officer, playing a little with his duty.

"Yes, sir," cried the look-out man, unconscious that Shakespeare had been before him, "very like a whale!"

The captain and the officer exchanged glances at the poor fellow aloft having fallen into the trap laid for him; and the temptation must have been great to have inquired whether it were not 'like a weasel'; but this might have been stretching the jest too far; so the lieutenant merely called to the signal midshipman, and desired him to skull up to the mast-head with his glass, to see what he made of the look-out man's whale.

"It looks like a small rock," cried young skylark, as soon as he reached the top-gallant yard, and had taken the glass from his shoulders, across which he had slung it with a three-yarn fox.

"Stuff and nonsense," replied the officer, "there are no rocks hereabouts; we can but just see the top of Muckish behind Tory Island. Take another spy at your object, youngster. The mast-head man and you will make it out to be something, by-and-by, between you, I dare say."

"It's a boat, sir!" roared out the boy. "It's a boat adrift, two or three points on the lee-bow."

"Oh ho!" said the officer, "That may be, sir?" turning, with an interrogative air, to the captain, who gave orders to keep the frigate away a little, that this strange-looking affair might be investigated. Meanwhile, as the ship was not to be tacked, the watch was called, and one half only of the people remained on deck. The rest strolled sleepily below; or disposed themselves in the sun on the lee gangway, mending their clothes or telling long yarns.

A couple of fathoms of the fore and main-sheets, and a slight touch of the weather top-sail and top-gallant braces, with a check of the bow-lines, made the swift-footed *Endymion* spring forward, like a greyhound slipped from the leash. In a short time we made out that the object we were in chase of was, in fact, a boat. On approaching a little nearer, some heads of people became visible, and then several figures stood up waving their hats to us. We brought to, just to windward of them, and sent a boat to see what was the matter.

It turned out as we supposed; they had belonged to a ship which had foundered in the recent gale. Although their vessel had become water-logged, they had contrived to hoist their long-boat out, and to stow in her twenty-one persons, some of them seamen and some passengers. Of these, two were women, and three children. Their vessel, it appeared, had sprung a leak in the middle of the gale, and in spite of all their pumping, the water gained so fast upon them, that they took to baling as a more effectual method. After a time, when this resource failed, the men, totally worn out, and quite dispirited, gave it up as a bad job, abandoned their pumps, and actually lay down to sleep. In the morning the gale broke; but the ship had filled in the meantime, and was falling fast over on her broadside. With some difficulty they disentangled the long-boat from the wreck, and thought themselves fortunate in being able to catch hold of a couple of small oars, with a studding-sail boom for a mast, on which they hoisted a fragment of their main-hatchway tarpaulin for a sail. One ham, and three gallons of water, were all the provisions they were set adrift with on the wide sea. The master of the ship, with two gentlemen who were passengers, two sailors, and one woman, remained on board, preferring to stick by the vessel while there was any part of her above water. This, at least, was the story told us by the people we picked up.

The wind had been fair for the shore when the long-boat left the wreck, and though their ragged sail scarcely drove them along, their oars were only just sufficient to keep the boat's head the right way. Of course, they made but small progress; so that when they rose on the top of the swell, which was still very long and high, in consequence of the gale, they could only just discover the distant land of Muckish, a remarkable flat-topped mountain, on the north-west coast of Ireland, not very far from the promontory called the Bloody Foreland.

There appeared to have been little discipline amongst this forlorn crew, even when the breeze was in their favour; but when the wind chopped round, and blew off shore, they gave themselves up to despair, laid in their oars, let the sail flap to pieces, gobbled up all their whole stock of water. Meanwhile the boat, which had been partially stove in the confusion of clearing the ship, began to fill with water; and, as they all admitted afterwards, if it had not been for the courage and patience of the women under this sharp trial, they must have gone to the bottom. As it was both cold and rainy, the poor children, who were too young to understand the nature of their situation, or the inutility of complaining, incessantly cried out for water, and begged that more clothes might be wrapped round them. Even after they came to us, the little things were still crying. "Oh! Do give me some water!" words which long sounded in our ears. None of these women were by any means strong; on the contrary, one of them seemed to be very delicate; yet they managed to rouse the men to a sense of their duty, by a mixture of reproaches and entreaties, combined with the example of that singular fortitude, which often gives more than masculine vigour to female minds in seasons of danger. How long this might have lasted, I cannot say; but probably the strength of the men, however stimulated, must have given way before night, especially as the wind freshened, and the boat was drifting further to sea. Had it not been for the accident of the officer of the forenoon watch on board the *Endymion* being unaware of the captain's wish to tack before dinner, these poor people most probably would all have perished.

The women, dripping wet, and scarcely capable of moving hand or foot, were lifted up the side, in a state almost of stupor; for they were confused by the hurry of the scene, and their fortitude had given way the moment all high motive to exertion was over. One of them, on reaching the quarterdeck, slipped through our hands, and, falling on her knees, wept violently, as she returned thanks for such a wonderful deliverance. But her thoughts were bewildered; and fancying that her child was lost, she struck her hands together, and, leaping again on her feet, screamed out, "Oh! Where's my bairn! My wee bairn?"

At this instant, a huge quarter-master, whose real name or nickname (I forget which) was Billy Magnus, and who was reputed to have no fewer than five wives, and God knows how many children, appeared over the gangway hammocks, holding the missing urchin in his immense paw, where it squealed and twisted itself about, like Gulliver between the finger and thumb of the Brobdingnag farmer. The mother had just strength enough left to snatch her offspring from Billy, when she sunk down flat on the deck, completely exhausted.

By means of a fine blazing fire, and plenty of hot tea, toast, and eggs, it was easy to remedy one class of these poor people's wants; but how to rig them out in dry clothes was the puzzle, till the captain bethought him of a resource which answered very well. He sent to several of the officers for their dressing gowns; and these, together with supplies from his own wardrobe, made capital gowns and petticoats, at least till the more fitting drapery of the ladies was dried. The children were tumbled into bed in the same apartment close to the fire; and it would have done any one's heart good to have witnessed the style in which the provisions vanished from the board, while the women wept, prayed, and laughed, by turns.

The rugged seamen, when taken out of the boat, showed none of these symptoms of emotion, but running instinctively to the scuttle-butt, asked eagerly for a drop of water. As the most expeditious method of feeding and dressing them, they were distributed amongst the different messes, one to each, as far as they went. Thus they were all soon provided with dry clothing, and with as much to eat as they could stow away; for the doctor, when consulted, said, they had not fasted so long as to make it dangerous to give them as much food as they were disposed to swallow. With the exception of the ham, de-voured in the boat, and which, after all, was but a mouthful a-piece, they had tasted nothing for more than thirty hours; so that, I suppose, better justice was never done to His Majesty's beef, pork, bread, and other good things, with which our fellows insisted upon stuffing the new-comers, till they fairly cried out for mercy, and begged to be al-lowed a little sleep. Possibly some of us were the more disposed to sympathise with the distress of these people when adrift in their open boat on the wide sea, from having ourselves, about a month before, been pretty much in the same predicament.

In a fine autumnal morning, just a week after we had sailed from Lough Swilly, to cruise off the north of Ireland, a sail was reported on the lee-beam. We bore up instantly; but no one could make out what the chase was, nor which way she was standing; at least, no two of the knowing ones could be found to agree upon these matters. The various opinions, however, presently settled into one, or nearly so; for there were still some of the high-spyers who had the honesty to confess they were puzzled. The general opinion was, that it must be a brig with very white sails aloft, while those below were quite dark, as if the royals were made of cotton, and the courses of tarpaulin; a strange anomaly in seamanship, it is true, but still the best theory we could form to explain the appearances. A short time served to dispel these fancies; for we discovered, on running close to our mysterious vessel, that we had been actually chasing a rock; not a ship of oak and iron, but a solid block of granite, growing, as it were, out of the sea, at a greater distance from the mainland than, I believe, any other island, or islet, or rock, of the same diminutive size, is to be found in the world. This mere speck on the surface of the waters, for it seems to float on the sea, is only seventy feet high, and not more than a hundred yards in circumference. The smallest point of a pencil could scarcely give it a place on any map, which should not exaggerate its proportions to the rest of the islands in that stormy ocean. It lies at the distance of no fewer than 184 miles very nearly due west of St. Kilda, the remotest of the Hebrides, 290 from the nearest part of the main coast of Scotland, and 260 from the north of Ireland. Its name is Rockall, and it is well known to those Baltic traders that go north about. The stone of which this curious peak is composed is a dark-coloured granite; but, the top being covered with a coating as white as now, from having been for ages the resting place of myriads of sea-fowl, it is constantly mistaken for a vessel under all sail. We were deceived by it several times during the same cruise, even after we had been put upon our guard, and knew its place well. I remember boarding three ships in one day, each of which, in reckoning the number of vessels in sight, counted Rockall as one, without detecting their mistake till I pointed their glasses to the spot.

As we had nothing better on our hands, it was resolved to make an exploring expedition to visit this little islet. Two boats were accordingly manned for the purpose; and while the ship stood down to leeward of it, the artists prepared their sketch-books, and the geologists their hammers, for a grand scientific field-day.

When we left the ship, the sea appeared so unusually smooth that we anticipated no difficulty in landing; but on reaching the spot we found a swell rising and falling many feet, which made it an exceedingly troublesome matter to accomplish our purpose. One side of the rock was perpendicular, and as smooth as a wall. The others, though steep and slippery, were sufficiently varied in their surface to admit of our crawling up when once out of the boat. But it required no small confidence in our footing, and a dash of that kind of faith which carries a hunter over a five-bar gate, to render the leap at all secure. A false step, or a faltering carriage, after the spring was resolved on, might have sent the explorer to investigate the secrets of the deep, in those fathomless regions where the roots of this mysterious rock connect it with the solid earth. In time, however, we all got up, hammers, sketch-books, and cronometers, inclusive.

At is was considered a point of some moment to determine not only the position, but the size of the rock, by actual observations made upon it, all hands were set busily to work, some to chip off specimens, others to measure the girth by means of a cord, while one of the boats was sent to make soundings in those directions where the bottom could be reached.

After we had been employed for some time in this manner, we observed a current sweeping past us at a considerable rate, and rather wondered that the ship, which was fast drifting away from us, did not fill and make a stretch so as to preserve her distance. But as the day was quite clear, we cared less about this addition to the pull, and went on with our operations. I forget exactly at what hour a slight trace of haze first came across the field of view. This soon thickened into a fog, which felt like a drizzle, and put some awkward apprehensions into our heads. It was immediately decided to get into the boats and return to the *Endymion;* for, by this time, we had finished all our work, and were only amusing ourselves by scrambling about the rock.

The swell had silently increased in the interval to such a height, that the operation of returning to the boats was rendered twice as difficult as that of disembarking; and, what was a great deal worse, occupied twice as much time. It required the greater part of half-an-hour to tumble our whole party back again. This proceeding, difficult at any season I should suppose, was now reduced to a sort of summerset or flying leap; for the adventurer, whose turn it was to spring, had to dash off the rock towards the boat, trusting more to the chance of being caught by his companions than to any skill of his own. Some of our Dutch-built gentry, known in the cockpit by the name of heavy-sterned Christians, came floundering amongst the thwarts and oars with such a crash, that we half expected they would make a clear breach through the boat's bottom.

As none of these minor accidents occurred, we pushed off, with our complement entire, towards the ship; but, to our astonishment and dismay, no *Endymion* could now be seen. Some said, "only a minute ago she was there!" others asserted, as positively, that they had seen her in a totally different direction. In short, no two of us agreed as to where the frigate had last been seen, though all, unhappily, were of one mind as to the disagreeable fact of her being now invisible. She had evidently drifted off to a considerable distance; and, as the first thickening of the air had destroyed its transparency, we could see nothing in the slightest degree even like what is called the loom of a vessel. The horizon was visible, indistinctly indeed; but it was certainly not the same horizon along which we had seen the ship sailing but half an hour before. The atmosphere had something of that troubled look which is given to a glass of water by dropping a little milk into it. So that, although there was no fog as yet, properly so called, there was quite enough of moisture to serve the unpleasant purpose of hiding the object of our search; and we remained quite at a loss what to do. We rowed to a little distance from the rock, supposing it possible that some condensation of vapour, incident to the spot, might have cast a veil over our eyes. But nothing was to be seen all round.

It then occurred to some of our philosophers, that as dense air, by its very definition (as they gravely put it) is heavier than light air, it might so happen that the humid vapours had settled down upon the surface of the sea, and that, in fact, we were groping about in a shallow stratum of untransparent matter. The top of the rock, which was seventy feet higher, it was thought, might be in the clear region, and the ship's mast-heads, if not her hull, be visible from thence. There was a sort of pedantic plausibility about the technology of these young savants, which induced the commanding officer of the party, a bit of a dabbler himself in these scientific mysteries, to decide upon trying the experiment. At all events, he thought it might amuse and occupy the party. So one of the men was landed, the most alert of our number, who skipped up the rock like a goat.

All eyes were now turned to our look-out man, who no sooner reached the summit, than he was asked what he saw, with an impatience that betrayed more anxiety on the part of the officers than they probably wished should be perceived by the boats' crews.

"I can see nothing all round," cried the man, "except something out thereabouts," pointing with his hand.

"What does it look like?"

"I am afraid, sir, it is a fog-bank coming down upon us." And so it proved.

The experienced eye of the sailor, who in his youth had been a fisherman on the banks of Newfoundland, detected a strip or extended cloud, hanging along the verge of the horizon, like the first appearance of a low coast. This gradually swept down to leeward, and at length, enveloped rock, boats, and all, in a mantel of fog, so dense that we could not see ten yards in any direction.

Although our predicament may now be supposed as hopeless as need be, it was curious to observe the ebbs and flows in human thought as circumstances changed. Half-an-hour before, we had been provoked at our folly in not having left the rock sooner: but it was now a matter of rejoicing that we possessed such a fixed point to stick by, in place of throwing ourselves adrift altogether. We reckoned with certainty upon the frigate managing, sooner or later, to regain the rock; and as that was the only mark at which she could aim, it was evidently the best for us to keep near.

We had been cruising for some time off the north of Ireland, during which we observed that these fogs occasionally lasted a couple of days, or even longer; and, as we had not a drop of water in the boats, nor a morsel of provisions, the most unpleasant forebodings began to beset us. The wind was gradually rising, and the waves, when driven against the rock, were divided into two parts, which, after sweeping round the sides, met again to leeward, near the spot where we lay, and dashed themselves into such a bubble of a sea, that the boats were pitched about like bits of cork in a mill-leat. This motion was disagreeable enough, but our apprehension was that we should be dislodged altogether from our place of refuge; while the gulls and sea-mews, as if in contempt of our helpless condition, or offended at our intrusion, wheeled about and screamed close to us, in notes most grating to our ears.

While we were speculating upon one another's characters in the boats below, our faithful watchman, perched on the peak of the rock, suddenly called out, "I see the ship!" This announcement was answered by a simultaneous shout from the two boats' crews, which sent the flocks of gannets and sea-mews screaming to the right and left, far into the bosom of the fog.

An opening or lane in the mist had occured, along which we could now see the frigate, far off, but crowding all sail, and evidently beating to windward. We lost as little time as possible in picking our shivering scout off the rock, an operation which cost nearly a quarter of an hour. This accomplished, away we rowed, at the utmost stretch of our oars, towards the ship.

We had hardly proceeded a quarter of a mile before the fog began to close behind our track, so as to shut out Rockall from our view. This we cared little about, as we not only still saw the ship, but trusted, from her movements, that she likewise saw the boats. Just at the moment however that we came to this satisfactory conclusion, she tacked, thereby proving that she had seen neither boats nor rock, but was merely groping about in search of her lost sheep. Had she continued on the course she was steering when we first saw her, she might have picked us up long before the fog came on again; but when she went about, this hope was destroyed. In a few minutes more, we, of course, lost sight of the frigate in the fog; and there we were, in a pretty mess, with no ship to receive us, and no island to hang on by!

It now became necessary to take an immediate part; and we decided at once to turn back in search of the rock. It was certainly a moment of bitter disappointment when we pulled round; and the interval between doing so and our regaining a resting-place was one of great anxiety. Nevertheless we made a good land-fall, and there was a wonderful degree of happiness attendant even upon this piece of success. Having again got hold of Rockall, we determined to abide by our firm friend till circumstances should render our return to the ship certain. In the meantime we amused ourselves in forming plans for a future residence on this desolate abode, in the event of the ship being blown away during the night. If the weather should become more stormy, and that our position to leeward was rendered unsafe, in consequence of the divided waves running round and meeting, it was resolved that we should abandon the heaviest of the two boats, and drag the other up to the rock, so as to form, when turned keel upwards, a sort of hurricane-house. These, and various other Robinson-Crusoe-kind of resources, helped to occupy our thoughts, half in jest, half in earnest, till, by the increased gloom, we knew that the sun had gone down. It now became indispensable to adopt some definite line of operations, for the angry-looking night was setting in fast.

Fortunately, we were saved from further trials of patience or ingenuity by the fog suddenly rising, as it is called, or dissipating itself in the air, so completely, that, to our great joy, we gained sight of the ship once more.

It appeared afterwards that they had not seen our little island from the *Endymion* nearly so soon as we discovered her; and she was, in consequence, standing almost directly away from us, evidently not knowing exactly whereabouts Rockall lay. This, I think, was the most anxious moment during the whole adventure; nor shall I soon forget the sensation caused by seeing the jibsheet let fly, accompanied by other indications that the frigate was coming about.

I need not spin out this story any longer. It was almost dark when we got on board. Our first question was the reproachful one, "Why did you fire no guns to give us notice of your position?"

"Fire guns?" said they; "why, we have done nothing but blaze away every ten minutes for these last five or six hours."

Yet, strange to say, we had not heard one single discharge!

THE LOSS OF THE "WHITE SHIP"

By CHARLES DICKENS

One of the most famous wrecks in English history is that of the "White Ship" in which Prince William, son and heir of King Henry 1, was lost.

Henry the First went over to Normandy with Prince William and a great retinue, to have the Prince acknowledged as his successor by the Norman nobles, and to contract the promised marriage — this was one of the many promises the King had broken — between him and the daughter of the Count of Anjou. Both these things were triumphantly done, with great show and rejoicing; and on the 25th of November, in the year 1120, the whole retinue prepared to embark at the port of Barfleur, on the voyage home.

On that day, and at that place, there came to the King, Fitz-Stephen, a sea captain, and said:

"My liege, my father served your father all his life upon the sea. He steered the ship with the golden boy upon the prow, in which your father sailed to conquer England. I beseech you to grant me the same office. I have a fair vessel in the harbour here, called the *White Ship*, manned by fifty sailors of renown. I pray you, sire, to let your servant have the honour of steering you in the *White Ship* to England!"

"I am sorry, friend," replied the King, "that my vessel is already chosen, and that I cannot, therefore, sail with the son of the man who served my father. But the Prince and all his company shall go along with you, in the fair *White Ship,* manned by the fifty sailors of renown."

An hour or two afterwards, the King set sail in the vessel he had chosen, accompanied by other vessels, and sailing all night with a fair and gentle wind, arrived upon the coast of England in the morning. While it was yet night, the people in some of those ships heard a faint, wild cry come over the sea, and wondered what it was.

364

Now, the Prince was a young man of eighteen, who bore no love to the English, and had declared that, when he came to the throne, he would yoke them to the plough like oxen. He went aboard the *White Ship*, with one hundred and forty youthful nobles like himself, among whom were eighteen noble ladies of the highest rank. All this gay company, with their servants and the fifty sailors, made three hundred souls aboard the fair *White Ship*.

"Give three casks of wine, Fitz-Stephen," said the Prince, "to the fifty sailors of renown! My father the King has sailed out of the harbour. What time is there to make merry here, and yet reach England with the rest?"

"Prince," said Fitz-Stephen, "before morning, my fifty and the *White Ship* shall overtake the swiftest vessel in attendance on your father, the King, if we sail at midnight!"

Then the Prince commanded to make merry; and the sailors drank out the three casks of wine; and the Prince and all the noble company danced in the moonlight on the deck of the *White Ship*.

When, at last, she shot out of the harbour of Barfleur, there was not a sober seaman on board. But the sails were all set, and the oars all going merrily. Fitz-Stephen had the helm. The gay young nobles and the beautiful ladies, wrapped in mantles of various bright colours to protect them from the cold, talked, laughed, and sang. The Prince encouraged the fifty sailors to row harder yet, for the honour of the *White Ship*.

Crash! A terrific cry broke from three hundred hearts. It was the cry the people in the distant vessels of the King heard faintly on the water. The *White Ship* had struck upon a rock — was filling — going down.

Fitz-Stephen hurried the Prince into a boat, with some few nobles.

"Push off," he whispered, "and row to the land. It is not far, and the sea is smooth. The rest of us must die."

But, as they rowed away fast from the sinking ship, the Prince heard the voice of his sister Marie, the Countess of Perche, calling for help. He never in his life had been so good as he was then.

"Row back at any risk! I cannot bear to leave her!" he cried.

They rowed back. As the Prince held out his arms to catch his sister such numbers leaped in, that the boat was overset. And in the same instant the *White Ship* went down.

Only two men floated. They both clung to the main yard of the ship, which had broken from the mast, and now supported them. One asked the other who he was. He said:

"I am a nobleman, Godrey by name, the son of Gilbert de l'Aigle. And you?"

"I am Berold, a poor butcher of Rouen," was the answer.

Then they said together, "Lord be merciful to us both!" and tried to encourage one another, as they drifted in the cold, benumbing sea on that unfortunate November night.

By-and-by, another man came swimming towards them, whom they knew, when he pushed aside his long wet hair, to be Fitz-Stephen.

"Where is the Prince?" said he.

"Gone! Gone!" the two cried together. "Neither he, nor his brother, nor his sister, nor the King's niece, nor her brother, nor any one of all the brave three hundred, noble or commoner, except we three, has risen above the water!"

Fitz-Stephen, with a ghastly face, cried, "Woe! Woe to me!" and sank to the bottom.

The other two clung to the yard for some hours. At length the young noble said faintly:

"I am exhausted, and chilled with the cold, and can hold no longer. Farewell, good friend! God preserve you!"

So, he dropped and sank; and of all the brilliant crowd, the poor butcher of Rouen alone was saved. In the morning some fishermen saw him floating in his sheepskin coat, and got him into their boat — the sole relater of the dismal tale.

For three days, no one dared to carry the intelligence to the King. At length, they sent into his presence a little boy, who, weeping bitterly and kneeling at his feet, told him that the *White Ship* was lost with all on board. The King was never afterwards seen to smile.

MAN OVERBOARD

By W. H. G. KINGSTON

Men often fell overboard while working aloft in sailing ships, especial-ly in men-of-war. Here is an account of the heroism of an officer.

We were on our return home, by the way of the Cape of Good Hope, when, on the 8th of May of that year, we were off Cape L'Agullus. It was blowing a heavy gale of wind, with a tremendous sea running, such a sea as one rarely meets with anywhere but off the Cape, when just at nightfall, as we were taking another reef in the top-sails, a young seaman, a mizen-topman, James Miles by name, fell from the mizen-topsail-yard, and away he went overboard. In his descent he came across the chain-span of the weather-quarter davits, and with such force that he actually broke it. I could scarcely have supposed that he would have escaped being killed in his fall; but as the ship flew away from him, he was seen rising on the crest of a foaming wave, apparently unhurt. The life-buoy was let go as soon as possible, but by that time the ship had already got a considerable distance from him; and even could he reach it, I felt that the prospect of saving him was small indeed, as I had no hope, should we find him, of being able to pick him out of that troubled sea; and I had strong fears that a boat would be unable to swim to go to his rescue, should I determine to lower one. I was very doubtful as to what was my duty. I might, by allowing a boat to be lowered, sacrifice the lives of the officer and crew, who would, I was very certain, at all events volun-teer to man her. It was a moment of intense anxiety. I instantly, how-ever, wore the ship round; and while we stood towards the spot, as far as we could guess, where the poor fellow had fallen, the thoughts I have mentioned passed through my mind. The sad loss of the gal-lant Lieutenant Gore and a whole boat's crew a short time before, about the same locality, was present to my thoughts. To add to the chances of our not finding the man, it was now growing rapidly dusk. As we reached the spot, every eye on board was straining through the gloom to discern the object of our search, but neither Miles nor the life-buoy were to be seen. Still, I could not bring myself to leave him to one of the most dreadful of fates. He was a good swimmer, and those who knew him best asserted that he would swim to the last. For my part, I almost hoped that the poor fellow had been stunned, and would thus have sunk at once, and been saved the agony of despair he must be feeling were he still alive. Of one thing I felt sure, from the course we had steered, that we were close to the spot where he had fallen. Anxiously we waited, — minute after minute passed by, — still no sound was heard; not a speck could be seen to indicate his position. At least half an hour had passed by. The strongest man alive could not support himself in such a sea as this for so long, I feared. Miles must long before this have sunk, unless he could have got hold of the life-buoy, and of that I had no hope. I looked at my watch by the light of the binnacle lamp. "It is hopeless," I thought, "we must give the poor fellow up." When I had come to this melancholy resolve, I issued the orders for wearing ship in somewhat a louder voice than usual, as under the circumstances was natural, to stifle my own feelings. Just then I thought I heard a human voice borne down upon the gale. I listened; it was, I feared, but the effect of imagination; yet I waited a moment. Again the voice struck my ear, and this time several of the ship's company heard it. "There he is, sir! There he is away to windward!" exclaimed several voices; and then in return they uttered a loud hearty cheer, to keep up the spirits of the poor fellow. Now came the most trying moment; I must decide whether I would allow a boat to be lowered. "If I refuse," I felt, "my crew will say that I am careless of their lives. It is not their nature to calculate the risk they themselves must run." At once, Mr. Christopher, one of my lieutenants, nobly volunteered to make the attempt, and numbers of the crew came forward anxious to accompany him. At last, anxiety to save a drowning man prevailed over prudence, and I sanctioned the attempt.

The boat, with Mr. Christopher and a picked crew, was lowered, not without great difficulty, and, sad to say, with the loss of one of the brave fellows. He was the bowman; and, as he stood up with his boat-hook in his hand to shove off, the boat give a terrific pitch and sent him over the bow. He must have struck his head against the side of the ship, for he went down instantly, and was no more seen. Thus, in the endeavour to save the life of one man, another was already sent to his long account. With sad forebodings for the fate of the rest of the gallant fellows, I saw the boat leave the ship's side. Away she pulled into the darkness, where she was no longer visible; and a heavy pull I knew she must have of it in that terrible sea, even if she escaped destruction. It was one of the most trying times of my life. We waited in suspense for the return of the boat; the minutes, seeming like hours, passed slowly by, and she did not appear. I began at length to dread that my fears would be realized, and that we should not again see her, when, after half an hour had elapsed since she had left the ship's side on her mission of mercy, a cheer from her gallant crew announced her approach with the success of their bold enterprise. My anxiety was not, however, entirely relieved till the falls were hooked on, and she and all her crew were hoisted on board, with the rescued man Miles. To my surprise I found that he was perfectly naked. As he came up the side, also, he required not the slightest assistance, but dived below at once to dry himself and to get out of the cold. I instantly ordered him to his hammock, and, with the doctor's permission, sent him a stiff glass of grog. I resolved also to relieve him from duty, be-lieving that his nervous system would have received a shock from which it would take long to recover. After I had put the ship once more on her course, being anxious to learn the particulars of his escape, as soon as I heard that he was safely stowed away between the blankets, I went below to see him. His voice was as strong as ever; his pulse beat as regularly, and his nerves seemed as strong as usual. After pointing out to him how grateful he should feel to our Almighty Father for his preservation from an early and dreadful death, I beg-ged him to tell me how he had contrived to keep himself so long afloat. He replied to me in the following words: — "Why, sir, you see as soon as I came up again, after I had first struck the water, I looked out for the ship, and, getting sight of her running away from me, I remembered how it happened I was there, and knew there would be no use swimming after her or singing out. Then, sir, I felt very certain you would not let me drown without an attempt to pick me up, and that there were plenty of fine fellows on board who would be anxious to man a boat to come to my assistance, if you thought a boat could swim. Then, thinks I to myself, a man can die but once, and if it's my turn to-day, why, there's no help for it. Yet I didn't think all the time that I was likely to lose the number of my mess, do ye see, sir. The next thought that came to me was, if I am to drown, it's as well to drown without clothes as with them; and if I get them off, why, there's a better chance of my keeping afloat till a boat can be lowered to pick me up; so I kicked off my shoes; then I got off my jacket, and then, waiting till I could get hold of the two legs at once, I drew off my trousers in a moment. My shirt was soon off me, but I took care to roll up the tails, so as not to get them over my face. As I rose on the top of the sea, I caught sight of the ship as you wore her round here, and that gave me courage, for I felt I was not to be deserted; indeed, I had no fear of that. Then I knew that there would be no use swimming; so all I did was to throw myself on my back and float till you came up to me. I thought the time was somewhat long, I own. When the ship got back, I saw her hove to away down to leeward, but I did not like to sing out for fear of tiring myself, and thought you would not hear me; and I fancied also that a boat would at once have been lowered to come and look for me. Well, sir, I waited, thinking the time was very long, and hearing no sound, yet still I could see the ship hove to, and you may be sure I did not take my eyes from off her; when at last I heard your voice give the order to wear ship again. Then thinks I to myself, now or never's the time to sing out. And, raising myself as high as I could out of the water, I sang out at the top of my voice. There was a silence on board, but no answer, and I did begin to feel that there was a chance of being lost after all. 'Never give in, though,' thinks I; so I sang out again, as loud, you may be sure, as I could sing. This time the answering cheers of my shipmates gave me fresh spirits; but still I knew full well that I wasn't safe on board yet. If I had wanted to swim, there was too much sea on to make any way; so I kept floating on my back as before, just keeping an eye to leeward to see if a boat was coming to pick me up. Well, sir, when the boat did come at last, with Mr. Christopher and the rest in her, I felt strong and hearty, and was well able to help myself on board. I now can scarcely fancy I was so long in the water."

I was much struck with the extraordinary coolness of Miles. He afterwards had another escape, which was owing less to his own self-possession, though he took it as coolly as the first. On our passage home, the ship was running with a lightish breeze and almost calm sea across the Bay of Biscay, when Miles was sent on the fore-top-gallant-yard. By some carelessness he fell completely over the yard, and those aloft expected to see him dashed to pieces on the fore-castle. Instead of that, the foresail at that moment swelled out with a sudden breeze, and, striking the bulge of the sail, he was sent forward clear of the bows and hove into the water. A rope was towing over-board. He caught hold of it, and, hauling himself on board, was again aloft within a couple of minutes attending to his duty, which had so suddenly been interrupted. On his arrival in England, Lieutenant Christopher received the honorary silver medal from the Royal Humane Society for his gallant conduct on the occasion of saving Miles' life.

OPEN BOATS IN LONELY SEAS

Among the hundreds of stories of heroism and suffering by seamen from lost ships, the tale of the Dutch Indiaman "John Hendrick" ranks very high.

One of the most heartrending shipwrecks that has happened for some time was made known at Lloyd's, by the arrival of the ship *Chance*, Captain Roxby, from Sydney, in the London Docks, having on board a portion of the crew of a Dutch Indiaman, named the *John Hendrick*, H. W. Edkelenbury, master, which was totally lost on the rocks forming St. Paul's island, on the morning of the 29th of May, 1845, while on her voyage from Amsterdam to Batavia. The manner in which the deplorable occurrence was discovered is remarkable. It appears that on the night of the 2nd of June, the crew of the *Chance* were anxious to ascertain whether such rocks as were laid down in the chart, forming St. Paul's Island, forty-five miles north of the equator, and twenty-nine degrees west, were really to be seen, as many doubts prevailed as to their existence. Captain Roxby informed them that if the same course they were then going was kept until the following morning, they would come in sight of the rocks. Accordingly at eight o'clock they descried them, and at half-past nine the captain was much surprised by observing, through a glass, a Dutch ensign flying from a spar on the island. It being surmised that a vessel had been wrecked near the spot, no time was lost in bearing up to the rocks, and, on nearing them, several persons were noticed on them, evidently in an exhausted state. The captain ordered the pinnace to proceed to their assistance. About twenty poor creatures were found lying about, exhausted, and apparently in a dying condition. The boat not being able to take them all off, the captain, the chief officer, steward, carpenter, two seamen, and three apprentice boys, were first rescued, the remainder being assured by the boat's party that they would return and preserve them also. The ship was speedily gained, and on the captain learning that eleven persons were still on the island, he promptly ordered the long boat to be lowered,

and with the pinnace started for the rocks. Only twelve minutes elapsed ere they had set out a second time for the island, but in the meanwhile a sharp breeze had sprung up, a tremendous sea ran, and a
strong current set in to the westward. Both boats kept beating about
for five hours, and it appearing evident that if they kept out much
later they would be swept away, they returned to the ship, having
been unable to render the promised assistance. It being probable
that the gale might in some measure abate, Captain Roxby kept his
ship beating about the island, as it was impossible to anchor, there
being no soundings, for ten entire days; and having seen nothing of
the poor creatures, who by that time must have perished from the
intense heat and the want of water and food, he sailed for England,
his own provisions by this time becoming very short.

On questioning those whom he had saved, he learned that they
belonged to the Indiaman in question; that on the morning of the 29th
of May she was running under a press of sail, when at three o'clock
the watch on deck discovered the rocks ahead so close as made it
impossible to clear them. The helm was instantly brought to, but
almost at the same moment she struck, and the succeeding wave
pitched her on her beam ends. Every endeavour was instantly made
to get her off; her rigging and masts were cut away in order to
lighten her, but as the sea kept dashing her against the rocks with
terrific force, she soon broke up. The captain succeeded in reaching
the rocks with a line, and secured it round one of the loftiest cliffs, in
effecting which he was no less than seven times swept down the rock,
frightfully lacerating his body. The line being also made fast to the
wreck, most part of the crew contrived to haul themselves on the
island by it. Four brave fellows attempted to land in a boat with the
ship's papers and some provisions, but on nearing the breakers a
heavy sea capsized her, and they all perished. A poor boy, who had
been saved, had his arm broken by being dashed against the rocks.
On assembling on the frightful spot which they had been cast upon,
which presented not the remotest chance of escape, starvation stared
them in the face. Of wearing apparel they had saved none, save the

few drenched rags that covered them; and of food, the only things they could rescue from the wreck were a cask of butter, a cask of flour, a small biscuit, and a small keg of gin. Immediately under the line, a burning sun pouring upon them, and not having a drop of water to quench their thirst, the heat was intense, and which they could only allay by wading into the sea up to the chin, and thus remain the whole day. At night time the spirit was distributed amongst them. The single biscuit was broken up and divided equally, and then they commenced scouring the rocks in the hope of finding further food. They succeeded in getting a few wild fowls and eggs; they were almost driven to madness. At dusk a few drops of rain were felt descending; they instantly laid out a kind of sail to catch it, and held their heads up to the heavens with their mouths open. It soon, however, passed over.

On the third day, to their great joy, a vessel bearing American colours hove in sight in the offing. They hoisted the signal on the spar, and in order to make doubly sure, the mate, seven seamen, and a passenger, put off in the only boat they had been enabled to save, with a small piece of wood to dabble along, the oars being lost, to the approaching ship, but she passed onwards and was not seen afterwards. The poor creatures in the boat then strove to regain the island; the current was too strong for them, and they were speedily lost sight of. That they have perished there can be no doubt. They had not the slightest provision with them — no compass, and no oars, the nearest place being Cape Roque, more than 600 miles distant. The sufferings of those left on the rocks, on perceiving the fate of those in the boat, were tenfold; and on the fourth day, they gave themselves up to death. They were rapidly sinking from the effects of the heat, the skin on their face, hands, &c. actually peeling off. On the morning of the fifth day the *Chance* hove in sight, and, as before noticed, saved seven. Eleven, amongst whom was the doctor, were left on the island. On the arrival of the poor fellows in London, they waited on the Netherlands consul, who having relieved their destitute condition, housed them at the Yorkshire Grey Tavern, Lower Thames

Street, from whence they proceeded next day to their native country, by the Rotterdam mail steamer. The illfated Indiaman belonged to Rotterdam, was 800 tons burden, and had only been built about two months previous to her loss. To Captain Roxby the highest commendation is due for the humane and prompt steps he adopted to rescue the unfortunate persons on the island. Those who are indebted to him for the preservation of their lives, declare that nothing could exceed his endeavours to re-make the island, Night and day he was on deck attempting it. Of the fate of the eleven poor creatures left on the rocks, it is the opinion of Captain Roxby, as also the Dutch captain, that they must have perished in a day or two afterwards; for had they been rescued by any other vessel, she must have been fallen in with by the *Chance*. The rocks being situated some hundred of miles out cf the track of vessels trading to the Cape, perhaps scarcely two out of one thousand ever met with them.

SMALL BOAT BATTLE

by W. H. G. Kingston

During the long years when the Royal Navy strove to suppress the terrible slave trade in the Indian Ocean, many fights took place. This is the story of one such fight and how it led to the death of a senior officer.

Another incident to be recorded is the death of Captain Charles J. Brownrigg, senior naval officer on the East Coast of Africa. This officer had greatly distinguished himself by the energy and success with which he had carried on operations against the slaving dhows during the term of his command on the Zanzibar coast. On the 27th of November 1881 he started in the steam pinnace of the *London,* accompanied by his steward, a native interpreter, and a writer, with a crew consisting of a coxswain, Alfred Yates, three seamen, and three stokers. Captain Brownrigg was going upon a tour of inspection among the boats engaged in repressing the slave trade, and the various depôts. On his way he examined any dhows he met which he suspected to contain slaves. On the 3rd of December a dhow was sighted flying French colours. In such cases it was not Captain Brownrigg's custom to board, but only to go alongside to see that the papers were correct. He therefore ordered the boat's crew to be careful not to board without direct orders, intending a mere cursory examination, and no detention whatever, as he did not arm the boat's crew, and directed the time alongside to be noted.

He went alongside without hailing or stopping the dhow in any way, the wind being light and the craft scarcely forging ahead.

Prior to getting alongside he sent the coxswain forward to make a hook, with a chain and rope attached, fast to the dhow, his object in doing so seemingly being to prevent the necessity of the vessel stopping, and to enable him to converse with the captain and to quietly verify her papers. He took the tiller himself, and was alone, with the exception of his steward (a Goanese) and a native interpreter, in the

377

after-part, which is separated from the rest of the boat by a standing canopy, over which one has to climb to get fore or aft. It was still more cut off by the fact of the main-boom having been raised to the height of the top of the ensign staff on the main mast, and over it the afterpart of the rain-awning was spread, being loosely gathered back towards the mast.

When the boat was quite close to the dhow, a man, supposed to be the captain of her, stood up aft with a bundle or roll of papers in his hand, and said something as he unfolded them, and pointed to the French flag. What he exactly said is unknown.

There were then visible on board the dhow four men, two aft and two forward, all armed with the usual Arab swords and creases. The forecastle sun-awning was spread at the time from the foremast to a stanchion shipped abaft the stern-piece, and under it were two blue-jackets and the writer; the leading stoker was at the engines, whilst the two stokers appear to have been sitting on the inside of the gunnel of the well, *i.e.* the space for boilers and engines.

As the coxswain was standing on the stem of the boat, in the act of making fast with the hook rope, he caught sight of some eight or ten men crouched in the bottom of the boat with guns at the 'ready' position. He sang out to the captain aft, when they rose up and fired; he flung the hook at them, and closed with one, both falling overboard together.

The Arabs, the number of whom is variously estimated at from fifteen to twenty-five, then jumped into the pinnace with drawn swords and clubbed guns. As their first fire killed one man (a stoker) outright, mortally wounded another, and severely wounded two others of the boat's crew, the Arabs found but little difficulty in driving the rest, unarmed as they were, overboard.

Captain Brownrigg and his steward were the only two left, and both were in the after-part of the boat. He seized a rifle, and at the first shot knocked an Arab over; but before he could reload three or four of them rushed aft to attack him, getting on the top of the canopy and at the sides, but he, clubbing his rifle, kept them at bay, fighting with a determination that filled the survivors, who were then in the water unable to get on board, with the greatest admiration, they describing him as 'fighting like a lion'.

He knocked two of his assailants over, but was unable to get at them properly owing to the awning overhead, whilst they were above him on the canopy cutting at him with their long swords, but fearing to jump down and close with him. As he knocked one over, another took his place.

The first wound that seems to have hampered him in the gallant fight was a cut across the forehead, from which the blood, pouring over his face, partially blinded him. He was then cut across the hands, the fingers being severed from the left and partially so from the right one, and, badly wounded in both elbows, he could no longer hold the rifle.

He then appears to have tried to get hold of any of his foes or of anything wherewith to fight on, but, blinded as he was, his efforts were in vain. He fought thus for upwards of twenty minutes, keeping his face to his assailants, and having no thought, or making no effort, to seek safety by jumping overboard. At length he was shot through the heart and fell dead, having, besides the fatal one, received no less than twenty wounds, most of them of a severe, and two of a mortal nature.

During this time, of the men in the water, Thomas Bishop, seaman, was badly wounded, and was supported to the dinghy astern of the pinnace by William Venning, leading stoker, who was himself slightly wounded in the head by a slug. There he held on, but the Arabs, hauling the boat up alongside the pinnace, cut him over the head until he sank.

Samuel Massey, A.B., was severely wounded, and was supported to the shore, a distance of about 700 yards, by Alfred Yates, leading seaman, and William Colliston, ordinary; the remaining stoker swam there by himself, as also did the interpreter. The writer (third class), John G. T. Aers, having been mortally wounded, there was left on board only the captain's steward, who lay quiet, pretending to be dead.

The Arabs then left the boat and sailed away in their dhow, when the leading stoker got on board of her, — he having been in the water all the time, — got up steam, and picked up the men on the beach. When they were on board they proceeded to find Lieutenant Henry W. Target, the senior officer in charge of the boats at Pemba, but who, being twenty-five miles off, could not get up in time to capture the dhow.

The perpetrators of this outrage were afterwards captured by the Sultan of Zanzibar, and brought to justice.

JOE ORGAN'S ARCTIC YARN

This story tells in graphic style of the hardships of Polar pioneers. It is interesting to compare it with the modern situation — permanent settlements at the South Pole and regular air routes across the North Pole.

"Yes," began Joe, after a peep into the saucepan, "yes; the admiral told you true enough, I've been on three Arctic voyages in my time, between the years 1848 and 1854. You want me to reel off the yarn straight from the beginning? Well, the first voyage was with Captain Sir James Clark Ross. He was one of the old school; rather a sharp 'un, sir; I might say a bit of a Tartar. This was the first expedition in search of Sir John Franklin. The *Enterprise* and the *Investigator* were the ships, both sailing vessels. Captain Ross had the *Enterprise*, Captain Bird the *Investigator*. I was quarter-master on board the *Enterprise*.

"We started from Greenhithe on the 12th of May, 1848 and bore up first for Stromness, in the Orkney Islands, to take in fresh supplies. We got a little to the westward of Leopold Island — well, I can't say no nigher than Leopold Island, tho' I believe the place had a name of its own — and in that harbour we wintered; but we had a dreadful journey, and many difficulties afore we got there, coming through the bays, cutting the ship's way through the ice. Progress? Bless your soul, I couldn't give you no idea. We were three weeks off the Devil's Thumb; sometimes we'd gain a few miles and next day we'd lose 'em and more than we'd gained. But we got there somehow for our winter quarters.

"In the fall of the year we laid out depots in different points about Prince Regent's Inlet and leading on towards Cape Walker for the spring expeditions. We laid a depot on the Point of Leopold in case of anything happening to the ships and another no great way off with six months' provisions for twenty men and a steam launch all ready for setting out in case that any of Franklin's expedition might come that road. You see we reckoned as how they might turn up at any moment poor chaps. In the spring one party from the *Investigator* went up to Fury Beach to look for Franklin but had no luck. Lieutenant Robinson was in command. Then on May 12th what they called the 'grand parties' started for the long travel. I went with the one under Sir James Ross with Sir Leopold M'Clintock second in command; but had to get back to the ship when we had made five days' march for I had got my feet frostbitten some time afore.

"Let me see — you are asking about our outfit for an expedition. Well in them days we had leather boots and box-cloth jackets and trousers with fur boots for sleeping in but we never wore them. They were more trouble than they were worth. You may find them on Leopold's Island now if the bears haven't eaten them. The sledges at that time were much the same as the bodies of the brewers' drays you see in the streets, great clumsy heavy things with the stores piled up on 'em mostly in black bags. Our grub was navy salt pork that had all to be cooked on board ship afore we started concentrated peasoup that was carried in frozen chunks in bags and a piece was chopped off and put into warm water to thaw it and make it eatable or drinkable somehow. The meat was so bad that we had to what you call 'soldier' it in the messing — call out the chaps' names and make each man stick to the mess that was called to him. Grog? Yes; navy rum twice a day half a gill each time. Were we forced to drink it on the spot? My faith, we didn't need no forcing; we had nothing else to put a bit of heat into us.

"The sledges — we dragged them, you know — were different sized; but most of them were 'seven men' sledges — that is the team including the officer was eight but the officer doesn't drag. Only Admiral Osborne he was always a good 'un to lay into it when the chaps had a heavy drag. About ten miles a day is the regular allowance but I've been sixteen hours in harness and only made three miles. We had canvas tents shaped like the roof of a house 14 feet by 7 each tent for eight men and of course we pitched them on the ice. The sleeping wraps on my first expedition was a tarpaulin underneath with a blanket bag — the blankets sewn up at the bottom and the sides and you had to get inside like a fellow you know getting ready for a sack race and lie regularly in a bag — yes, head and all. Then we had besides a buffalo robe above and below with the hair turned inwards for the sake of warmth.

"We turned in all standing of course — it wasn't quite the place to undress and go to bed like folks do at home. You carry no kit with you but what is on your back except a flannel, a pair of drawers, two pair of mittens and a towel. In them days we carried lignum vitæ for fuel and used the ordinary boats' coppers for cooking. We boiled them twice a day morning and night — in the evenings we thawed the peasoup, in the morning we had cocoa. Soft tack! Lord love you, sir, it was all biscuit. On board ship we were supposed to have soft tack twice a week; but it was not once in ten times that it could be baked for want of fuel.

"It was a regular starvation voyage was that, sir. Me and another chap used to take each other's grub day about so that both of us might get as much as we could eat once in the two days. This time we stopped out only one winter and a dreadful job it was getting back. In August 1849 we broke out and in September we got set fast in the ice again and drove away on through Lancaster Sound and I should think well into Davis's Straits afore the ice gave from about us. We lost seven or eight of the crew, chiefly I believe through bad provisions — aye, and the bad treatment didn't help to keep the chaps hearty and merry. When you come to flog men out in the Arctic regions why, sir, you see, it disheartens them; men hain't got no more confidence then. I don't say that if they had been away from this special work the chaps as got flogged didn't deserve it; but there, sir, flogging is the worst mistake that an Arctic captain can make.

"My second Arctic voyage began in the *Resolute* with Captain Austin. There were four ships in the expedition altogether. Captain Ommaney had the *Assistance,* Commander M'Clintock the *Intrepid* and Lieutenant Sherard Osborne the *Pioneer.* The *Intrepid* and *Pioneer* were steam tenders for towing the two big ships. I was Captain Austin's coxswain at first and when a vacancy occurred in the

Pioneer as ice-quartermaster I was recommended for it and got the berth. My feet that had been frost-bitten were very tender at first. A part that has been once touched is more liable ever after and you know a burnt child dreads the fire.

"How do we treat frost-bites? Well, sir, the part is first bathed in warm water and rubbed — friction, I believe they calls it — and then oatmeal poultices are clapped on. The using of snow is an old saying, I know, but I never saw it tried, and it's a thing as I shouldn't use myself. I've seen men's toes come clean out of the sockets with frost-bites. But I must lie a little closer to the wind, sir, else we'll never get into port. An ice-quarter-master's duties are just like a pilot's. His place is up aloft in the crow's nest, and he guides the ship through the ice.

"This second expedition sailed pretty nearly about the same time of the year as the first. Our winter quarters — all the ships were together — were at Griffith's Island. There was quite a fleet of ships that year wintering in the Arctic regions. Lady Franklins two ships, under Captain Penny, were close by us. The Americans, the *Rescue* and the *Advance*, were beset in the ice all the winter, and were drove down similar to what we had been in my first expedition. But before we got to winter quarters we came on traces of Franklin at Beachy Island. There were three graves — no, not in the ice, in the gravel of the shore — with headboards, and the name on one was Hartnel, I forget the other two names.

"Of course I went to have a look at them. We knew the poor chaps belonged to Franklin's crews, because *Erebus* and *Terror,* the names of his ships, were on the headboards, and that they had wintered there in 1846. And there was a place where a garden had been laid out, and what had been a carpenter's workshop, and a cairn on the top of the island, but nothing in it — not a line to say where they had come from, or where they were trying to go to. I reckon they must have been drove out in a hurry, afore they had time to put anything into the cairn. We turned the island almost upside down expecting to find something or other, but there was not so much as a shred. We left the graves just as we had found them, and then the ships of the expedition separated in various directions.

"One went across Wellington Sound to Cape Hotham, another groped up Wellington Channel; but we had no success in the search, and all came together again for wintering. In the fall of the year, after we had laid up at Griffith's Island, we did a great deal in travelling parties, looking round in different places for more traces of Franklin, but in vain. In the spring the provision depots were laid out, and in May the grand parties began. One went to Cape Walker, another to Melville Island, and in fact we went about in all directions searching. Commander M'Clintock's party was out the longest, eighty-two and a half days.

"We had better equipment this time, better provisions, and better treatment. The sledges were quite another thing, half as light again. If you're passing the British Museum you might look and see a model — one inch to the foot scale — of a sledge of this expedition, fully equipped for a hundred days. I made the model with my own hands, and Sir John Barrow sent it to the Museum. We had the best of grub — good meat and good soups, beefsteaks and onions, pemmican of various sorts, and a gill of grog allowed per man. Our tents were lighter, and the sleeping appliances much better. We had mackintoshes this time above and below, with felt blanket bags covered with brown holland to keep the frost out, and buffalo robes as well. Our clothing, too, was much improved. Our boots had cork soles, and we had mocassins for travelling. And our cooking gear was quite different, and ever so much better. In the second expedition we used tallow and glycerine for fuel, burnt in a copper lamp, which heated a tin galley.

"We had no luck as to Franklin, but Commander M'Clintock, in that long travel of his, reached Melville Island and took out of a cairn the despatches which Captain Parry had left in his voyage of 1818. He left instead a document about our expedition. I ought to tell you that shortly after Captain M'Clure, of the *Investigator*, came with a party to Melville Island, expecting to find Parry's despatches, and

385

13

found M'Clintock's instead. Captain M'Clure had tried the North-west passage, you know, by the Bering Straits, and when he had got as far as Mercy Bay his ship was there beset in the ice — stuck hard and fast. He would have followed M'Clintock up to Griffith's Island, but his men were too far gone for the long journey. I'll have more to tell you presently about M'Clintock.

"My third Arctic expedition sailed in 1852, under Captain Belcher, as he was then. We had the same ships, only the senior captains had changed ships. I was again in the *Pioneer* with Captain Osborne. We left Greenhithe about the same time of the year as before. By this time there were two expeditions missing — three indeed. There was Franklin's, of which there was not much hope for anything but the relics; there was M'Clure in the *Investigator*, and there was the *Enterprise* under Captain Collinson, who had not been heard of for three years. The *North Star* came with us to act as a depot and reserve ship, and it was lucky for us she did — we came to find her very handy. We held on towards Barrow's Straits as well as we could, cutting and blasting the ice; and this time we had not so much difficulty in getting to Beachy Island.

"We found lots of open water in Wellington Sound, and the expedition parted. The *Resolute* and *Intrepid*, under Captain Kellett, took their way up to Melville Island, and there wintered by Parry's Cairn, which had been the end of M'Clintock's previous journey, and there, of course, it was found that M'Clure had been and taken away M'Clintock's despatches and left his own. Everybody with Kellett thought that, as the season had been such an open one, M'Clure had got right round all safe, and had struck homeward, and no thought, therefore, was taken of looking for him; but in the spring Lieutenant Pim, with a party, started to have a look at the spot where M'Clure had mentioned his ship was lying, and to see if he had left any information there. Well, instead of finding a paper in a cairn, they found the *Investigator* there — in Mercy Bay — frozen in high and dry. She had not started tack nor shift for two years, and the crew were in a very bad state, some of them well on to rottenness with scurvy. So you see, M'Clure never got right round the north of the American continent with his ship, but he himself did with his crew, who were brought off by Kellett. The worst cases were sent at once to the *Resolute*, but several died.

"In the meantime, we of the *Assistance* and *Pioneer* were up in another part of the world altogether. We passed through Wellington Channel, and after what we call ordinary difficulties, poking about bays and points for traces of Franklin with no result, we made our way to what is now called Northumberland Sound, and there we got the ships snug for the winter, and made our preparations for the fall travelling. I was away with Captain Osborne, and we were out about fifteen days. We were to have stayed longer, but broke through the young ice, and wetted our provisions; so we had to come back. Still no traces of Franklin.

"In the spring we made great preparations for long travelling, by throwing out feeding depots to supply the parties as far forward as possible without breaking on the grub they carried. Each sledge carried grub for forty-five days. We travelled that trip ninety-one days. Captain Richards was out ninety-three days. We explored new land, and carried the coast on to the northward from where Penny left off the year before, surveying it accurately.

"We had another winter of it, but I am not come to that yet. Owing to the length of our journey, the ships had left their winter quarters and were working their way down channel when we caught them up. It was at twelve o'clock at night we overtook them; and what do you think? Old Belcher had hoisted the letter K, which is the signal for the plague being aboard.

"Mayhap it was this as brought us bad luck. We got beset, and were three weeks cutting three miles of ice; but the ice gradually opening let us down within some seventy or eighty miles of Beachy Island, and there it drove us very near high and dry, and jammed us so tight that next summer we found it impossible to get them out. We had to leave the whole fleet stuck hard and fast this voyage — all our own four ships, and the *Investigator* as well. When we found it was 'a case', we began in the spring to move the sick down to the depot-ship, the *North Star*. We had to travel them on sledges on the ice.

"On the 26th of August, 1854 — I think that was the date — we abandoned the old ships for good and all, and all hands marched for the *North Star*. She was pretty full, I can tell you, for she had five crews aboard, besides her own, deducting the worst cases of the *Investigator* and our invalids, who had gone home the year before in the *Phœnix* and *Talbot* hove in sight, ranged up alongside, and delivered their letter bags. Then we all went back to the floe, made fast again, and distributed the crews afresh, and, after a long spell of talking, and a bit of a jollification, we stood away for home. And so ended my Arctic experiences. I was paid off 17th October, 1854.

"How did we spend our winters? Well in my first voyage we had a school 'tween decks, and the officers came and taught us anything from the alphabet right up to the higher branches. In the other voyages we had pastimes as well as school; on the first voyage we had no heart for pastime. We have had theatricals, philharmonic societies, masquerades and fancy balls, and what not, taken up and carried out by the officers. Lectures, too, were given by them — some on astronomy, some on surveying, some on history, and so on. We were very comfortable, I can tell you. Captain Austin was a thorough good old gentleman, and would enter into them things just like a lad. We used to take exercise out of doors, and do a lot of sleeping.

"In the matter of clothing, I myself would prefer good thick under-clothing, thick knitted socks, mocassins for the feet in travelling, and good loose jumpers, and trousers, which the men ought to be allowed to line according to their own taste. The snow does not settle on duck as on cloth; as for them sealskin things we had last voyage, I wouldn't give tuppence for the lot. But I'm all for sealskin caps with flaps, and what we call 'Welsh wigs', or Arctic nightcaps. Worsted mittens are the things. I can't see as any improvement can be made on the last voyage; or in the matter of sledge equipments or provisions. I'd let 'em have the rum for sure, and with that and good grub and good usage, the men will go to the Pole if it be possible. I would advise as much extra brown holland being sent as would make a sail for each sledge when there happens to be a fair wind. I invented this dodge myself, and they all used it after I showed them the example. It is easy to rig the sail on the sledge with the boarding-pikes as mast and yard, and as the wind catches it, the men's shoulders are eased wonderfully. Up the sail, and away you go; I've been kept on the trot for hours, and sometimes the crew would jump on the sledge and leave only a couple of hands to guide it straight.

"To the Pole? — of course they'll go to the Pole — what's to hinder them, if they go through Smith's Sound? The Admiral and me has had many a talk over it — they get right up into the basin then, and have clear water. Says I to the Admiral, 'If you're agoing, sir, I'm agoing too,' and so I would, either with him or with Admiral Richards. I would like to be ten years younger, sir, I would. If it were the money to bury me, I'd give every sixpence I ever had, or ever shall have, to be able to go that way once more. It would go against my heart to see any other nation drop into that job, sir." And as the flush rose on the old man's face, and the glow kindled in the eyes of him, the expression of the wistful eager face, and the eyes looking into the far off, as if the Pole was to them a visible entity, called vividly to mind a certain famous picture, which was one of the masterpieces of this year's Academy.

OLD ZEKE'S YARN

Another tale once enjoyed by sailormen in the Dog-watches who joyed in ghost stories.

It was a great day when the brig *Lydia* was launched — great was the throng of people, and great the exultation of the Pooduckers, Old Zeke shook his head when she stuck in her course to the sea; but when she reached it, his hurrah, thrice repeated, was loud and long. Then came the rigging. Zeke was as much on the alert, as if the property had been his own, splicing ropes, uncoiling cables, and always joining the workmen in every song, whether in tune or out, for it would be a severe day when a sailor couldn't make his own tune. Well, the brig was rigged and went to sea, and Old Zeke again renewed his rounds, from the ferry-house to the fish-house, and thence to the ship-yard, where he would stand looking off upon the water with a sad and half-vacant look. Then was the time for a story, and though Old Zeke would call us all sorts of landlubber names when we gathered about him, yet there was always a twinkle of the eye, that showed that it pleased him.

I must tell one of Old Zeke's last stories, because it was the one that made the deepest impression upon my mind; first premising, that Zeke was a firm believer in omens and presentiments, in mermaids and ghosts. As to that, so were most of his hearers, very few of us having become so unfortunately wise as to lose the zest of a wild story by any unreasonable doubts as to its verity. So, then, we were all able to listen with staring eyes, "goose flesh", and hair crawling upon our heads.

OLD ZEKE'S YARN.

I was mate in the trim ship *Morgianna*, Richard Lee, commander. The *Morgianna* was as nice a craft as ever dipped the water, but a doomed ship from the very first. She was owned by old —, as big a rascal as ever escaped the halter. He cheated the workmen out of nigh about half their wages by his parlavering blarney, and that too after keeping them on half allowance of grog. No good would come of it, and so in truth she stuck when going off the stocks, which was saying as plain as dumb thing could say, that she hadn't a long cruise to run. I was right loath to go in her, anyway, but Richard Lee was to be captain, and no sailor could refuse to sail under him. He was as true as steel, nobody ever knew him to flinch, let the case be what it might; and then, he carried an eye that took the soul out of the toughest seaman that ever opened a pair of clam-shells.

"Do sailors always have to open clam?" said Tommy D., who was on a visit from the country. We all laughed, and Zeke chucked him under the chin, and said — "Yes, when he opens his lips." But, as I was saying, Cap'n Lee had a terrible eye, full and black as a squall; but then he had a true sailor heart, — didn't climb into the ship through the cabin winder, but come regully up from the forecastle.

Well, we'd been cruising about the West Indy Islands, exchanging freight and so-forth, and on our return voyage, somewhere in latitude — "Oh, never mind the latitude, nor longitude neither," cried a dozen little shrill, sharp, eager voices, all in one breath. Well, well, we was somewhere in the Gulf-Stream. It was my watch on deck, and a pale young man, that went out for his health, because he writ poetry, and sat up nights makin faces at the moon, came and stuck himself down astern of me. I didn't like it jeest right, for I was thinkin' of Sukey Bacon, and a nice gal she was. Howsomever, I tried to look civil, and said nothing. He had sat there about half an hour, when I, tipping an eye all around the horizon, to keep a look-out for squalls, that are always keeping the deuce to pay in them seas, I see a brisk light off to the nor'-east.

"What's the kick-up off there," says I sposin' it to be some craft a-fire. With that the young man run down, and up comes Cap'n Lee his great eyes looking as if they wasn't never made to shut, no how.

"What have we here?" says he, seizing the speakin'-trumpet, and puttin' it to his mouth, as if he fear'd nobody; for the thing was bearing down upon us, before a light wind, and we could see her spars and sails, and her light rigging in the midst of the flame. Soon as she came in speakin' distance, Cap'n Lee hailed her.

"Ship-ahoy, Mr. Beelzebub; where are you from, where bound, and what's your cargo?"

My hair stood right on end, and the strange sail came down upon us, and almost touched our stern. 'Twas an awful sight. I must say she'd a 'ben a nice model for a ship, barrin' the pattern was made by old Nick himself; but everything was so trim and easy, and she lay down to the water so handsome, that I was sure he must some time or other have been a sailor himself, to do the thing so handsomely. To be sure, where her hull touched the water, there was a terrible frizzlin'. Well, down she came alongside, and, sure enough, we could see old Nick himself standing to the helm, like any Cap'n; and there chained fast, with a red-hot chain, stood old—, the owner of the *Morgianna*. He gin us a terrible look as he went by, and lifted up both hands in a way that was piteous to behold. But I really believe his mouth was sewed up, or he would have spoke.

Cap'n Lee laid his hand, solemn-like, upon my shoulder, "Zeke," says he, "I believe Satan has got his due," and he took out the log-book, and set down the circumstance, and the latitude and longitude, day of the month, week, and hour of the night. Well, we had a rough time of it after this, squalls and gales; was blown off two or three times. After a time we got in, and the first news we heard was, that old — was dead. Cap'n Lee looked at me, and I looked at him. We found out jeest the time the old sinner died, and sure enough, 'twas jeest the same hour and minnit that we saw him off there, aboard that blazing craft, smokin' with brimstone.

So much for the story of Zeke. The old man got up and walked away, for the recital had wrought powerfully upon his own imagination, and we children stood huddled together with pale faces; and little Tommy D. had grasped my arm so tightly, as to leave black and blue spots for a long time afterwards.

THE PIRATE EMPRESS

By DOUGLAS V. DUFF

The story of a beautiful and cultured woman who reigned as the Queen of the China Seas in the early 1800s. Large-scale piracy in those waters started after a severe famine in 1800 caused by excessive spring floods which ruined the crops.

One day a large and well-found junk, laden with dried fish, rice and tea, ran ashore and stranded on a reef of rocks. From crevice and cranny in the rocky hills and cliffs the starving, desperate peasants emerged in a screaming mass, surged through the waist-high water and threw themselves at the wrecked ship. Her crew fought back desperately, killing hundreds of the attackers, many of whom had no more than their crooked fingers as weapons. They were unstoppable, the rest came steadily on, for death beneath the whirling sword-blades, or in front of the crew's muskets, was swifter and kinder than dying like dogs in a ditch. They never paused until the last of the seamen and passengers had been torn apart and thrown from the big junk's decks into the sand, rocks and water, and the precious food was being swiftly carried ashore and distributed far and wide.

The news of her capture spread like a forest-fire along the coast. The peasants put to sea in canoes and sampans, even on rafts, and though hundreds died from the sea and the defenders' fire, the rest succeeded in capturing other junks, especially one very large one bound for Hong-Kong with a hold-full of weapons. Piracy became general but for several months they were naught but a disorganized rabble. When a leader appeared he soon bound them into a taut and disciplined organization, one of the most evil and powerful ever known on all the Seven Seas.

This leader, a devil in human shape, was a most unlikely-looking pirate-chief, for Ching Yi was old, a hump-backed dwarf of the most hideous appearance. In spite of his grotesque appearance Ching Yi had a dominating personality and a brain able to outwit the most cunning of rivals. His deeply sunken eyes mesmerized those who looked into them, while his unnaturally deep, bass voice, a mighty sound from so small and twisted a man, commanded instant awe and implicit obedience. On top of that he was a dead-shot with the four pistols he carried in his belt and was deadly with both sword and dagger. He could draw and throw a casting-knife with uncanny speed and accuracy and he struck as swiftly and coldly as a snake when he deemed it necessary and that was not seldom. On top of all this he had a fiendish skill in devising tortures and protracted public deaths for his victims.

Ching Yi started by enlisting twelve extremely desperate and skilled fighting-men, well-known thieves and robbers, and exacting instant and faultless obedience to his every word. They swore to follow him wherever he chose to lead and they filled every detail of their oaths. He had a small, leaky sampan; his men were all armed with swords but there were only four ancient match-lock muskets between them, yet with Ching to lead them they soon showed their real strength. From his sampan, he told them, he would soon own first a small junk and then a large one, after which a frigate would be within their grasp — and he implemented every promise.

His main success was due to never attacking any enemy unless he was completely certain of victory. Ching Yi never risked a defeat for, with his handicaps of person and weakness, he knew a single setback would be his end. Always he attacked with complete surprise and some of the stories of the ways in which he lulled enemies to complacency by appearing as a helpless cripple, or as a juggler and tumbler among them, equal those of Robin Hood. Gradually, in ever-increasing acceleration of progression, he owned other vessels and manned them with the hardiest of the peasants and the best-qualified prisoners he took. He mercilessly slaughtered any of his own men who cut down gunners or marksmen among the crews they captured, and, so great was the terror of his name and his reputation for success, that most of the professional fighting-men hired to defend the ships were very willing to join him. After a year his flag, flying from his increasing fleet, was enough to ensure instant surrender, often without the need to fire a single shot.

He kept the best junks he captured and used all the bronze cannons from those he did not wish to incorporate in his fleet, to increase the armament of his chosen ships. Very soon he had so powerful a squadron that the Mandarins of the Emperor's Court at Pekin sent a fleet of forty armed junks of the Imperial Navy to crush him. When this squadron arrived off Ching Yi's base they were instantly surrounded and attacked in headlong fashion by over 1,200 pulling boats and sampans, crammed with pirates who poured musketry and arrows into the Naval ships in a ceaseless sleet. The Mandarins aboard, who had come expecting a walk-over, were great noblemen, but they were by no means fighting sailormen, and panic gripped them at once. They ordered the warships turned about and tried to beat their way through the swarm of small craft. Twelve succeeded; the remaining twenty-eight, the most powerful men-o'-war on the China Coast, were added to Ching Yi's pirate-fleet.

After that victory his rise to complete sea-power was phenomenal. Men flocked to his standard so fast that within another year he was lord of 70,000 hard-fighting confident pirates, who manned six squadrons of first-class ships. His law was absolute, every word demanded obedience and the only punishment for any hesitation in complying with his will, cheating in the sharing of booty or the least suspicion of disloyalty, was a protracted and ingeniously planned public execution. The Emperor and the Imperial authorities dreaded him. Even the few foreign ships kept carefully away from the long line of coast controlled by Ching's men.

The only person who was not abjectly afraid of him was his young and superbly beautiful wife, Hsi Kai, who had been made prisoner when the ship in which she was a passenger was captured by pirates. They were so struck by her dainty and exquisite beauty that they reserved her for Ching himself. She was dragged aboard his flagship and stood, bound, on the deck facing the Lord of the Coast.

This hideous, misshaped, hunch-back dwarf, clad in gorgeous brocade and glittering with jewels, enthroned on a golden chair on the poop, stared for several minutes at the young and lovely maiden who faced him so dauntlessly, showing not the least trace of fear. That was something new to Ching Yi. He was accustomed to see every one who faced him cringe and plead for mercy. Hsi Kai said nothing. While he tried to stare her down, she stood mute in sullen and scornful rebellion. Ching Yi looked away first, very pleased at the new sensations he was feeling at the sight of someone whom he could not frighten and ordered her bonds to be cut off. The ropes on her wrists and ankles were sliced through, but, as they fell away, she snatched the curved, razor-edged knife from the seamen and then, like a tiger-cat, sprang straight at the little monstrosity on the golden chair. She would have killed him then and there, if four of Ching's officers had not grabbed her in the nick of time, at the very moment she thrust upwards in the horrible, belly-ripping back-stroke, the deadliest stroke of all. Hsi Kai would have died there and then, if Ching's deep voice had not suddenly roared:

"Hold. Who touches this lady — dies! She is to live, for I love a fighting-spirit, and I like courage whether it be that of man or woman."

He gave her luxurious quarters in his own flagship, rich clothing and slaves to wait upon her. He treated her like a queen and when he found that she had a quick brain able to grasp problems of attack and defence and to advise him shrewdly on great matters of strategy and tactics, his admiration of her became intense. Hsi Kai was a very clever and lovely woman and, above all else, she had the three advantages of ruthless common-sense, superlative physical beauty and cold logic with no human weaknesses, a combination which, fortunately for the rest of the world, occurs very, very infrequently in any one woman. In her own fashion she was another Roxanna, Zenobia or Theodosia. She was also very ambitious and realized that she could never return to her former mode of life. Consequently she decided to do the best she could for herself under the circumstances open to her.

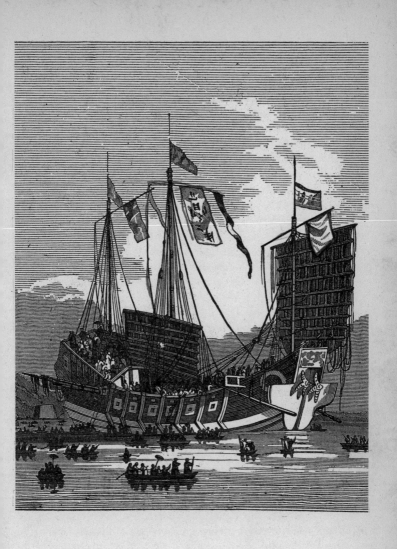

Realizing that as Ching Yi was very old he could not last for many years, she made herself, behind his outward authority, the real ruler of that vast Pirate Empire. So when the hunchback proposed marriage she accepted, for by then she had him so greatly under her influence that he willingly agreed that she should hold equal executive authority with himself. It was probably the only time in his life Ching ever trusted another human being. His wife, with her beauty and her aristocratic lineage, her brain and her charm, was idolized by him because of her deep loyalty and sincere regard for his wishes and welfare. Hsi Kai never, not for a single moment, lowered her guard so that all intrigues to poison her husband's mind against her were defeated, stillborn. Rumour-mongers were reported by Ching himself to his wife who devised ever new and more devilish methods of having them killed in public. There was a perfect trust between them during the few months they were together. In that time Hsi Kai achieved supreme power among the pirate fleets.

The pirates ran into a typhoon off the Pescadores, in the Foros Strait, about ten months after the marriage, and Ching went down in his flagship. Hsi Kai was not with him; she was cruising with another squadron, of which she was commander-in-chief, hundreds of miles away. When a swift junk brought the news of her husband's death, she ordered all the squadrons back to their base where she signalled all captains to repair aboard her flagship, announcing that she was now their admiral. Only three disobeyed her summons and she was ready for them — her executioners were waiting and instantly be-headed the waverers. The rest were already convinced of the wisdom of having her in command and willingly followed her.

Hsi Kai immediately changed her outward appearance, all the gorgeous and dainty robes she had worn to charm the old hunchback were put aside. She always appeared in the dress of a fighting chief-tain of the coast, wearing an unsheathed and naked sword slung from her shoulder. What was more she quickly showed that she was mas-ter of the art of using the blade and she cut down one junk-captain who had a reputation as a champion swordsman when he attempted to challenge one of her orders. It is probable, even likely, that she deliberately provoked the man into fighting, in order to impress her superb skill-at-arms on her followers and to show them she asked no indulgence for being female.

She soon proved herself a perfect Amazon of a woman, handsome, quick-tempered, fearless, with the courage of a lioness. She was, calculatedly, extremely cruel and, more importantly, proved herself to be an even better strategist and tactician than her dead husband, while the Intelligence Service she organized was extremely efficient.

This enabled her to lead her fleets up the great rivers of China, forsaking the seaboard for bigger rewards. She sacked rich cities hundreds of miles upstream and forced their survivors to pay colossal ransoms. She constrained wealthy rice-planters who had never seen the sea or an ocean-going ship, to surrender their entire crops, but she won over the temple-priests by a strict respect for their safety and property. If a prisoner's relatives were not swift in paying a ransom she sent them, first, the right ear of the victim, and exactly ten days later, the head!

Perhaps her greatest hold over the motley and ferocious empire lay in her reputation for cold and fierce chastity. She lived in the lonely isolation of a modern admiral, guarded by a tough band of eunuchs and women who resembled her in their skill-at-arms. Then, one day, she fell in love with a young fisherman her flagship picked out of his sampan while the fleet was on passage. Her own story was repeated, for when the young man was brought, fettered, before her as she sat in the golden chair, he refused to grovel on the deck and beg for his life.

When she said, coldly, that he would be beheaded if he persisted in refusing to bow, the young man looked straight up at her:

"Strike off my head if you wish, Lady Hsi Kai," he said proudly. "It is the only way you can make it bow to the deck before you. But you are naught but a woman, powerful and mighty as your qualities have made you, whereas I am a man who will die rather than shame his manhood by bowing at her order to any woman on earth. Do what you will — I cannot prevent you carrying out your will. But a woman you are while I remain a man for as long as it pleases you to allow me to live."

She recognized the same spirit with which she had faced that terrible hunchback. The tense scene on the speeding warship, with its great matting sails drawing full, the blue water hissing past, lasted for more than a minute, before she ordered him to be taken below, and kept under strict guard but to be treated kindly and well fed. Within a week she sent for him to meet her again on the poop, and when he appeared, his hands still fettered, Hsi Kai cut the cords with her own knife. A servant stepped forward with the elaborately-embroidered robes of a nobleman and she handed him the bejewelled sword of that rank. There was no romance between them; Hsi Kai maintained her reputation for frigid chastity, but she quickly realized the worth of Paou the Fisherman. He proved himself the best seaman in her whole fleet and, though the officers were jealous of him, he had the sovereign ability to command the affection and respect of the ordinary men, who would, and did, follow him to the death whenever his sword was out and flashing in the sun above a prize's bulwarks. The intrigues of the disgruntled officers were quickly shattered by Hsi Kai herself.

Paou must have been an astute person, for he was always careful to treat Hsi Kai as though she was his admiral and never to show that her feminitity entered into their relationship. Consequently her trust in him became absolute and when the High Admiral of the Imperial Navy, Kwolang Lin, swore to smash the pirate empire for good and all, she chose Paou as her commander-in-chief.

High Admiral Kwolang Lin had a cage made and placed on his flagship's poop, parading it around several cities as the one in which he would bring back Hsi Kai, Queen of the Pirates. He mustered the full strength of the Emperor's Navy and sailed with not the least doubt that they would smash the pirates. They were met at sea by the six pirate squadrons, with 75,000 men aboard, and Hsi Kai flying her flag in one of the most heavily-armed junks. The Imperial ships were all much larger and carried heavier guns than those of the sea-robbers, but the pirate vessels were much handier and manned by far more expert seamen.

It was as big-scale a naval action as the defeat of the Spanish Armada, and even more ships and more numerous cannons were engaged. Under Paou, who led her vanguard, the ships of Hsi Kai darted swiftly in and out of the rolling gun-smoke, struck at the Imperial leviathans and withdrew before suffering any serious damage themselves. The battle ended as night fell with Paou running his vessel alongside the Imperial flagship and leading his ravening, maddened boarders over her rail, sword blades whirling. The Imperial troops and seamen were driven back until, making their last stand on the lofty poop, the High Admiral Kwolang Lin, put the hilt of his jewelled sword on the deck-planking and threw his breast onto its point — his suicide ending all resistance.

With the total defeat of the Imperial Navy, Hsi Kai became undisputed mistress of the China Seas. She married Paou, but even after doing so she remained the commander and Paou was always her loyal Vice-admiral and competent Chief of Staff until, forced at last to make peace with her because he was unable to smash her power, the Emperor offered generous terms, hoping to transform the unconquerable Queen of the China Seas and her horde of fighting sailor-men into his servants. He did so much against his inclination and will; he struggled and delayed for as long as he could on the sole ground that it was beneath the dignity of a man, let alone an Emperor, to treat on equal terms with any woman.

Hsi Kai met him on his own ground. When he continued to dally, she broke off the negotiations and ordered her ships to sea and her pirates back to battle stations. Not until the Emperor consented to deal directly with her, woman though she was, would she free the sea-lanes or stop the raids on the cities of the coast and rivers. She insisted upon her husband being ennobled and appointed a high official, in the first class of Mandarins. With this was to go a large palace in Pekin, an exalted title for herself, a vast grant of money and land and unbreakable oaths of security, ensuring her future status.

Once she had all this, the amazing woman made a complete change in herself. Doffing her male war-chieftain's clothing and putting aside her sword, she resumed the daintiest of feminine apparel, settled down as the pleasing wife of Paou, bore him four children and lived until she died in the utmost respectability, accepted and liked by the ancient nobility of Pekin. Grandchildren came and the riches of the Lady Hsi Kai and her husband, the Admiral Paou, steadily increased until he died, a very aged man, in 1869, the dainty Hsi Kai surviving him until 1873, when she must have been somewhere in the region of ninety years old.

A GLOSSARY OF NAUTICAL TERMS

Many of the terms and names used in this book are now long forgotten even by sailors, though still more are in current, everyday usage. Here are some of the older terms and phrases:

ABACK: When a sailing ship is suddenly taken with the wind filling her sails from forward, pressing them back against the masts and spars. A very dangerous predicament, liable to dismast her. Usually caused by careless handling or lack of seamanship and happening with devastating suddenness. Hence the expression, "taken aback" - "taken flat aback" indicating one's being perilously surprised.

ABAFT: Towards the sternmost part of the ship from amidships. It is also used to indicate the bearing of some object from the vessel. "Ship three points abaft the starboard beam" indicates that it bears approximately 124 degrees from right ahead.

AFORE or FOR'ARD OF: The opposite of ABAFT.

AMIDSHIPS: In the centre, or the middle of the vessel.

ATHWART: Lying across — for instance, a boat that has drifted against a ship's anchor-cables as it lies moored is said to be "athwart her hawse".

AVAST: The command to stop. "Avast hauling" indicates to stop pulling at a rope.

BACKSTAYS: Ropes running from a mast-head, lower, top, or topgallant mast in a fore-and-aft direction, secured to the ship's sides, designed to stay the spar against longitudinal stresses and strains (see *Shrouds*) from aft. FORESTAYS do the same for stresses from forward.

BARE POLES (under): Indicates a ship driving before a storm with no canvas set. Only the bare poles of her yards or gaffs are showing.

BARQUE: A three- or four-masted ship square-rigged on all the masts except the aftermost one, which carries only fore-and-aft sail (see *Full-rigged Ship*).

BARQUENTINE: Three- or four-masted, with square rig on only her foremast, all the rest being fore-and-aft rigged (see *Schooner*).

BATTENS: Thin strips of wood or metal engaging in cleats around the hatch-coamings to hold down the tarpaulin coverings. They are secured by hammered-in wedges. Hence the term indicating everything is secured: "battened-down".

BEAMS: The strong cross-members running from side to side in the hull which support her ribs, knees and outer hull, and also her decks. Thus when a ship is said to be "over on her beam-ends" she is lying on her broadside in a state of complete capsize. But "the beam" also means a direction, at right angles from her fore-and-aft line. Thus "on the lee-beam" means something at right angles from the ship on the side sheltered from the wind: on the windward side at right angles, it would be "on the weather-beam".

BEND: To make fast a line or rope.

BIGHT: The loop or the doubled part of a rope when held. It also means a bay or an inlet. The Bight of Benin is perhaps the largest of these, as usually they indicate a small inlet or bend in a coastline.

BINNACLE: The case containing the compass by which the ship is steered. Originally it was a square, rough box, but later became a helmet-shaped brass container, fitted with a permanent lamp.

BLOCK: A pulley. A piece of wood with one or more sheaves, or wheels in it, through which ropes run, or are rove, to ease the labour involved in lifting heavy objects, or those under severe strains. Usually blocks are made to take a specified size of rope but SNATCH BLOCK is specially adapted, with a lifting slide, to accommodate several thicknesses at will.

BOBSTAY: The line holding the bowsprit down to the stem, preventing it being lifted or destroyed by the upward tugging of the jibs or headsails.

BOLTS: Large nails or bars of metal used to unite various parts of the ship. Bolts made of wood, used in ancient times more than nowadays, were TREE-NAILS. It is also a measure of canvas.

BOLT-ROPE: The rope surrounding a sail to which the canvas is sewn.

BOOM: A soar, rigged fore and aft when stretching a sail set in that direction. Also used in olden days for studding-sails, spread from the end of the yardarms when the wind was fair. Booms were also used to hold boats when at anchor out from the ship's side. TO BOOM OFF means to thrust something away with the aid of a pole or boom. BOOMs were also used as floating obstructions in harbour defence.

BRACES: Ropes at the yardarms by which the yards where swung, or "braced" to bring them to the correct angle to set the sail to the wind.

BRAILS: The ropes by which the lower corners of fore-and-aft sails are hauled up and so shortened.

BRIG: A two-masted sailing-ship carrying square-rig on both.

BRIGANTINE: Two-masted ship square-rigged on the foremast only.

BULKHEAD: Temporary or permanent partitions dividing a ship into separated compartments. Some are "watertight" and meant to act as dams in case of flooding.

BULWARK: The wood or metal solid protection around the outer and upper edging of the upper deck.

BUNT: The middle section, or belly, of a sail.

BUNTLINES: The ropes for hauling up the bunt.

CABLE: Until the 1820's these were almost invariably of thick hemp rope. Now normally of chain cable, securing the ship to her anchor. The cable is also a unit of measurement, but one that varies greatly, ranging from 120 fathoms or 720 feet in American ships to 200 fathoms in the Royal Navy of Nelson's time.

CAT-HEAD: A large, usually squared baulk of timber projecting from the side of the forecastle, or the fore-part, to which the anchor was hoisted and secured (catted) by its ring, the flukes being led further aft.

CHAFING-GEAR: Old rope-yarns and other material wrapped around the rigging or the spars at friction-points to minimise chafing.

CLEAT: A piece of timber secured to the deck or the bulwarks, fashioned with projecting arms from the centre, around which ropes could be turned-up, or belayed, to secure them.

CLEW: The after lower corner of a fore-and-aft sail and the lower corners of square ones.

CLOSE HAULED: A ship with her sails trimmed to creep as close to the wind's flow as possible. She is trying to make headway against an unfavourable breeze without losing ground by being drifted down to leeward.

COIL: Rope stowed away in a ring. The act of stowing it in this fashion.

CRINGLE: The rope that runs around a sail but varying from a *Bolt-rope* (q.v.).

CROSS-TREES: Small projecting timbers supported by the "trestle-trees" and "cheeks", supporting-timbers, at the mast-head to hold the "tops" at the head of the lower-mast and also at the top-mast head to spread more widely the topgallant rigging.

DAVITS: Timbers or metal cranes, with sheaves at their ends outboard, meant to support and hoist the ship's boats so they project clear of her sides to enable them to be lowered in safety.

DEAD RECKONING: A calculation of the ship's various courses and speeds, taken at fixed and frequent intervals, if possible with due note of tides, currents and winds, which can give some indication of her position. The method is very prone to inaccuracy, but was essential in olden times, when it was impossible, or very difficult, to fix the longitude, either because of the lack of a chronometer or inability to "shoot" the stars, moon or the sun.

DOG WATCHES: Half-watches of two hours instead of the normal four. They came between 16.00 and 20.00 each day. Their purpose was to vary the actual hours so that the same watch was not on duty from midnight until 04.00 every day of the voyage. The watches changed at each four-hour period after midnight, when eight bells were struck. Thereafter each half-hour added a stroke to the bell, thus at 15.00 six bells were struck; at 15.30 seven. The custom arose in the days when times at sea were measured in thirty-minute sand-glasses, the quartermaster striking a bell for the number of the glass just emptying itself; eight of the sand glasses were kept in the rack before him and reversed as needed. The term "dog watch" has the same connotation as the "dog" in "dog roses", "dog violet", etc., i.e. pseudo. Thus four bells were struck at 18.00, but only one at 18.30. But instead of four following the three at 19.30 the full eight were sounded at 20.00 to mark the ending of a watch. At midnight on December 31st/January 1st sixteen bells were struck — eight for the Old and eight for the New Year.

DOWN-HAUL: A rope to haul down jibs, staysails and other canvas such as studding-sails.

DROGUE: A canvas sleeve, or drag, towed astern to slow a ship. This was also often used by privateers or men-of-war under sail when they wanted to lure an enemy to destruction.

EARRING: The rope attached to the CRINGLE (q.v.) of a sail by which it is bent or netted. (A network of small lines by which sails and hammocks are lashed and stowed away).

EYE-BOLT: An iron bar with a loop or an eye at one end driven through the side or deck of a ship with the eye projecting to allow a hook to be affixed. If there is a ring through this eye it is called a RINGBOLT.

EYE-SPLICE: A rope with a permanent loop formed at one end by tucking individual strands in succession into the lay of the rope. A SHORT SPLICE is used to join two ends of a rope by interweaving the opposing strands. A LONG SPLICE is the same, but, by a system of halving the strands, the joined rope is no thicker than the original, so allowing it to be rove through a similar sheaved block. A BACK SPLICE is formed by tucking the strands back into the lay to prevent the end of the line being frayed by remaining loose.

FID: A wooden pin of various sizes employed to lift the lay of ropes while a strand is being tucked through to form one part of a splice. Also a fid can be a block of metal, usually of iron, or wood, which was thrust through the heel of a mast to support it. The metal counterpart of the fid used in splicing is a marline-spike.

FISH: To repair or strengthen a damaged spar or yard by passing cordage arund it. TO FISH AN ANCHOR entails raising its flukes upon the gunwale or bulwarks, the flukes being the point at each end of the bill, which is at the end of the upright shank, which is surmounted at right angles by the stock.

FOOT-ROPE: Formerly called the "horse". It is the looped rope slung beneath a yard on which the seamen stand while reefing, furling or doing any other work upon the sail.

FORECASTLE: The part of the deck, usually raised in sailing-ships, right in the bows forward of the foremast. It is the name used, as a rule, to designate the accommodation for the seamen, which was in this part of the vessel.

FOUNDERING: The act of sinking when a ship fills with water.

FURL: The rolling up of a sail and securing it.

GAFF: The spar to which the head of a fore-and-aft sail is bent. BOOM is the name for the lower spar.

GASKETS: The ropes securing a sail to a spar or a yard when it has been furled.

GRAPNEL: Small anchor with several flukes, or claws, usually found in boats and very small craft. Used for grappling.

GRATING: A wooden lattice-work used for covering open hatches in fine weather. In old men-of-war, the place where flogging was carried out.

GUNWALE: The uppermost part of the side of a boat or small ship.

GUY: A rope used for steadying a spar or mast, or to swing a derrick or spar either way when hoisting something from its upper end.

HALYARDS: Ropes and tackles employed in hoisting and lowering yards, sails and gaffs. Also thinner ones for hoisting flags, known as the SIGNAL HALYARDS.

HATCH OR HATCHWAY: Opening in the decks to allow passage to spaces beneath. The coverings of the holds are also called HATCHES.

HAWSE PIPE or HOLE: The holes in the bows through which the anchor-cables run.

HAWSER: A larger and much stronger rope used for towing, warping and other heavy duties where more slender ones would not suffice.

HAZE: Bullying a man.

HEAD SAILS: Used for all canvas setting forward of the fore-mast.

HEEL: The part of the keel nearest the rudder-post. TO HEEL means to list, or to lean over.

HELM: The complete mechanism by which a ship is steered.

HITCH: To secure; or a particular form of knots used for a special purpose.

HOLD: The interior, open part of a ship, where, for instance, her cargo or stores are stowed.

HOLY-STONE: A block of sandstone used for scrubbing and whitening wooden decks by abrasion. There were names for their various shapes and sizes, e.g. "Boston Bible", "Bristol Prayer-book", the eccleciastical implication being appropriate because holystoning was a chore often performed kneeling on the deck.

IRONS: A ship was "in irons" when, after messing up an attempt to tack and come around on the opposite course, she failed to swing through the wind's eye and hung there unable to help herself and usually "caught flat a-back", a position of considerable danger in a strong breeze. TO PUT A MAN IN IRONS was to fetter him.

JACKSTAYS: Ropes stretched tautly along a yard, or elsewhere, to bend sails or other ropes on to.

JIB: A triangular head-sail set fore and aft. Set on a stay forward of the foremast.

JIB-BOOM: The spar or boom rigged out beyond the bowsprit to which the tack of the jib is lashed.

JOLLYBOAT: One of the smallest boats carried, usually lashed across the stern in merchantmen.

JURY RIG: Temporary repairs to masts and sails and spars executed at sea. Jury masts and other replacements were erected to replace those damaged, but vitally needed.

KEDGE: A small anchor with an iron stock used for warping a

vessel out of a narrow channel or to gain an offing when required.

KEEL and KEELSON: The keel is the spine of a ship, the lowermost of her timbers, running her entire length, the backbone on which she rests. The keelson is a timber sheath over the keel.

KNEES: The crooked timbers, or ribs, of a ship used to connect the beams to the rest of her framework.

KNOT: The nautical unit of speed which means the time needed to cover one nautical mile in terms of the number made good in one hour. Its name comes from the knots formed at certain intervals in the log-line which was streamed astern to find the speed. By measuring the time taken, using a sand-glass, for a certain number of these knots to run out from the reel, the hourly speed at that moment could be calculated. It is as wrong to speak of distances as being so many knots as it is to say a ship travels at so many knots *an hour*. The knot is a combined time-distance unit of measurement.

LANYARDS: Ropes rove through the DEAD EYES to set up the rigging and hold it taut. DEAD EYES are round pieces of timber, usually pierced with three holes and used in pairs. By tautening the lanyard between the upper and lower lanyard, the proper tension needed to keep the SHROUDS (q.v.) can be maintained. In vessels with hemp rigging the shrouds and stays would be stretched while to windward and require tightening after the ship came on to the other tack.

LARBOARD: The old name for port, or the left side of a ship when one looks forward from aft.

LAUNCH: A large boat. Often the LONG-BOAT.

LAY: To come or go. To LAY-TO is to heave-to, bring the ship up to ride to wind and sea, seeking safety untill a storm abates.

LEAD: The hand-lead is a small version used for soundings in not more than 20 fathoms. It has a hollow at its lower end meant to be charged with a piece of tallow to recover a specimen of the sea-floor. The DEEP-SEA LEAD was much larger and could sound depths up to 100 fathoms. The LEAD-LINE attached to it was marked at intervals to indicate the depths attained.

LEE: The side opposite to the one from which the wind is blowing. That would be the WEATHER SIDE. LEEWAY is the distance lost by a ship's drift to leeward. In a small craft it may easily be calculated by the angle between the wake and the fore-and-aft line of the vessel. This shows how far she is being set down from the course she appears to be lying and can be corrected with ease, once known.

LIFE LINES: Ropes carried along yard, or decks, to help men to their footings.

LOG: The log-book is the official diary and record of all that happens aboard a ship. In merchantmen it is usually kept by the Second Officer nowadays, though in earlier times it was the Mate's sole responsibility. The LOG, however, is a piece of timber, thrown overboard and secured by a rope, by means of which the speed is calculated in knots (q.v.)

LUFF: To alter the helm so as to bring the ship's head closer to the direction of the wind. "To bring her up".

MARTINGALE: A short, perpendicular spar set under the end of the bowsprit and used for a guy for the head-sails to prevent the bowsprit and jib-boom from being sprung upwards by their pull.

MESS: Any number of men who eat together.

MIZEN or MIZZEN MAST: the aftermost of the three masts of a three-master. In ships with four, the after one is usually called the JIGGER, though there are variations. In a BRIG (q.v.) the after of the two masts is the MAINMAST and there is no mizen.

PAINTER: The rope from the bow of a boat for the purpose of

attaching her to a wharf, to a stake, or to her parent-ship.

QUARTER-DECK: That part of the upper deck abaft the main-mast, the second mast. The name stems from the sixteenth century, when ships had half- and quarter-decks as well as a poop. The HALF-DECK is now the name given to quarters of the apprentices or cadets.

RATLINES: The rope lying across the shrouds (q.v.), like the rungs of a ladder, used to help men get aloft.

ROYALS: Light sails for fine weather set above the top gallant sails.

SCHOONER: Fore-and-aft rigged ship without tops, but with two or more masts. There were variants, such as the TOPSAIL SCHOONER, which carried a pair of topsails on her fore-mast. One that was two-masted and had a pair of topsails on each of her masts was an HERMAPHRODITEBRIG.

SCUPPERS: Holes cut in the waterways to enable the decks to clear themselves.

SHEET: The rope used to set a sail by keeping the CLEW (q.v.) down to its place.

SHEET ANCHOR: The ship's largest anchor.

SHROUDS: The ropes from the mastheads of lower, top and top-gallant masts secured to the ship's sides and intended to sustain all lateral strains and stresses, as opposed to STAYS, which take those longitudinally applied.

SKY-SAIL: A light sail setting above the royals.

SLOOP: A small, one-masted fore-and-aft rigged vessel. A KETCH had a tall foremast and a short mizzen, its difference from a YAWL being that the ketch's steering gear was placed forward of the mizzen-mast, while a yawl had hers abaft it. A CUTTER was also one-masted, but differed in several particulars from a SLOOP.

SPANKER: The aftermost sail, fore and aft, of any ship of size. It set with BOOM and GAFF.

STANCHIONS: Upright posts meant to support the BEAMS, or the bulwarks.

STANDING RIGGING: The parts of a ship's rigging intended to remain fast and immovable, as opposed to the RUNNING RIGGING used to manoeuvre her.

STAYSAIL: A triangular, fore-and-aft sail which sets upon a STAY (q.v.).

STEERAGE: The parts below decks just forward of the after cabin.

STEM: The cutwater; a piece of staunch timber from the forward end of the keel up to the bowsprit heel.

STERN POST: The aftermost timber of a ship or the after-end of the vessel.

STRAND: A number of yarns twisted together to form part of a rope.

STRIKE: To lower sails or colours.

STUDDING-SALES (often written **STUNSAILS**): Light sails set outside the ordinary sails on the yards, set from booms sliding along the yard themselves and used only in fair weather. Nelson carried his fleet into action at Trafalgar under studding-sails because of the light favourable S.W. wind.

TACK: To put the ship about by turning head to wind and so bringing it on to the other side. By turning stern to wind, one WEARED or WORE ship. The TACK is also one of the ropes used to control fore-and-aft sails.

TAFFRAIL: The rail running around a ship's rails astern.

TAUNT or ATAUNTO: Meaning high or tall, and usually applied to a ship's masts.

TAUT: Tight.

TILLER: The bar of wood or metal which moves the rudder by means of the TILLER ROPES, which lead from the tiller-head to the barrel of the steering wheel, from whence she is controlled by the helmsmen.

TOPMAST: The second mast above the deck, above the lower mast. Above is sometimes stepped the third or TOPGALLANT MAST.

TOPSAILS (lower and upper): Usually the second and third sails above the deck. Over them went the upper and lower topgallants in ships rigged after 1885. Above them again were some variants, such as royals and skysails. All were square sails.

TRANSOMS: The timbers crossing the stern-post to strengthen the hull.

TRAVELLER: An iron ring fitted to slide up and down a rope or along a bar.

TRESTLE TREES: Two strong pieces of timber placed horizontally and fore-and-aft on opposite sides of the lower masthead to support the cross-trees (q.v.) and tops. In ancient times seamen stricken with mortal injuries and dying on deck without a confessor or chaplain believed they could win remission of all the punishment due to sin and complete absolution by turning their eyes to the cross-trees and expressing their contrition.

TRYSAIL: Fore-and-aft sail, setting with boom and gaff.

UNBEND: To cast-off or untie a line.

WAIST: The part of the upper-deck between the quarter-deck and the forecastle.

WARE or WEAR: See TACK.

WEATHER GAUGE; TO WEATHER: A vessel which is to windward of another holds the weather gauge of her. To weather a cape or an obstruction means a ship can claw far enough up into the wind not to be driven on to the rocks. WEATHER

HELM signified that an individual ship had a tendency to bring her head up into the wind and needed constant correction of the helm and much vigilance if she was not to be caught aback.

WEIGH: To raise anchor or to lift a mast or spar.

WINDLASS: The machine used, like a capstan, to weigh the anchor.

WRING BOLTS: Bolts securing the planks to the timbers.

YAWING: The motion of a ship lurching off her course.